in Canterbury

Maurice Crosland

May 1979

HISTORICAL STUDIES
IN THE LANGUAGE OF
CHEMISTRY

HISTORICAL STUDIES IN THE LANGUAGE OF CHEMISTRY

by

MAURICE P. CROSLAND

Professor of the History of Science,
University of Kent at Canterbury

DOVER PUBLICATIONS, INC.
NEW YORK

Published in Canada by General Publishing
Company, Ltd., 30 Lesmill Road, Don Mills,
Toronto, Ontario.
Published in the United Kingdom by Constable
and Company, Ltd., 10 Orange Street, London
WC2H 7EG.

This Dover edition, first published in 1978, is
an unabridged republication of the work originally
published by Heinemann Educational Books, Ltd.,
London, in 1962. The author has made corrections
and written a new preface to this edition.

International Standard Book Number:
0-486-63702-6
Library of Congress Catalog Card Number:
78-55246

Manufactured in the United States of America
Dover Publications, Inc.
180 Varick Street
New York, N.Y. 10014

To E.F.C.

Preface to the Dover Edition

In the sixteen years since the publication of this book, little has been published concerning the language of chemistry to cause the author to wish to revise any of his original arguments. Some readers have found *Historical Studies in the Language of Chemistry* a useful source of reference and have kindly acknowledged this in their own works.[1] In addition to its role as a reference text for students and scholars in the field, the work includes areas of inquiry that are of interest to a wider readership. The first section of the book certainly has some relevance to the wave of interest of the late 1960s and 1970s in the study of alchemy and the occult. Also, readers with a general interest in language may find the discussion in the main section of the book concerning the problems of a rational universal language interesting from a philosophical and social, as well as a historical, viewpoint.

Although the book does not need substantial revision, it may well be useful to suggest here several areas for further reflection and research. As the title implies, the writer made no claim to have covered *all* aspects of chemical language; he was, in fact, concerned mainly with chemical substances. Other research topics still to be investigated include the history of chemical equations and the names of apparatus, chemical processes and types of reaction. On the basis of the law of conservation of matter so effectively advocated by Lavoisier, chemical names and particularly chemical symbols could be incorporated into equations as a new and powerful calculus of operations. The author himself is gathering materials for a history of chemical equations.[2] The study of the names of pieces of apparatus is

1. For example, B. J. T. Dobbs, *The Foundations of Newton's Alchemy*, Cambridge, 1975, p. xii.
2. A first sketch was given in M. P. Crosland, 'The Use of Diagrams as Chemical "Equations" in the Lecture Notes of William Cullen and Joseph Black', *Annals of Science*, *15* (1959), 75–90.

quite a different matter. The task of following the alphabet from Alembic, Beaker and Crucible [3] on, would probably best be done by a museum curator. Still different is the task of studying the terminology used in describing chemical processes. This might be an undertaking for a chemist with philosophical interests. Finally, the naming and classification of types of reaction offers the possibility of a new perspective; the theory of Woodward and Hoffmann (1965) has far reaching implications for organic chemistry.

There are still many terms used in chemistry which would not fit into any of these categories. The concept of *equilibrium* is an obvious incursion from mechanics. [4] At one time solutions were described as *weak* or *strong*; these somewhat anthropomorphic designations were replaced by the 'scientific' terms *dilute* and *concentrated*, which could be given more precise meanings and be expressed numerically. The concept of *purity* is used by thousands of modern scientists without any thought being given to its origins [5] and its metaphorical implications. New chemical terms could have their source in common discourse, as in 'degrees of *freedom*'. Reciprocally, the rich language of chemistry could provide metaphors for extra-scientific purposes; the terms to *distill* or *dissolve* or *react* can have meaning outside chemical usage. Coleridge said that he attended Davy's chemical lectures to improve his metaphors and Goethe gave the title *Die Wahlverwandschaften* (Elective Affinities) to one of his novels, transferring the idea of attraction from the realm of chemical substances to that of men and women. Only a few centuries before, the term 'affinity' (*affinitas*) had been used exclusively to deal with human relationships. Thus a general term borrowed for scientific purposes can gain greater effect because of its added scientific connotations.

Although guides to the nomenclature of both inorganic and organic chemistry are available, these have understandably been written not from a historical perspective but from a severely practical point of view to provide working guides and standards

3. The *Oxford English Dictionary* suspects that the word *crucible* is derived from *crux* (cross), but it is unable to justify this etymology historically.

4. After some crude post-Newtonian attempts to reduce chemistry to mechanics, Berthollet's *Essai de statique chimique* (1803) was a major attempt to understand the many factors involved in chemical reactions.

5. E. F. Caldin, *Proceedings of the Chemical Society* (1961), 234–5.

for chemists. In the twentieth century, however, the problem of nomenclature affects many more people besides bench chemists. Science librarians, information officers, editors of journals and manufacturers of chemicals are continually concerned with problems of chemical nomenclature. The subject has been examined carefully from the point of view of information retrieval,[6] understandably with some thought given to the use of computers. However, it may be useful to remind enthusiasts of a principle of nomenclature that was re-stated as recently as 1957: a name should be pronounceable as well as easy to typeset.[7] Because of continuing problems with nomenclature, the *Journal of Chemical Education* decided in 1971 to begin a regular feature: 'Notes on Nomenclature'.[8] There may even be room for a new book devoted exclusively to the development of chemical nomenclature in the twentieth century and future prospects.[9] Here one can do no more than mention a few salient points and provide some references for further study.[10]

It has traditionally been the organic chemists who have been most concerned with nomenclature. Although organic chemistry is basically the chemistry of the compounds of a few elements centred on carbon, the complexity of their structure and particularly of the many ring systems has produced very great problems. The sheer number of compounds is also formidable. In 1896, at the time of the Geneva Congress, the number was thought to be enormous; there were then approximately 60,000 registered organic compounds. By 1910, however, there were

6. For example J. E. Ash (ed.), *Chemical Information Systems*, Chichester, 1975; E. G. Smith, *The Wiswesser Line Formula Chemical Notation*, New York, 1968.

7. International Union of Pure and Applied Chemistry, *Nomenclature of Inorganic Chemistry* ('Red book'). 2nd edn., London, 1971, Introduction to 1st edn., p. 2.

8. *Journal of Chemical Education*, *48* (1971), 433–4.

9. The most thorough recent study of the modern history of nomenclature is a long series of articles by P. Verkade relating to organic chemistry: 'Etudes historiques sur la nomenclature de la chimie organique', *Bulletin de la Société chimique de France*, *I* (1966), 1807–12; *II* (1967), 4009–20; *III* (1968), 1358–67; *IV* (1969), 3877–81; *V* (1969), 4297–4308; *VI* (1970), 2739–46; *VII* (1971), 1634–47; *VIII* (1971), 4299–4307; *IX* (1973), 1961–71.

10. A review of nomenclature literature is given in 'Notes on Nomenclature' (ref. 8) and in Sieghard Neufeldt, 'Wichtige Schritte in der Entwicklung der chemischen Nomenklatur', *Chronologie Chemie 1800–1970*, Weinheim, 1977, 312–18.

approximately 144,000, and by 1930 around 300,000 compounds. By the late 1960s the total number of known organic
compounds was approximately two and a half million, and it
was estimated that 800 new ones were being added every day.[11]

The authors of handbooks and dictionaries and the editors
of journals have a major influence on nomenclature. Thus it
was a triumph for the Geneva nomenclature when Beilstein
began to use it in the third edition of his standard *Handbuch der
organischen Chemie*, started in 1893. In 1923 the American
Chemical Society and the Chemical Society of London made
some contribution towards uniformity by adopting a common
basic list of names for organic compounds. Although national
societies obviously had the greatest authority in the twentieth
century, individuals continued to exert important influences.
An American, Austin M. Patterson, helped prepare the way for
the conference of Liège in 1930, and his influence was instru-
mental in securing the adoption of the Liège system in *Chemical
Abstracts* from 1937. A further attempt to grapple with all
aspects of the problem of nomenclature of organic compounds
was made after World War II by the International Union of
Pure and Applied Chemistry and resulted in the I.U.P.A.C.
1957 Rules, now partly superceded by the I.U.P.A.C. 1965
Rules.[12]

The 1965 Definitive Rules of the International Union of
Pure and Applied Chemistry on the Nomenclature of Organic
Chemistry accept many traditional or 'trivial' names but
discourage the introduction of new ones. They state that in
coining new names one should begin by considering the type of
nomenclature to be used (substitutive, additive, and so forth),
and then identify a principal group and the principal chain
or parent ring system. A relatively simple example demon-
strating the application of prefixes, suffixes and a numbered
chain is the compound

$$\overset{6}{HO-CH_2}-\overset{5}{CH}-\overset{4}{CH}=\overset{3}{CCl}-\overset{2}{CO}-\overset{1}{CH_3}$$
$$\underset{CH_3}{|}$$

11. *Journal of Chemical Education*, *45* (1968), 193.

12. International Union of Pure and Applied Chemistry, *Nomenclature
of Organic Chemistry* ('Blue book'). 3rd edn., London, 1971, sections A, B and
C.

Here the principal group is —CO— (a ketone), giving the suffix, *-one*. Since there are six carbon atoms in the principal chain it is regarded as a derivative of *hex*ane. Appropriate prefixes are used to denote the substitution of Cl-, HO-, and CH_3- groups. The name of the compound (accepted with a minor modification in Britain) is

3-Chloro-6-hydroxy-5-methyl-3-hexen-2-one.

When there is more than one chain, the concept of 'seniority' is introduced. Similarly, there are conventions for ring systems, and it was in the nomenclature of these that the Geneva system needed greatest revision.[13] The modern development of polymeric materials has created further problems for nomenclature.

However, despite the repeated attempts by academic chemists to rationalise the naming of chemical compounds, most accepted the concept that some link with the past must be preserved. The requirements of indexing and of computers have, however, encouraged some chemists to develop entirely new systems. In industry, where immediate convenience and cost factors outweigh long-term considerations of rationality and uniformity, many of the older names persist. It is very tempting to use the popular term D.D.T. (based on the apparently systematic name which is really ambiguous: *d*ichloro*d*iphenyl*t*richloroethane), rather than the I.U.P.A.C. official name, 1,1-bis(4-chlorophenyl)-2,2,2-trichloroethane. There may be a good case for abbreviations of standard names, but to prevent misunderstanding it is still desirable that the first reference to any substance in a chemical journal be by the official name.

In inorganic chemistry in the late nineteenth century the problem of understanding the molecule was a difficult one. Complexes provided a special problem and it was appropriate that A. Werner, who had done so much in this field, should have made suggestions for the naming of these compounds (1897, 1907). The electronic theory of valency, in relation to the work of A. Stock (1919), provided a basis for the most far reaching development in the nomenclature of inorganic compounds in

13. The special problems of ring compounds are discussed by A. M. Patterson, L. T. Capell and D. F. Walker in *The Ring Index*, 2nd edn., Washington, 1960, with supplements.

the twentieth century. Lavoisier would have been delighted to find the system based on an 'oxidation number,' although he would hardly have understood the definition of this in terms of electrons. Thus, for example, rather than use the suffixes *-ous* and *-ic* to distinguish between the compounds $FeCl_2$ and $FeCl_3$, it is now recommended that they be known as iron(II) chloride and iron(III) chloride. Chemists are further encouraged to use the Latin *ferrum* instead of iron. Although the 'trivial' English names lead, silver and tin remain, in the interests of international understanding the Latin terms *plumbum*, *argentum* and *stannum* are used to describe substances derived from these elements, e.g., plumbate. According to the 1970 Definitive Rules of the International Union of Pure and Applied Chemistry[14] it is still permissible to use names derived from the French word *azote* for compounds of nitrogen and from the Greek word Θεῖον for compounds of sulphur. In modern revision some slight differences of usage between English and French have been accepted, the rules being issued in both languages, English as the model for Germanic tongues and French as the model for Romance languages. While all of us do not speak the same language as yet, scientists around the world are making considerable progress in establishing a uniform system of nomenclature.

Canterbury   M.P.C.
March, 1978

ACKNOWLEDGEMENTS

I should like to thank various friends and colleagues and especially Dr. W. A. Smeaton for drawing my attention to a few minor errors in the first edition which I have been able to correct. I am also grateful for comments on this preface by two visiting scholars who have been working on the history of chemistry at the University of Kent in the academic year 1977–78, Dr. Clarke Gage and Dr. Christoph Meinel.

14. Op. cit. ref. 7, p. 10.

Preface to the First Edition

It has been said that 'to write a full description of the origin, growth and misadventures of the language of chemistry is to write a history of the science'.* Whilst this book represents an attempt to trace the part played by language in various stages of the history of chemistry, the author makes no claim to have written a history of chemistry. In order to concentrate on one aspect of the subject, it has often been necessary to pass over quickly or even to ignore major advances in the laboratory, and hence this book cannot be considered as anything more than a series of essays in the history of science. It is possible that it may make some contribution towards a fuller understanding of the modern science of chemistry.

Although it is the chemistry and the chemical language of the past rather than the present that comes under review, it is hoped that at least some parts of the book may be of interest to a wider public than the professional historians of science. Any modern student of chemistry will have been struck by some of the quaint expressions still found in the text-books, even if he has tended to take for granted the structure of its terminology comprising such systematic names as *sodium chloride* and *diethyl ether*. It is intended that the contents of this book should deal adequately with both aspects of the subject.

The study of the language of chemistry often throws interesting light on the problems and development of the science. To take one example, it seems likely that difficulties of language gave rise to many of the misconceptions upon which later alchemical practice was based. Again, it was inevitable in the early history of chemistry that substances should be given names before their precise chemical nature had been ascertained. In this way, many of the old names tended to perpetuate the misconceptions of a previous age about the nature of particular

* M. M. Pattison Muir, *A history of chemical theories and laws*, New York, 1907, p. 189.

substances. It was difficult for each new generation to think afresh about the basic problem in chemistry, that of chemical composition, without carrying the prejudices implied in the current terminology. To see this, however, is no more than to view the negative side of the question. Lavoisier considered that by creating a new language for chemistry, it would be possible not only to correct the mistakes of the past, but also to map out the future progress of the science. In the sense that a nomenclature provided a classification of chemical compounds, Lavoisier's hope was justified and the new chemical nomenclature can be compared in scope at the end of the eighteenth century with the periodic table of Mendeleev in the nineteenth century. The importance of language in the history of chemistry is not merely a twentieth-century idea conceived under the influence of the philosophical school of linguistic analysis; it has always been insisted upon by chemists themselves, men like Robert Boyle in the seventeenth century, Torbern Bergman and Lavoisier in the eighteenth century and Berzelius in the nineteenth century.

The book is divided into five parts, each being a more or less self-contained essay. The section dealing with alchemical language comes first because the spirit of alchemy is furthest removed from that of modern chemistry. Some of the contents of Part Two are, however, concerned with an even earlier period. Part Five, which deals with organic chemistry, includes references to chemical symbolism which might be thought more appropriate in Part Four. The author considers, however, that the continuity of the book is better served by the order adopted.

In Part One of the book the characteristics of the terminology of the alchemists are examined. The author believes that the beginnings of the science of chemistry in the seventeenth and eighteenth centuries can be better appreciated against a background of earlier alchemical practice. It is true, of course, that modern chemistry did not develop from alchemy alone, but the materials, apparatus, operations and language of the medieval and renaissance alchemists formed an inheritance which chemistry was not able to reject entirely. Alchemy did not originate in Western Europe, however, and it has been thought desirable to mention some Greek and Arabic precursors of the alchemists who wrote in Latin. Chinese alchemy had little or no direct impact on the growth of chemistry in Western Europe and has not been included in this study.

A second important source of modern chemistry were the chemical arts and crafts associated with metallurgy, glass-making, dyeing, distilling and pharmacy. Although nearer to modern times in the sense of being more rational, the terminology used to describe chemical materials was primitive and names were largely based on physical properties, colour being especially important. This early chemical terminology is described in Part Two. Criticisms of the worst examples of chemical terminology were not uncommon in the seventeenth century, but little by way of reform was done before the mid-eighteenth century. About this time the number of earths, metals, acids and salts known to chemists was rapidly increasing. The old terminology which comprised names for a few dozen chemical substances could not easily be extended to cover the new discoveries unless certain definite principles of nomenclature were agreed upon.

Part Three is concerned with the introduction of a systematic nomenclature. A parallel is drawn between the state of botany and that of chemistry in the early eighteenth century and it is suggested that Linnaeus' binomial nomenclature in botany formed a precedent for Bergman's binomial nomenclature in chemistry. Bergman's ideas were adopted and extended by the French chemist Guyton de Morveau, who eventually collaborated with Lavoisier in establishing what is essentially the nomenclature used in inorganic chemistry to-day. The French terms were soon translated into other languages and in Britain, for example, the new terms were fairly generally accepted at the close of the eighteenth century. The early years of the nineteenth century witnessed an extension of Lavoisier's nomenclature to express the composition of compounds in quantitive terms.

In Part Four various systems of chemical symbols are examined. Alchemical symbols were used by chemists up to the eighteenth century. The geometrical symbols of Hassenfratz and Adet (1787) to denote compounds were perhaps more systematic than the alchemical symbols, but they were never popular because they were clumsy and could not easily be incorporated into printed works. The same consideration applies to a rather less extent to Dalton's symbols, first published in 1808. Dalton used his symbols to convey to the minds of his students the idea of atoms or groups of atoms each with a definite weight. Finally, we come to the modern system of chemical symbols used by Berzelius. Berzelius was by no means the first chemist to denote chemical substances by their initial letters. His important contribution to chemistry was to apply this method systematically to all the known elements and their compounds.

Part Five is concerned with the question of nomenclature in the field of organic chemistry. Here it was not enough to know what elements a compound contained or even the proportion of the elements. Organic compounds had to be classified according to reactive groups, e.g., ketones, alcohols, etc. The use of Berzelius' symbols to express the formula of an organic compound itself led to difficulties, since the formula of the same compound could be written in so many different ways. This was one of the problems to be discussed at the Karlsruhe congress of 1860. The time had come when decisions could only be made by international conferences rather than by the authority of a small group of men and the Karlsruhe congress led indirectly to another congress held in Geneva in 1892 at which the modern structure of organic chemical nomenclature was first established on an international basis.

The Bibliography, whilst including books consulted, does not give detailed references to periodical literature. To have quoted the author's name, title and source of every article consulted would have led to an inflated bibliography at least treble the size of the present one and probably to little purpose, since, by the very nature of the subject, all that has been extracted in many cases from a whole paper is perhaps an odd sentence or a footnote. It is hoped that the footnotes in the present work will enable the reader to trace references in the periodical literature as well as from other sources.

Parts One to Four of the book are based on a Ph.D. thesis in the University of London, which has been abbreviated in an attempt to make the work more suitable for publication. In particular the actual number of footnotes has been drastically reduced and certain aspects of the subject not relevant to the main theme have been omitted. In addition, some of the contents of the book have already been presented at a seminar at University College London in June 1958 and at an international colloquium on the history of chemistry held in Paris in September 1959. Part Five was written in 1960 especially for this book, as it was felt that a work on the language of chemistry, however incomplete in other ways, could hardly fail to include a section devoted to organic chemistry.

In the preparation of this work my thanks are due chiefly to Professor Douglas McKie of University College London who has given me every assistance and encouragement and to Dr. W. P. D. Wightman of the University of Aberdeen who has also read the original thesis and made many helpful suggestions. The typescript was also read by two readers on behalf of the Harvard University Press and their encouraging comments and constructive criticisms were much appreciated. For any errors that remain I must, of course, assume full responsibility. I should like to take this opportunity of thanking the staffs of various libraries, particularly the British Museum, University College London, London University, and also the Wellcome Historical Medical Library, the Patent Office Library and the library of the Pharmaceutical Society. Without the resources of these libraries the compilation of the present work would have been clearly impossible. Where no translations of texts were available, I have undertaken this responsibility myself and I have received valuable help from my wife in translations from the German.

I should like to thank Professor E. Briner and Professor Cherbuliez of the University of Geneva for kindly providing a copy of the photograph of the Geneva Congress of 1892. Acknowledgement is also due to the Asiatic Society of Bengal for permission to reproduce *in extenso* a translation by H. E. Stapleton from the Arabic which was published in the *Memoirs* of the society.

Contents

1—The Language of Alchemy

2—*Early Chemical Terminology*

3—The Introduction of Systematic Nomenclature into Chemistry and the Acceptance of the 1787 Reform

4—*Chemical Symbolism*

5—*The Language of Organic Chemistry*

List of Illustrations

Abbreviations

A.C.R.	Alembic Club Reprint.
Ann. Chem.	*Annalen der Chemie und Pharmacie*, ed. J. von Liebig.
Ann. chim.	*Annales de chimie*, Paris.
Ann. chim. phys.	*Annales de chimie et de physique*, Paris.
Ann. Pharm.	*Annalen der Pharmacie*, ed. Liebig.
Ann. Phys. Chem.	*Annalen der Physik und Chemie*, ed. Poggendorff.
Berth., *A.G.*	Berthelot, *Collection des anciens alchimistes grecs*, 3 parts, Paris, 1887–8.
Berth., *M.A.*	Berthelot, *La chimie au moyen âge*, 3 vols., Paris, 1893.
Comp. rend.	*Comptes Rendus des Séances de l'Académie des Sciences*, Paris.
H.M.	*The Hermetic Museum*, ed. A. E. Waite, London, 1893.
J. Chem. Soc.	*Journal of the Chemical Society*, London.
M.H.	*Musaeum Hermeticum*, Frankfurt, 1678.
Manget	J. J. Manget, (ed.), *Bibliotheca Chemia Curiosa*, 2 vols., Geneva, 1702.
Mém. Acad.	*Mémoires de l'Academie Royale des Sciences*, Paris.
Mem. Bengal	*Memoirs of the Asiatic Society of Bengal*.
Phil. Mag.	*Philosophical Magazine*, London.
Phil. Trans.	*Philosophical Transactions of the Royal Society*.
Th. Ch.	*Theatrum chemicum*, ed. Zetzner, 6 vols., Argentorati, 1659–61.

Part I

THE LANGUAGE OF ALCHEMY

'O doubtful names which are like the true names, what errors and anguish have you provoked among men!'

Book of Crates, Berth. *M. A.*, iii, p. 50

CHAPTER ONE

Allegory and Analogy in
Alchemical Literature

Introduction

The term 'Alchemy' comprises a variety of aspects of human endeavour ranging from the practical to the mystical, and it is to be expected that the literature of alchemy will reflect this diversity. The field of alchemy is a vast one and it will be necessary to ignore many mystical writings which might have some claim to be alchemical in order to concentrate attention on those aspects of the subject concerned with practical chemistry. Rather more attention is paid to the writings of Geber than those bearing the name of Raymond Lull, and Glauber is thought to be more relevant than Flamel. As modern chemistry came into being in Europe in the late seventeenth and eighteenth centuries, particular attention has been paid to the chemical practice in Europe in the preceeding centuries, although Arabic and Greek influences have not been ignored.

At the very start of a study of alchemy we are faced with the fact that the final goal of the practical alchemists, the preparation of the 'Philosopher's Stone'[1] was unattainable. This does not, however, automatically exclude alchemy from serious attention in the history of chemistry. The various processes employed: solution, sublimation, distillation, calcination, etc. were undoubtedly chemical, as were the substances employed. While we cannot help regarding the ultimate aims and beliefs of the later alchemists as fantastic, we must admit that the chemical means adopted to reach this end were usually quite rational in the light of current chemical theory. Different alchemists might have stated their aims in different ways but, broadly speaking, it may be said that the object of alchemy was the perfection of

1. In early alchemy the 'Philosopher's Stone' was a substance capable of turning base metals into gold. Later, additional properties—such as the curing of diseases and the granting of immortality—were attributed to it.

matter, a process which, it was believed, occurred in Nature.
For this reason many of the alchemists saw their task as the
imitation of Nature within the walls of the laboratory.

It is important to note that the concept of perfection has not
only a chemical aspect but a moral and psychological one as
well. Largely for this reason[2] the body of literature which is
called alchemical is of a dual nature with, however, only a
minority of works which can confidently be classified as belonging completely to either of the respective fields of chemistry or
psychology. The relevance to chemistry has long been recognized; more recently the relevance to psychology has been emphasized by C. G. Jung.[3]

As it is clear that alchemy is a complex subject, it is to be expected that its literature should present special problems in its
interpretation.

The Difficulty of Recognizing an Alchemical Text

In the first place, every branch of knowledge has its own
technical terms which are either words coined for a particular
use or words taken from everyday language which are understood in a particular sense when used technically. Thus in the
science of electricity the term 'ion' and 'current' respectively
are examples of this habit. Similarly early technical chemistry
had its own terminology, but in alchemy this was the exception
rather than the rule. Alchemy was, for this reason, compared
adversely with other sciences whose books were set out clearly
and in a logical order.[4]

The alchemists generally preferred to use a language based on
analogy and more appropriate to poetry or mysticism than to an
exact science. Because of the widespread use of allegory it was

2. Chemical processes also seem to have provided a popular source of
allegory for mystical writers. An extreme view of the meaning of alchemy
was that adopted in the last century by Mrs Atwood, who stated that the
only thing in common between chemistry and alchemy is the 'borrowed
terms' (*A Suggestive Inquiry into the Hermetic Mystery*, London, 1850, p. 135).

3. *Psychologie und Alchemie*, Zurich, 1944; transl. *Psychology and Alchemy*,
London, 1953. The moral aspect of alchemy has also been stressed by cer-
tain writers e.g. Mrs Atwood, op. cit., and E. A. Hitchcock, *Remarks upon
Alchemy and the Alchemists*, Boston, 1857.

4. Theobaldus de Hoghelande, *De Alchemiae Difficultatibus*, Pars 2; *Th.
Ch.* i, p. 139. *De Alchemia*, Incerti Auctore; *Th. Ch.*, iii, p. 6.

possible, on the one hand, to fail to recognize an alchemical manuscript as referring to chemical reactions and it was possible, on the other hand, to read an alchemical meaning into allegorical works where no such interpretation was intended by the author.

To consider first the problem of recognizing an alchemical text as being such, we should recall that a division was continually emphasized between adepts, who were able to interpret alchemical symbolism, and the common herd of mankind, to whom alchemy was essentially mysterious. Those who had not received some guidance might find it very difficult even to recognize an allegorical description as referring to chemical processes, quite apart from being able to interpret the details of the allegory. Nowadays a textbook of chemistry can at once be recognized not only by its title but also by the language used in the text. This was not so with many alchemical works, and it still remains a matter of debate whether some of these texts could not be interpreted rather as referring to some other process, e.g. mental experiences. Nevertheless, anyone who has read several alchemical tracts begins to sense that they have certain features in common. Naturally, different authors had their own favourite themes of allegory and a religious writer might compare the stages in the preparation of the philosopher's stone to the passion and resurrection of Christ, whereas another writer might be content with comparing alchemical processes to the principal events in the life of man. Alchemy did sometimes tend to overlap with theology, but two more important instances where confusion arose were in connection with astronomy (or astrology) and, in a completely different way, with mythology.

Astronomy and Alchemy

The use of the names of the planets to describe metals and their derivatives has been common since early times. This important source of chemical terminology was due to a supposed analogy between the seven planets and the seven metals. The use of such terminology tended to strengthen the bonds between astrology and alchemy to the detriment of the latter. It also gave rise to confusion in so far as the names of the planets were those of the gods of mythology.

One alchemical author, at least, thought it advisable to warn the unwary reader:

> In the first place it should be known that this divine science uses the terms of astronomy.[5]

Owing to the fact that the vocabulary of these sciences over-lapped, it is often difficult to decide whether a particular text refers to astronomy or alchemy. Such a passage occurs in a celebrated alchemical work known as *Turba Philosophorum*:

> I signify that the envious have narrated and said that the splendour of Saturn does not appear unless it perchance be dark when it ascends in the air, that Mercury is hidden by the rays of the sun, that quick-silver (*argentum vivum*) vivifies the body by its fiery strength, and thus the work is accomplished. But Venus when she becomes oriental, precedes the Sun.[6]

A criterion which might be adopted to decide whether any given passage referred to astronomical phenomena would be to see if the description were reasonable if interpreted in this light. Thinking along these lines, Jean Brouault, in his *Abrégé de l'Astronomie Inférieure* (1644), argued that many documents which appeared to be concerned with astronomy were really about alchemy, because if they were taken literally, many of the statements of the ancients would be absurd. Rather than agree to this he suggests a metaphorical interpretation. Other authors attempted to expand the already crowded territory of alchemi-cal literature by including some astronomy, qualified as 'Inferior Astronomy', the subject matter of which was the 'earthly planets' (i.e. metals).[7] The term 'Inferior Astronomy' is also found in the early mediaeval *De Perfecto Magisterio* by the pseudo-Aristotle. In this tract the author compares the metals and other 'stones' to the fixed stars and draws an analogy between the planets and seven substances which were more usually classed as 'spirits', viz. quicksilver, sulphur, arsenic, sal ammoniac, tutia (probably zinc oxide), magnesia and marchasite.[8]

5. *Aurora Consurgens*, cap. 1; *Artis Auriferae*, Basle, 1572, p. 206.
6. *Turba Philosophorum*, ed. J. Ruska, Berlin, 1931, p. 166 (Latin text); English translation by A. E. Waite, London, 1896, pp. 193-4.
7. Rosencreutzer, *Astronomia Inferior*, Nuremberg, 1674. Also in *Th. Ch.*, vi, pp. 507-10, there is a tract with the title *Astronomia Inferior* which speaks about planets and constellations, but is really about alchemy.
8. *Th. Ch.*, iii, p. 76.

Mythology and Alchemy

If it is true to say that there was sometimes confusion between the literature of alchemy and that of astronomy to the detriment of both, this is even more so with alchemy and mythology. It was enough that some alchemical writers had made allusions to characters in classical mythology for the classics of Greece and Rome to be examined in a new light. Armed with the conviction that alchemy had been practised as long as there had been civilizations, the extremists of this movement regarded the entire field of classical literature as a potential source of information on alchemical matters.

This situation was brought about by a number of factors including the mediaeval attitude of respect for written authority, especially that of the 'ancients'. With the advent of the Renaissance this attitude was magnified rather than diminished. The connection between mythology and alchemy before the later Renaissance had been slight. It was only after the fifteenth century that authors began to combine their new knowledge of classical mythology with the writing and interpretation of alchemical texts. In the forefront of this movement was Michael Maier (b. 1568) and its last great propagandist was Pernety, a contemporary of Lavoisier. A second reason for the confusion was that, to many rationally minded people, the idea that the large body of mythology consisted of nothing but fables was repugnant. They therefore suggested that the ancients made use of poetry with some other end in view, e.g. a description of an alchemical process. Thus one writer[9] says, quite seriously, that it is ridiculous to believe in animals which breathe fire through their nostrils and from whose teeth armed men spring. The absurdity of a literal interpretation makes an allegorical interpretation (e.g. in terms of alchemy) all the more plausible. This is the conclusion reached by a later writer who gives 'proofs' that the details of the Trojan War as described by the classical poets cannot be historically accurate.[10] When one considers the diversity of alchemical allegory it is by no means impossible that a description of a chemical reaction should have taken the form of a conflict between chemical substances

9. Conti Natale, *Mythologiae*, Venice, 1568, Bk. 6, chap. 8, f. 179v.; also Petrus Bonus, *Preciosa Margarita Novella*, cap. 9; *Th. Ch.*, v, p. 615.
10. Pernety, *Fables Égyptiennes et Grecques*, Paris, 1758, t. II, pp. 476 ff.

represented symbolically. A third reason for the confusion between mythology and alchemy is that both drew on allegory
for their expression. Although themselves quite distinct, both
activities had a common root in the human psyche and it is
therefore not surprising sometimes to find similar symbolism in
each. It was always possible to claim that proper names referred
to chemical substances, as when it was claimed that, in a quotation from the poet Pindar, 'Hercules' stands for common salt
and 'Phoebus' for sulphur.[11]

A final reason for the confusion between mythology and alchemy was their common vocabulary. Thus fables relating to
Saturn could be explained as being about the alchemical Saturn
(i.e. lead), and references to Venus and Mars were also given a
similar chemical explanation.[12]

A favourite fable for alchemical interpretation was that of the
Golden Fleece. The suggestion that this fable had some connection with alchemy is found in the works of John of Antioch
(seventh century A.D.)[13] and it also occurs in Suidas. According
to the *Oxford Classical Dictionary* the lexicon bearing this name
was compiled about the end of the tenth century A.D. It is thus
clear that the confusion between mythology and alchemy had
begun even before alchemy was practised in Europe. The
origin of this particular error is not difficult to surmise. The
term 'Golden Fleece' did not have any obvious literal meaning
and it was therefore possible to suggest that the adjective 'golden' referred to a description of the art of making gold, and that
this account had been written on parchment or sheep-skin and
had therefore been called the 'Golden Fleece'. This is the explanation found in Suidas[14] and accepted by many alchemists.[15]
An alternative explanation was that the 'Golden Fleece' was a
metaphor for the philosopher's stone and that the adventures of
Jason referred to chemical changes which must be carried out
in order to arrive at the desired goal. Some writers exercised
their ingenuity in the interpretation of the details of the fable.

11. J. Tollius, *Fortuita*, Amsterdam, 1687, p. 99.
12. Conti Natale, op. cit., Bk. 2, chap. 3, f. 40v. Borrichius, *Hermetis,
Aegyptiorum et chemicorum sapientia . . . vindicata*, Hafniae, 1674, pp. 64–5.
13. According to Kopp, *Beiträge*, Brunswick, 1869–73, vol. i, p. 12.
14. *Suidae Lexicon*, Halle and Brunswick, vol. 1, 1853, cols. 1212–13.
15. e.g. Robertus Vallensis: *De veritate et antiquitate artis chemicae; Th. Ch.*,
i, p. 19. Giovanni Francesco Pico de Mirandula: *De Auro*, Bk. 3; *Th. Ch.*,
ii, p. 357. Libavius, *Alchymia Comment.*, Frankfurt, 1606, Part 2, Bk. 4.

Thus, according to one writer,[16] the plough of hardest iron in the story referred to the hermetic vessel, the four acres of land to the four elements, the spear of Jason signified the philosophical fire, etc. The metallurgist Agricola put forward the suggestion that the origin of the term 'Golden Fleece' was the use of animal skins to retain particles of gold.[17]

Having mentioned the names of Libavius and Agricola in connection with the legend of the Golden Fleece, we might conclude this section by referring to an interpretation of this legend by a third great figure in the history of chemistry, Rudolph Glauber. Glauber tried to convince the reader of the clarity of his own prolix and obscure writings by contrasting them with the story of the Golden Fleece, of which he gave the following account:

> When Ancient Philosophers, by Poetical Parables, described the laborious navigation of Jason to the Island of Colchos, where resided an huge dragon vomiting Fire, which, with Eyes never closed, diligently watched the Golden Fleece, they added this, viz. that Jason was taught by his wife Medea to cast to this waking dragon an edible Medicine to be swallowed, whereby he should be killed and burst; and that Jason should presently take the Dragon (thus slain) and totally submerge him in the Stygian Lake.
>
> Jason in this ingenious Fable, Hieroglyphically represents the Philosophers; Medea, accurate Meditations; the laborious and perilous Navigation, signifies manifold Chymical Labours; the watching Dragon vomiting Fire, denotes Salt, Nitre and Sulphur; and the Golden Fleece is the Tincture or Soul of Sulphur, by the help of which, Jason restored Health to his Aged Father, and acquired to himself immense Riches. By the Pills of Medea is understood the Preparation of Sulphur and Sal Mirabile.[18] By the total submersion of the Dragon in the Stygian Lake is intimated the Fixation of Sulphur by Stygian Water, that is, Aqua Fortis.
>
> Whence it is sufficiently clear how obscurely the Ancient Philosophers did describe their Fixation of Sulphur by Nitre, and how secretly they hid it from the Eyes of the unworthy.[19]

16. Guilielmus Mennens, *Aurei velleris libri tres*, Bk. 1, chap. 4; *Th. Ch.*, v, p. 254.

17. *De re metallica*, Bk. 8, transl. Hoover, London, 1912, p. 330.

18. The fact that this is Glauber's own interpretation of the fable, and not merely reported speech, is suggested by the inclusion of his own *sal mirabile* (Glauber's salt).

19. *Works*, transl. Packe, London, 1689, Part 3, p. 10b.; see also Part 2, p. 169b.

Theology and Alchemy

Although it is clear that theology and practical alchemy are in no way connected, it is equally clear that the history of alchemy includes many incursions into what is properly the field of theology. The feeling that the transformations brought about by alchemy involved something supernatural, and the tradition that alchemy was a divine art did much to bring together theology and alchemy. A religious atmosphere is present in almost all the Greek alchemical texts;[20] it is found in many Arabic alchemical writers including Jabir, and it continued in a Christian form when alchemy reached Western Europe. In the extreme, there were those mystics who used the concepts and operations of practical alchemy as a spiritual exercise. Such a man was Stephen of Alexandria who lived in the eighth century A.D. and used the transformation of metals as a symbol for the regenerating force of religion in transforming the human soul. Yet there were others who toiled in primitive laboratories and who also drew on religious concepts and sacred literature. The first chapter of Genesis was looked upon by many European alchemists as a guide to the chemical work they were to undertake. There were also ideas of purification and contrition. The concept of purification is one of immense importance because it was later taken over into the science of chemistry. Indeed the idea of a pure substance was fundamental to the development of chemistry in the eighteenth and nineteenth centuries. A process called 'the contrition of the philosophers' is referred to in the *Turba*,[21] and the *Rosarium Philosophorum*[22] speaks of the mortification of mercury leaving matter in the form of ashes, a process which the 'philosophers' called 'contrition'. Further examples of parallels drawn between Christian ideas and alchemy are found in statements that 3 days (Resurrection) or 40 days (Lent) are required for the alchemist's preparation to achieve perfection. Examples of an explicit comparison of Christian Doctrine and

20. e.g. see F. S. Taylor, 'A Survey of Greek Alchemy' in *Journal of Hellenic Studies, L* (1930), 110.

21. *Turba Philosophorum*, ed. Ruska, Berlin, 1931, p. 143, l. 15.

22. *Rosarium Philosophorum*, Frankfurt, 1550, f. 36v. As the title 'Rosary' was given to several distinct alchemical works, it may be mentioned that this particular compilation has the incipit: '*Qui desiderant artis philosophicae* . . .' and it cites frequently Arnald of Villanova.

alchemical theory are not hard to find. The following passage is attributed to Nicolas Flamel:

Behold . . . our Saviour . . . who shall eternally unite unto him all pure and clean souls, and will drive away all impurity and unclean-ness, as being unworthy to be united to his divine Body. So by com-parison (but first asking leave of the Catholic, Apostolic and Roman Church, to speak in this manner . . .) see here our white Elixir, which from henceforward will inseparably unite unto itself every pure Metallic nature, changing it into his own most fine silvery nature, rejecting all that is impure, strange, Heterogeneal, or of another kind.[23]

Some Other Allegories

Apart from specific analogies employed in alchemical texts (which are discussed later in this chapter), there are numerous examples in alchemical literature of the use of allegories. Indeed the allegory might be so complete as to convince all but the initiated that the text had no bearing on alchemy.

It is hard to believe, for example, that the visions related by Zosimos[24] (*c.* 300 A.D.) have any direct relevance to practical chemistry. Accounts of such visions can more profitably be studied by a psychologist than a chemist.[25] A better example is provided by an Arabic writer Ibn Umail who lived in the tenth century. The extract will be quoted *in extenso* because it pro-vides an excellent example of the mis-interpretation to which all allegory is exposed. It is also of relevance to the search for the philosopher's stone which some alchemist's pursued in the most disgusting substances.

The Sage Asfīdūs said: 'Take the things from their mines and raise them to their highest places and reap them from the tops of their mountains and return them to their sources.' This is a clear statement in which there is neither jealousy nor enigma; but he did not say what those things are. By 'mountains' he here meant curcurbits [i.e. the lower pots of the Aludel] and the 'tops of mountains' alembics. Their reapings are by way of similitude, that is, the transference of its water from the alembics to the receivers, and by 'return them to their

23. Flamel, *Exposition of the Hieroglyphical Figures*, London, 1624, (1890), p. 38.
24. Berth., *A.G.*, tradn., pp. 117 ff., pp. 125–7.
25. e.g. see C. G. Jung, *Psychology and Alchemy*, London, 1953, pp. 242, 239.

sources' he meant [to return] that which has come out of it. He named the curcurbits 'mountains' because in the mountains are mines of gold and silver. And in these mountains which are the curcurbits their gold and silver are produced. . . . He did not mean by 'mountains' 'men', nor by the 'tops of mountains' the 'heads of men', nor the thing that is reaped from them hair, as some who explained these things have stated. . . . Owing to this, they subjected hair to manipulation and their money was spent in vain and their days wasted, and their lives came to an end in search of a vain thing. The Science [of Alchemy] is more honourable, more lofty and more dignified than what they imagined. What you see has come from these people who speak these falsehoods on account of the [erroneous] interpretation which proceeds from their unintelligent hearts. . . . Similarly some said regarding this Art that it is from eggs, hair, dung, wine, blood, bile, sperm, sulphur and other defective combustible, corruptible and perishable minerals. After they came to know that it is a perfect science . . . and that it came from Allāh by revelation, they gave up the idea that it proceeds from . . . filthy and impure things which some people owing to their feeble intelligence and ignorance, have made it proceed from — even from dung and urine, Allāh forbid! The wisdom of Allāh is far above these things.[26]

The Difficulty of Interpreting the Texts

The first barrier to a study of alchemy was to appreciate the relevance of any given text to the subject. The second difficulty which had to be overcome was to interpret the various analogies used to refer to chemical substances and processes. It was the exception rather than the rule in alchemical literature for a substance employed in a chemical reaction to be given its common name. The usual practice was to use common language with an esoteric significance; alternatively use was made of analogies. Such analogies might be worked out in great detail and used to describe a series of chemical reactions or the analogy might amount to no more than a reference to the colour of a substance. Among the more common analogies employed were the comparison of metals to man and the 'imperfections' of metals to human ailments; some forms of sexual symbolism, and a comparison of the mineral kingdom to the animal and vegetable kingdoms were also quite common.

26. Ibn Umail, *Mā' al-Waraqī*, transl. Stapleton, *Mem. Bengal, 12* (1933), 41–2. There is a Latin translation in *Artis Auriferae*, 1572, pp. 275–6.

Man as a source of analogy

The concept of man as the microcosm analogous to the world or macrocosm is found in Plato's *Timaeus* and can be traced back to even earlier times. A later development from this analogy was a comparison of the parts of man to natural objects. Just as man was composed of body and soul (or spirit), so minerals could be classified as 'bodies' and 'spirits'. A 'body' was any solid object[27] such as a metal or stone and a 'spirit' was a volatile substance which could change the surface colour of a metal, giving it a new life as an apparently new metal. The use of the terms 'body' and 'spirit' in this sense is found in the writings of Zosimos.[28] The same writer describes the cutting up and cooking of a 'man', although the reader is not left without a hint as to the intended meaning, e.g., 'I am the man of lead and I undergo an intolerable violence'.[29] An explicit comparison made by Zosimos between copper (or bronze) and man had some influence in Arabic chemistry and was quoted, e.g. by Rhazes:

Consequently the Sage said: 'Copper is like a human being. It has a Spirit, a Soul and a Body' . . . that Spirit is the tincture.[30]

The analogical use of 'body' and 'spirit' was not made without some attempt to justify it:

The name 'body' is justly applied to metals because these are heavy whilst spirits are light; bodies return towards their [terrestrial] principle and spirits fly off towards their [celestial] world.[31]

The classification of substances played an important part in Arabic alchemy and the division of substances into 'body' and 'spirit' was worked out in detail. Rhazes included four important chemical substances in the category of 'spirits': sulphur, arsenic sulphides, sal ammoniac and mercury. In the Latin works of Geber seven spirits are mentioned which include the four mentioned above.

The analogy on which this classification was founded was ex-

27. This analogical use of 'body' continues to the present day and is to be found, unremarked, in any elementary text-book of physics.
28. e.g. Berth., *A.G.*, texte grec, p. 124; tradn., p. 132.
29. Ibid., tradn., pp. 118, 126. This analogy survived in Latin alchemy, e.g. *Artis Auriferae*, Basle, 1572, p. 152: 'Accipe hominem, tonde eum. . . '.
30. Al-Rāzī', *Shawāhid*, transl. Stapleton, *Mem. Bengal*, *12*, 137–8.
31. *Treatise of Syriac and Arabic Alchemy*, Berth., *M.A.*, ii, p. 159.

tended and given new life in the sixteenth century by Paracelsus, who is famous for his theory that the metals are composed of
Mercury, Sulphur and Salt: 'Mercury is the spirit, Sulphur is
the soul and Salt is the body. . . .'[32] Such comparisons provided
mystical writers with a rich store of verbal inspiration as is found,
for example, in the works of Jacob Boehme.[33]

In this section it has been maintained that man provided a
significant source of analogy for alchemical ideas. It is only fair
to mention, in conclusion, that the exact contrary of this thesis
has been seriously maintained, i.e. that 'man is the central object of all alchemical books' and that authors 'most commonly
speak of him as a Metal or Mineral.'[34] Such a radical difference
in interpretation only serves to emphasize the heavy cost that is
paid by those who resort to extended analogy and allegory.

The chemical medicine

The concept of an allegorical chemical medicine is to be
found in Latin and Arabic alchemy and can be traced back to
Greek sources. There are some references to similarities in the
treatment of men and metals in the Greek authors, as when
Zosimos quotes from 'Mary the Jewess' a comparison between
the nourishment of man and the tincture of metals. In particular, Mary repeatedly uses the idea of a remedy or medicine
(πύριον φάρμακον) when referring to the means by which
metals are to be transformed.[35] The comparison between the
(supposed) imperfections of metals and the diseases of man became more explicit in Arabic alchemy.[36]

Among alchemical writings in Arabic, those attributed to
Jabir make the most use of this analogy. The theory underlying
Jabir's references to medicines is based on the idea that in the
most perfect metal (gold) there was a balanced proportion of
each of the four elementary qualities. Jabir saw a close analogy
between these four qualities and the four humours of Galenic

32. *De Natura Rerum*, Lib. 1; *Sämtliche Werke*, ed. Sudhoff, Munich and
Berlin, 1922–33, Bd. xi, p. 318.
33. *Concerning the Three Principles of the Divine Essence*, London, 1910, chap.
1, para. 6.
34. E. A. Hitchcock, *Remarks upon Alchemy and the Alchemists*, Boston, 1857,
pp. 40–1.
35. Berth., *A.G.*, tradn., p. 169. and texte grec, p. 103, l. 4; p. 196, l. 11;
p. 201, l. 9.
36. A. Mieli (*La science arabe*, Leyden, 1938, p. 135) says that one of the
names by which the elixir was known was 'dawâ' (medicine).

physiology, on the equilibrium of which the health of man was considered to depend. Jabir asserts that if a proper equilibrium could be obtained in a man's body he would no longer have to fear disease; he would be immune from even such a terrible disease as leprosy and his life would be prolonged indefinitely.[37] Thus it came about that gold was compared with man in a perfect state of health. One of the synonyms of gold was 'the healthy', while silver (the second metal in order of perfection) was described as 'leprous gold'. The use of the term 'medicine' to denote the means of perfecting metals also occurs in the works of Geber (whose identity with Jabir is still in dispute), notably in the *Sum of Perfection*. Often Geber's use of the term 'medicine' corresponds to that of 'tincture', as when he speaks of a citrine and a white medicine.[38] Another Latin work in which the concept of a chemical medicine plays some part is the *Preciosa Margarita Novella*, in which the excess of humours possessed by each of the imperfect or 'leprous' metals is detailed, and gold is described as 'having perfect health'.[39] As always, the introduction of allegory gives rise to a problem of interpretation and we find Jabir, for instance, interpreting a quotation relating to fever in terms of the properties of metals.[40]

The term 'elixir' which was often used to describe the goal of the alchemists was also closely connected with the analogy of a chemical medicine. Although the term has so far not been discovered in any of the older Greek alchemical works, it is generally thought[41] to be derived from the Greek ξήριον ('powder for wounds'). The word *iksīr* is defined in the *Mafātīh al-'Ulum* as the drug which transforms molten metal into gold and silver when it is boiled with it. The word *al exir* or *elixir* was frequently used by Jabir and Ibn Sina and thence passed to the Latin authors. In works attributed to Albertus Magnus[42] and Roger Bacon the terms elixir and medicine are used as synonyms. Bacon defines alchemy as follows:

Alchemy is the science which teaches how to make and generate a certain medicine called the elixir, which, when projected onto metals

37. Berth., *M.A.*, iii, p. 148, and ii, p. 157.
38. *The Works of Geber*, transl. Russell, London, 1678 (1928), p. 147.
39. Op. cit., cap. 13; *Th. Ch.*, v, p. 632.
40. *Book of Mercy*, sec. 20; Berth.,*M.A.*, iii, p. 172.
41. *Encyclopaedia of Islam*, Leyden and London, 1908–38, vol. 2, p. 23. Kopp, *Beiträge*, Brunswick, 1869–73, vol. i, p. 209.
42. *Compositum de Compositis*; *Th. Ch.*, iv, p. 827.

or imperfect bodies, brings them to perfection in the moment of projection.[43]

It seems very probable that the properties later attributed to the philosopher's stone of curing diseases (and whence prolonging life) arose when references to a chemical medicine were interpreted literally instead of metaphorically.

Analogies drawn from the Animal and Vegetable Kingdoms

Among the sources drawn upon by the fertile imagination of the later alchemists were certain animals and plants. That such analogies were not unknown in Arabic alchemy,[44] however, is shown by the use of such names for chemical substances as 'the green lion' (copper), 'the eagle' (sal ammoniac) and 'the fish' (mercury). By the time the printed book became common in Western Europe such symbols were widely used, not only verbally, but in illustrations as well.

Birds were found useful by many alchemists to denote colours (e.g. peacock, raven, swan) or to denote volatility. For the latter purpose the eagle was usually chosen. Indeed the terms *aquila coelestis* and *aquila alba* were used as late as the latter seventeenth century to denote the volatile substances sal ammoniac and calomel respectively. One alchemical book[45] devotes a section to 'philosophical birds' and explains the use of the raven, the swan and the eagle to represent earth, water and air respectively. Birds could be used not only to suggest substances but operations as well. The process of distillation was sometimes considered separately as evaporation and condensation and represented by a bird flying upwards or downwards respectively. The complete process of distillation might therefore be shown by two birds in contrary senses.

Even a practical chemist like Glauber thought it fitting to employ such extravagant analogies, as in the following description of saltpetre:

Whatsoever the acid spirit thereof, or the Eagle with its sharp claws cannot effect, its fixed salt, or the fiery Lion, will accomplish; and whatsoever is impossible to be done by these two, the Griffin,

43. *Speculum Alchemiae*, cap. 1; Manget, i, p. 613.
44. J. Ruska and E. Wiedemann, 'Alchemistische Decknamen', *Sitzungsberichte der physikalisch-medicinische Societät*, Erlangen, 56 (1924), 25–33.
45. Rosencreutzer, *Astronomia Inferior*, Nuremberg, 1674, p. 380.

which hath its rise from the Eagle and the Lion, will artificially perform.[46]

This may seem to be allegory brought to extremes but Becher, the originator of the phlogiston theory, explains in his *Oedipus Chemicus* that when substances are symbolized by the names of animals this is done not fortuitously but by strict analogy between the properties of the substance and the behaviour of the animal. According to him, a red lion stands for gold, a toad or a crow symbolizes putrefaction, and mercury is denoted variously by a dove, an eagle, a green lion and a serpent. Arsenic is symbolized by a serpent, antimony by a wolf and nitre by a dragon. The dragon is often mentioned in alchemical texts, but the favourite animal in later alchemical allegory was probably the lion, a term usually employed to denote a fixed substance which could 'resist the attack' of a strong fire. Lions of various colours are mentioned. If one is to attempt a systematic interpretation of these symbols it seems reasonable to suppose that a 'red lion' might describe a substance of that colour such as cinnabar, a 'green lion' might denote salts of iron and copper,[47] and a yellow lion would probably denote yellow sulphides. To any such attempt at a rational interpretation of alchemical symbolism, however, there are many exceptions. It is rather disconcerting for example, to encounter a 'green lion' which is explained as refering to yellow orpiment.[48]

Many titles of the later alchemical books mention flowers, trees or gardens[49] and the theme of vegetable growth is not uncommon in alchemical writings. This was largely based on a supposed analogy between the growth of metals in the bowels of the earth and the growth of plants. Even part from the analogy of the metallic seed it was often found convenient to describe the colour changes in a chemical process by analogy with flowers of corresponding colours.

Sexual Symbolism

Sexual symbolism was used frequently by medieval writers,

46. *The Prosperity of Germany*, Part 4; *Works*, transl. Packe, London, 1689, Part 1, p. 406b.

47. The term 'green lion' was also used for glass (often tinted green) e.g. Robert of Chester, *Liber de Compositione Alchemiae*, Manget, i, p. 518.

48. *Allegoriae Sapientium*, Distinctio 20; *Th. Ch.*, v, p. 79.

49. For numerous examples see Kopp, *Die Alchemie*, Heidelberg, 1886. Part 2, pp. 375–8.

and often the parallel between sexual union and the processes of alchemy was worked out in some detail. Works such as the *Rosarium Philosophorum* printed in Frankfurt in 1550 provide illustrations as well as a verbal comparison.

References to male and female constituents of a mixture were not unusual. Gold was compared to the male and silver to the female. As long as the early chemists believed that metals were produced by the union of sulphur and mercury, it was natural for them to speak metaphorically of these two substances as 'father and mother' or 'male' and 'female':

Sulphur enim est quasi pater, argentum vivum quasi mater metallorum.[50]

This analogy is quite common in later European alchemy, but sometimes it is stated that it is mercury which is the masculine principle whilst sulphur is feminine.[51] There was, after all, no outstanding reason why one should be called male and the other female, the main point being that the union of the two was considered to be necessary to produce a metal.

Different sexes were also attributed to the Aristotelian elements. 'Artefius'[52] considered fire and air as masculine and water and earth as feminine, probably because the first two were more active and spiritual whilst the latter corresponded to the realms of generation of fish, animals and plants. The *Turba Philosophorum* associates the male with 'lead'[53] (probably not the element Pb) and the female with orpiment. Another association was between the volatile parts of a chemical reaction (female) and the fixed or non-volatile parts (male). Yet another analogy was to call a substance which was able to coagulate another substance male, and a substance which would be coagulated was female. Probably vinegar and milk would satisfy these respective categories. A few alchemical writers who used such sexual analogies went to the extreme of basing chemical reasoning upon it. Thus, in a certain chemical reaction, not more

    50. *Compositum de Compositis*, attrib. to Albertus Magnus; *Th. Ch.*, iv, pp. 825–6.
    51. See Reusner, *Die Gab Gottes*, Basle, 1588, pp. 302, 293, and also the contradiction: 'pater = sulphurum', p. 305.
    52. *Clavis Maioris Sapientiae, Th. Ch.*, iv, p. 206.
    53. Op. cit., ed. Ruska, Berlin, 1931, p. 126. It is typical of the contradictions met with in alchemical literature that this was later quoted by Garlandius as 'lead is female' (because it is soft and frigid), *Das Buch der Alaune und Salze*, ed. Ruska, Berlin, 1935, p. 75.

than two substances are said to be necessary because wedlock is the union of two people only![54]

Analogies for chemical processes

The analogies so far discussed are concerned mainly with chemical substances. There were other analogies which were thought appropriate to describe chemical processes. An important analogy was the comparison of the process of creation willed by the alchemist in his curcurbit to the creation of the world by God. The two main texts on which this comparison was based were the Book of Genesis and the *Tabula Smaragdina*. The former described the creation of the world and the latter gave some authority to the analogy with alchemical creation. In the alchemical work it was necessary to start from the black prime matter and then, in keeping with the philosophy of Aristotle, the requisite form had subsequently to be imposed upon it. As the creative process got under way, light entered and in the first stage, the Sun and Moon showed themselves. This analogy was used by several later authors and in extreme cases degenerated into a discussion of the text of Genesis. The importance of Genesis in the history of alchemy cannot be ignored, although it would be a gross exaggeration to assert that 'the first chapter in Genesis is the greatest page in alchemy'.[55] Yet, even in the eighteenth century, an able chemist like Kunckel criticized Helmont's ideas on the elements, not on the basis of experiment, but by reference to the text, 'God created heaven and earth'.[56]

A second important source of analogy for chemical processes was the life cycle of man. The successive stages in a child's life from its birth and its subsequent growth were compared with the various stages in the alchemical work. Of the many analogies employed by alchemical authors it was one that could be most easily applied and understood. Jabir says that the matter used in the alchemical work should be like the microcosm, man and that it must be formed from male and female and must be 'educated' along the right lines.[57] In another Arabic text there

54. *Arcanum Hermeticae*, Manget, ii, p. 652.
55. Grillot de Givry, *Witchcraft, Magic and Alchemy*, London, 1931, p. 350.
56. Kunckel, *Laboratorium Chymicum*, Hamburg and Leipzig, 1716, Part 3, chap. 40, p. 537.
57. *Book of Mercy*, Berth., *M.A.*, iii, p. 179.

is found a detailed comparison of the 'Work' with human gestation.[58] The mysterious Morienus also compared the preparation of the magistery to the creation of man.[59] A similar kind of analogy is found in the *Speculum Alchemiae* (attributed to Roger Bacon) in which there is a comparison of the light diet of the infant and the more substantial diet at a later age to the fire which should first be low and then increased by degrees until the Work was accomplished.

Allegorical Time

As the preparation of the Philosopher's stone had been assimilated to the birth of a child or the growth of a plant, it comes as no surprise to find this symbolism used to describe the length of time which must be spent to achieve the goal of the alchemists. Thus Zosimos uses the following terms to describe the alchemical process:

The time of gestation is not less than nine months when there is no miscarriage[60]

Several centuries later an arabic alchemist wrote:

As for the number of days, some say that 40 days are necessary, others 80, 180, 100, 150; but the general opinion is that nine months are necessary.[61]

'Ortulanus', who may have written at the end of the fourteenth century, is one of those who writes of the four seasons of the alchemical work.[62] It begins in the winter and passes through the spring to the summer when flowers (a reddish colour in the alembic) are to be seen. The Work is finished in the autumn, the season when the farmer gathers in the harvest. The much quoted *Turba Philosophorum* also includes this analogy with the advice 'to dissolve in winter, to cook in spring, to coagulate in summer, and to gather and tinge the fruit in autumn'.[63]

During the whole period of Arabic and Latin alchemy the question of time required for chemical reactions, and, in particular, the fabrication of the supposed elixir, would appear to

58. *Book of El-Habîb*, Berth., *M.A.*, iii, p. 79.
59. Morienus Romanus, *De metallorum transmutatione*, Paris, 1564, f. 23v.
60. Berth., *A.G.*, tradn., p. 198.
61. *Book of El-Habîb*, Berth., *M.A.*, iii, p. 85.
62. *Practica Alchimica*; *Th. Ch.*, iv, p. 917.
63. Op. cit., ed. Ruska, Berlin, 1931, p. 127.

have been a major point of dispute among various authorities. Jabir makes no attempt to conceal this divergence:

The method followed in the operation which generally is the longest can last as long as 70 years according to the variations. . . . The shortest method lasts 15 days. You see, dear brother, the divergence which these figures present: 70 years and 15 days.[64]

It is no wonder that many writers give a list of times which have been claimed as sufficient to complete the 'Work' and leave it to the reader to decide which to believe.

It was always possible to say that when a 'philosopher' spoke of a 'year' or a 'month' he meant a 'philosophical year', etc., which was different from an ordinary year. Thus Ruland explains that a philosophical year is equivalent to a common month.[65] Faced with such contradictions and circumlocutions the sceptical modern reader tends to regard this as one more piece of evidence that alchemy was nothing but fraud. Others, who have been more sympathetic in their attitude to alchemy, have tried to give a plausible explanation of apparent inconsistencies in alchemical authors:

The philosophers have determined several periods of time for the preparation of our Art. Some have fixed this period at one year, others at one month, others again at three days, and still others at a single day. But in the same way as we call a day the length of time taken by the sun to traverse the heavens from the east to the west, the Sages have called a day the interval of time that elapses from the beginning of the cooking to the end. Those who speak of a month refer to the course of the sun through one sign of the Zodiac. Those who mention three days consider the beginning, the end and the middle of the work; and finally those who fix the time at a year, say this in respect of the four colours which form their four seasons.[66]

That such a defence was even possible indicates how little as well as how much could be contained in allegories. Although we are not likely to accept such an explanation it is clear that in the matter of time, as with chemical substances, the general practice was to conceal by allegory rather than reveal by literal statement.

64. *Book of Royalty*, Berth., *M.A.*, iii, p. 128.
65. Ruland, *Lexicon Alchemiae*, Prague, 1612, p. 43, but cf. p. 330: 'Philosophers month = 40 days', i.e. a philosopher's month would seem to be longer than a philosopher's year!
66. Quoted by Pernety, *Dictionnaire Mytho-Hermétique*, Paris, 1787, pp. xix-xx.

Description of the Goal of Alchemy

In addition to the 'philosopher's stone' several other names were given from time to time to the ultimate aim of the alchemists, names such as 'magistery',[67] 'quintessence', 'elixir' and chemical 'medicine'. The *raison d'être* of most of these names is not hard to find but the origin of the most important name, that of 'philosopher's stone' is obscure. According to Berthelot,[68] the expression is not found in texts before the seventh century A.D., although the idea of such a stone is more ancient. References to the goal of the alchemists as 'a stone which is not a stone' (λίθον τον οὐ λίθον) occur in the writings of Zosimos, who on one occasion puts this phrase into the mouth of Demokritos, the alchemist. It might be argued that such a phrase merely indicates the difficulty of expressing an unfamiliar concept in ordinary language. This phrase might have meant no more than that the substance sought was a solid (a 'stone') which was volatile (not a stone). This tincture would give metals a superficial white or yellow colouring. In the course of transition from Greek to Arabic and then to Latin the concept of transmutation changed but the old formula remained to describe the material which was to make transmutation possible. The phrase 'stone which is not a stone' is often quoted in Latin alchemy, in which it figured as a paradox and a model for the many deliberately contradictory statements made about the Philosopher's stone. This is how a late alchemical work explains the term 'stone' and comments on its nomenclature:

> Know that it is called a stone, not because it is like a stone, but only because, by virtue of its fixed nature, it resists the action of the fire as successfully as any stone. Its appearance is that of a fine powder, impalpable to the touch, sweet to the taste, fragrant to the smell, in potency a most penetrating spirit. . . . It has no name of its own; yet there is nothing in the whole world whose name it might not with perfect propriety bear.[69]

On the subject of the many names given to the goal of the alchemists it has been truly said that 'many alchemical writers

67. Literally: 'work of the master'. The term later became incorporated into chemical nomenclature, e.g. 'magistery of bismuth'.
68. Berth., *A.G.*, tradn., p. 194 n.1.; texte grec, p. 114, l. 3 (tradn., p. 122) and texte grec, p. 122, l. 5 (tradn., p. 130).
69. *A Brief Guide to the Celestial Ruby*, M.H., p. 780; H.M., vol. i, p. 249.

appear to have regarded it both as a duty and as a mark of their originality to advance a new name for the Stone, or to provide it with a new antithetical description.'[70]

Petrus Bonus compares the stone to a foundling, since both have no proper name of their own.[71] He explains away the many conflicting names given to the stone by comparing it with gold, which is called a ring or a goblet or a bracelet according to its particular form. Similar excuses for the almost infinite nomenclature of the stone were given by other writers.[72] A more reasonable practical explanation for the necessity of different names for what was apparently the same thing, was that the matter passed through different stages in its preparation:

> To each of the stages in the operation is given a name in keeping with the nature of the metal which it resembles; for example, if the metal blackens, it is called black lead.[73]

Analogies based on colour were frequent, but by no means universal. Each author had his own nomenclature:

> Some have given it a designation relating to its taste, others according to its characteristics or its use without worrying about it more deeply.[74]

Analogies on which the description was based were limitless, as Petrus Bonus makes clear:

> The ancient philosophers saw that this stone may be compared in its origin, its sublimation and in the conjunction of its elements to all things in the world, material and abstract, and to their properties.[75]

A complete list of possible names for the stone was, therefore, not a practical proposition; it was, nevertheless, attempted from time to time.[76] An Arabic manuscript gives a list of some sixty names to denote the stone[77] and the author says that this was only a minority. Included in the catalogue are the names of animals, metals, parts of the body and also common chemical

70. J. Read, *Prelude to Chemistry*, London, 1939, p. 127.
71. *Preciosa Margarita Novella*, cap. 9; *Th. Ch.*, v, p. 595.
72. e.g. 'Senior', *Th. Ch.*, (1622 edn.), v, p. 249.
73. *Book of Mercy*, Berth., *M.A.*, iii, p. 181.
74. *Book of Crates*, Berth., *M.A.*, iii, p. 51.
75. Op. cit., cap. 9, *Th. Ch.*, v, p. 592.
76. e.g. *The Names of the Philosopher's Stone*, collected by William Gratacolle—*Five Treatises of the Philosopher's Stone*, H.P., London, 1652, pp. 65–8.
77. *Book of Ostanes*, Berth., *M.A.*, iii, pp. 118–19.

substances like vinegar, salt, sulphur and glass. As both practical chemical experiments and theoretical alchemical speculation continued, the names for the philosopher's stone were
multiplied so that by the eighteenth century the number of
names in use had increased at least ten-fold.[78] The fact that
Greek, Hebrew, Arabic and Latin words were used indescriminately in European alchemy had the effect of expanding
the nomenclature of the Stone even further.

78. e.g. see Pernety, *Dictionnaire Mytho-Hermétique*, Paris, 1787, pp. 272–
280, where some six hundred names are given for the stone in its various
stages.

CHAPTER TWO

Further Difficulties of Language

The Special Use of Common Language

In many alchemical texts it was on comparatively rare occasions that a substance to be employed in a chemical reaction was mentioned by its usual name. The common practice was to use a language which was not intended to be understood literally. Use would be made either of allegory or of common words in a special sense known only to the 'adepts'. Thus it should not be assumed that the term 'water' always denotes H_2O, and even 'fire' often cannot be understood literally. 'Water' is usually used in the two more fundamental senses of a liquid substance such as mercury, or as a solvent and in the latter case even fire was included. Although fire and water were opposites in the restricted sense of the Aristotelian elements, to the alchemist they both suggested the concept of dissolution. He saw no clear distinction between the melting of a metal in the heat of a fire and the 'melting' of a salt when water is added to it. Thus we are not surprised to read in an Arabic text of a 'fiery water, which works like the work of fire'.[79] There are numerous examples of special meanings assigned by the alchemists to common words. 'Lead' or Saturn was the term used to describe the black prime matter from which new substances could be generated by having suitable forms impressed upon them. The 'vinegar' of the philosophers (often referred to as *acetum acerrimum*) was the name used for a solvent whose powers were claimed to be much greater than those possible for acetic acid. It may sometimes have stood for one of the mineral acids but it is more likely that it referred to mercury which has the power of dissolving metals such as gold by forming an amalgam. Another term which was used by early chemists in at least two quite different senses is 'magnesia'. In a technical sense it was usually the black oxide of manganese or iron, but in an al-

79. Ibn Umail, see *Mem. Bengal, 12* (1933), 194, n. 3.

chemical context it was often used to denote the black prime matter sometimes represented as 'lead'. The term 'magnesia' is found in Greek texts, whence it passed into Arabic and Latin alchemy. The black prime matter had to be dyed white to bring it nearer the perfection of the noble metals, and it may have been the use of the term 'magnesia' for the white alloy which led to its use to denote such substances as tin amalgam, and silver amalgam.

It must have been extremely disconcerting to the earnest practical reader of an alchemical tract to read about a preparation involving not common chemical substances, but substances which were designated as being of a particular kind used by the philosophers. Many authors chide the reader, telling him that if he uses common mercury he will be wasting his time; instead he should use 'the mercury of the philosophers' or 'our mercury'. As a sixteenth-century alchemist said, adhering to contemporary theory:

> Everybody knows that if imperfect metals are to be perfected, they must be perfected starting from sulphur and quicksilver; yet not everyone knows what that quicksilver is.[80]

It would seem, therefore, that there existed, parallel to the language of early chemistry, a mystical language[81] based on analogies with chemical substances. Attempts were, of course, made to relate 'philosophical' terms to common substances, as in the following 'interpretation':

> Our quicksilver is the clearest water, and our arsenic is pure silver, and our sulphur is pure gold; and in these three things is constituted total perfection.[82]

On closer examination, however, such a statement is seen to be of little value, because we can never be sure that any term does in fact refer to the chemical substance of that name.

In a few cases it is possible to attempt a rational explanation for what would otherwise be meaningless nonsense. One such

80. Laurentius Ventura, *De Lapide Philosophico*; *Th. Ch.*, ii, p. 226.

81. e.g. Jacob Boehme speaking of mercury: 'Yet here I do not altogether understand the Mercurius . . . which the apothecaries use (although that hath the same virtue or power, and is of the same essence) but I speak of that in the first Principle . . . of God . . . .' (*Concerning the Three Principles of the Divine Essence*, London, 1910, Ch. 1, § 14.)

82. *Speculum Alchymiae*; *Th. Ch.*, iv, p. 528.

case is a phrase that was often repeated that 'our gold is not common gold' (*aurum nostrum non est aurum vulgi*).[83] The following interpretations are suggested:

(i) Alchemical gold was, at best, a poor imitation alloy.
(ii) Alchemical gold, once made, had the power of transmuting base metals into gold.
(iii) The goal of the alchemists was not material but spiritual. They were seeking a mystical perfection.

Paradox

An increasing amount of paradox is found in later alchemical literature, although it is not entirely absent even in the period of Alexandrian alchemy. The habit of giving conflicting descriptions to the philosopher's stone has already been mentioned. A common example of this practice was the statement that the Stone was more precious and more vile than anything in the world.[84] Such a statement in a religious context might well be made about man, and we know that paradoxes are found in many religions. The psychologist Jung considered the paradox as 'one of our most valued spiritual possessions'[85] and stated that a religion 'becomes inwardly impoverished when it loses or reduces its paradoxes', because an unambiguous language is unsuited to express the incomprehensible. It seems clear that, whereas mystical alchemy may well have thrived on paradox, its existence in the literature was stultifying to alchemy as a science. What conclusion can we draw from a typical paradox such as that presented by Isaac Hollandus in a treatise on the philosopher's stone?

If you say that it is water you speak truly; if you say that it is not water your denial is not false. . . .[86]

A simple explanation of this might be that the use of the term 'water' in the first sentence is by analogy and refers to any liquid; in the second sentence it refers literally to ordinary water. Thus, in many cases, apparent paradoxes can be solved if one appreciates the metaphorical use to which language was

83. e.g. *Rosarium Philosophorum*, Frankfurt, 1550, f. 34.
84. *Mem. Bengal. 12*, 194; *Th. Ch.*, (1622), v, p. 262.
85. C. G. Jung, op. cit., p. 15.
86. *De Lapide Philosophorum: Th. Ch.*, ii, p. 134.

put by many alchemical authors in order to cast a veil of mystery over even the simplest chemical reactions. Another example in which a paradox might have been avoided by the precise use of terms is provided by some of the Alexandrian alchemists in their conception of the composition of gold. On the one hand, because gold was fusible, it was associated with water. On the other hand the precious metal was associated with fire because it was bright and yellow. Gold was therefore said to be composed of Fire and Water—two diametrically opposed Aristotelian elements:

How are Water and Fire, enemies and contrary to each other, opposed by nature, re-united in the same body in concord and affection? Oh, unbelievable mixture: whence comes the unexpected friendship between enemies?[87]

Sometimes paradoxes can be explained as instances of a formula which has persisted after its original significance has been lost, e.g. the phrase 'the stone which is not a stone'. But finally, it must be said of the practitioners for whom alchemy was a projection of the self into a scheme of chemical processes and a path of ascent to perfection, that in their belief that their Art comprised the supernatural as well as the natural, ordinary language became insufficient to them and their writings are probably more to be appreciated as contributions to mysticism or poetry than to an exact science.

Geometrical Representation

A survey of alchemical symbolism would be incomplete without a mention of the geometrical figures sometimes used to convey the idea of the properties of a chemical substance or its constitution. The two Aristotelian elements which tended to move upwards were represented by triangles the apexes of which suggested this movement, whilst water and earth which naturally moved downwards were shown as inverted triangles (see Fig. 2). The perfection of gold had been represented since Egyptian times by the completeness of a circle. Even in the nineteenth century, Dalton's symbols sometimes suggested pictorially a property or a resemblance.

87. Berth., *A.G.*, tradn., p. 102.

The Aristotelian doctrine of four elements lent itself very easily to geometrical symbolism by a figure of four sides. This was usually a square, although the figure was often roughly drawn.[88] As these four elements owed their existence to a combination of four qualities, this led to a further representation of a square within a square:

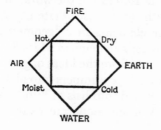

In some of the works attributed to Raymond Lull[89] geometrical figures are used. Gold, being perfect, is composed of an equal proportion of the four elements, shown by a circle on a square. Silver, the composition of which is represented by a triangle, differs from the yellow metal gold in that it does not contain fire.

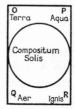 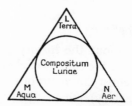

When the concept of three principles, propagated by Paracelsus, was generally accepted and used by most chemists of the sixteenth and seventeenth centuries, the completeness of the conjunction of four elements in a square was supplemented by a triangle, the apexes of which represented sulphur, mercury and salt.

A geometrical description of the preparation of the philosopher's stone is found in the *Rosarium Philosophorum*, where it

88. e.g. *Clavis Sapientiae*, attrib. Alphonso X of Castille; *Th. Ch.*, v, pp. 766–786.

89. e.g. *Practica*; *Th. Ch.*, iv, p. 139.

is said that the circle must be squared to make the two sexes (mercury and sulphur?) into one whole:

> Out of the man and woman make a round circle and extract a quadrangle from this and from the quadrangle a triangle. Make a round circle and you will have the Philosopher's Stone.[90]

An illustration of this is found in the works of Michael Maier in the early seventeenth century (see Plate 1a). A further reference to joining the four elements in a 'geometrical proportion' is found in one of Newton's alchemical MSS.[91]

Not entirely separate from the ideas of geometrical symbolism were attempts to introduce numbers into alchemy. With the extremists this degenerated into lists of numbers more cabbalistic than alchemical. A more moderate example is provided by 'Basil Valentine':

> Know that the stone is composed out of one, two, three, four and five. Out of five, that is the quintessence[92] of its own substance. Out of four, by which we must understand the four elements. Out of three, and these are the three principles of all things. Out of two, for the mercurial substance is twofold. Out of one, and this is the first essence of everything which emanated from the primal fiat of creation.[93]

Colour Symbolism

Throughout the history of alchemy great importance was attached to the colours of chemical substances. For the practical early chemist the colour of a substance was a convenient (though unsatisfactory) means of identifying it, as may be seen from early attempts at chemical nomenclature. For many alchemists, to whom the ideas of Galileo, Boyle and Locke were unknown, the colour of a substance was a primary quality or fundamental property of a substance and was often of deep symbolical significance.

Black was always associated with impurity, putrefaction or the 'death' of a substance. In alchemical theory the primal matter

90. Op. cit., Frankfurt, 1550, f. 30v.
91. *Sententiae Notabiles*, reprinted in Ambix, 5 (1956), 69.
92. *quinta essentia* = fifth essence. See also F. Sherwood Taylor, 'The Idea of the Quintessence' in *Science, Medicine and History*, ed. E. A. Underwood, London, 1953, vol. i, pp. 247–65.
93. *The Twelve Keys*, Appendix, *M.H.*, pp. 426–7, *H.M.*, vol. i, p. 353.

was black and on this new qualities could be imposed. Black was also the colour associated with Saturn (lead). Although white was a universal symbol of purity, it was not generally used in alchemy to denote perfection, since white was associated with silver and silver was second in perfection to the yellow metal gold. Gold, however, was more often associated in European alchemy with red rather than yellow, the idea being that red was an intense yellow. This is clearly shown in a quotation from the *Speculum Alchemiae* attributed to Roger Bacon:

> The red elixir makes substances yellow infinitely[94] and transmutes all metals into the purest gold.

Green was associated with fruitfulness, and as long as it was considered that generation and growth took place in minerals as in vegetables and animals, green substances were of some importance, as may be judged from the following passage from the *Rosarium Philosophorum*:

> All that is perfect in copper (*aes*) is that green which is in it alone. . . . Oh blessed greenness, which generates all things. . . .[95]

The colour of copper compounds was thought so important that Geber refers to a salt of copper as 'greenness made of copper, calcined and dissolved'.[96]

Colours often figured prominently in allegorical descriptions. Thus Bernard Trevisan refers to the succession of colours which was said to appear in the making of the philosopher's stone in the following passage:

> I asked him what colour the king was? And he replied that he was clothed in the first place with a sheet of gold. Then he had a doublet of velvet and a shirt white as snow and flesh as sanguine as blood.[97]

Another allegorical description from 'Basil Valentine' may be cited in which copper is referred to as

> . . . Lady Venus, who appeared in a crimson robe intertissued with threads of green, and charmed all by the beauty of her countenance and the fragrance of the flowers which she bore in her hand.[98]

---

94. *rubeum quidem elixir citrinat in infinitum*, op. cit., cap. 7, Manget, i, p. 616.
95. Op. cit., Frankfurt, 1550, f. 9v.
96. *The Works of Geber*, trans. Russell, London, 1928, p. 219.
97. *Book of the Natural Philosophy of Metals*, Bk. 4, Zacaire, *Opuscule de la vraie philosophie*, Lyons, 1612, pp. 269–70.
98. *The Great Stone of the Ancient Sages*, *M.H.*, p. 390; *H.M.*, i, p. 321.

It might be argued[99] that such preoccupation with colour in later alchemy was directly in the tradition of the Alexandrian alchemists who were concerned with dyeing metals till they had the desired tint. Any attempt to explain the interest in colour as a degenerate continuation of a technical tradition could not be accepted as a complete explanation. We should not forget the importance in human society of colour, as exemplified in heraldry, the vestments and decorations traditional in the Roman Catholic Church, etc.

Pictorial Representation

In European alchemy pictorial representation became an increasingly important mode of communication. It has been truly said that 'Alchemy was pictorial in its expression to a degree which is not realized in this age'.[100] As the words of the alchemical authors became more obscure, there was some attempt made to express alchemical theory and practice in pictures, thus supplementing verbal symbolism by pictorial symbolism:

> The philosophers express themselves more freely and with more significance in a mute discourse, that is by allegories and enigmatic figures, than in words. Examples of this are the table of Senior, the allegorical pictures of the Rosarium, those of Abraham the Jew reported by Flamel, and those of Flamel himself. More recently there are the emblems of the learned Michael Maier. . . .[101]

The illustrations represented in the following pages attempt to give a much abbreviated view of some aspects of pictorial symbolism. Most of these examples are taken from printed books of the early seventeenth century, a period when such work was at its zenith. The symbolism on which these illustrations are based is, with a few exceptions, of a much earlier date.

Plate 1a shows a geometrical aspect of alchemical symbolism referred to above. Plate 2a is intended to describe four stages in the alchemical process and also the four elements which are indicated on the spheres. The four operations depicted are (from left to right) *Solutio*, *Ablutio*, *Conjunctio* and *Fixio*, as the accompanying verse tells us. The elements are Earth, Water,

99. A. J. Hopkins, *Alchemy, Child of Greek Philosophy*, New York, 1934.
100. J. Read, *Prelude to Chemistry*, London, 1939, p. xxi.
101. Espagnet, *Arcanum Hermeticae Philosophiae Opus*, p. 7, cap. 12. N. Albineus, *Bibliotheca Chemica Contracta*, Geneva, 1653.

PLATE 1a. Squaring the circle to make the sexes one whole. (From M. Maier, *Atalanta Fugiens*)

PLATE 1b. 'The whole philosophical work'. (From *Viridarium Chymicum*)

PLATE 2a. The four elements. (From D. Stolcius, *Viridarium Chymicum*)

PLATE 2b. The Seven Metals. (From *Viridarium Chymicum*)

Air and Fire respectively. Another work, printed in 1570[102] depicts the three principles of Paracelsus. The Spirit (Sulphur) is illustrated by a winged male figure in a cloud of fumes emanating from a bowl which he is carrying. The Body (Salt) is shown as a knight in armour. The Soul (Mercury) is shown as a female figure from which light radiates.

Plate 2b shows the seven gods in Hades, each god corresponding to a planet and a metal. They are in order (from left to right):

(front row)	Diana	Luna	Silver
	Apollo	Sol	Gold
	Venus		Copper
(second row)	Jupiter		Tin
	Mars		Iron
	Saturn		Lead
	Mercury		Mercury

An interesting aspect of the study of alchemical pictures is to compare the impressions of different artists showing the same alchemical process. Plates 3a and 3b both symbolise the purification of metals. In Plate 3a gold is purified by fusing it with antimony, the latter being intended to combine with any impurities in the gold. This is depicted by a wolf (antimony) devouring the king (gold). They are then cast into the fire from which the king emerges revivified, as can be seen in the background. The first of the twelve 'Keys' of 'Basil Valentine' (Plate 3b) is slightly more complex. Two fires are shown and the picture may be interpreted in two halves. On the left the king is to be purified by throwing his body to a fierce grey wolf. The accompanying instructions say that this is to be done three times and then the king will be fit for the rest of the work, i.e. antimony is to be added to gold and strongly heated in the crucible shown. The queen on the right of the picture represents silver and the old man with the scythe is Saturn or lead (see Plate 2b). Silver is therefore to be purified by heating it with lead in the adjacent cupel.

Attempts to communicate the whole alchemical Work in one picture were occasionally made and Libavius undertook this ambitious task[103]. More detailed instructions could be con-

---

102. Thurneysser zum Thurn, *Quinta Essentia*, Munster, 1570, f. 67, f. 81, f. 87.

103. *Alchymia*, Frankfurt, 1606, Commentarium, Part II, p. 55.

tained in a series of pictures.[104] The most famous example of this type of communication is the *Mutus Liber*, which is reprinted in Manget's collection of alchemical works.[105] In this form it consists of 15 folio pages of illustrations depicting various processes carried out by an alchemist and his wife. In one picture they are shown extracting dew by ringing out sheets which had been exposed in a field. Dew was thought to be endowed with wonderful properties because it was reputed to contain the 'Universal Spirit'. In succeeding illustrations in the *Mutus Liber* Sol, Luna and a child undergo further operations but at no time is any verbal clue given to the substances used.

Another illustration which summarizes the contents of tomes of alchemical literature is shown in Plate 1b. It incorporates a square, a triangle, a seven-pointed star and a circle. At the four corners of the square are the four Aristotelian elements. At each apex of the triangle is one of the three principles of Paracelsus. The pointed star includes the symbols of the seven metals and between the points of the star are depicted stages in the preparation of the Stone, e.g. the two birds bearing a crown aloft suggest sublimation. Finally there is the circle which encloses the words: *Visita Interiora Terrae Rectificando Invenies Occultum Lapidem.* This translated means: 'Visit the interior of the earth; by rectifying thou shalt find the hidden Stone' but it would seem more reasonable to regard this as an acrostic, since the first letters of the Latin words form: V.I.T.R.I.O.L. 'Vitriol' was a general term used to denote any shiny crystalline substance and as this illustration is entitled 'The Whole Work of Philosophy' it suggests that this 'vitriol of the philosophers' was an important ingredient in their preparation.[106] Another acrostic is explained by Kircher.[107] It consists essentially of three concentric circles with the legend: *Sola Vera Laudat Philosophia Homines Veritatis Rectae/Fiet Inde Xenophontis Verum Mandatum/Lege Omnes Sophos*

104. e.g. *Viridarium Chymicum* by Daniel Stolcius, Frankfurt, 1624, in which each illustration is accompanied by an explanatory verse. This is a derivative work, taking illustrations *inter alia* from J. Mylius, *Philosophia Reformata*, Frankfurt, 1622, and M. Maier, *Tripus Aureus*, Frankfurt, 1618.

105. *Mutus Liber in quo tamen tota Philosophia hermetica, figuris hieroglyphicis depingitur* by 'Altus' (possibly the 'Senior' of alchemical literature?) Manget, i, pp .938ff.

106. Kunckel called vitriol the 'Lock and Key of all Metals' and says that he had used many hundredweight of it in his experiments (*An Experimental Confirmation of Chymical Philosophy*, London, 1705, p. 115).

107. *Mundus subterraneus*, Amsterdam, 1665, vol. ii, p. 293, fig. 2.

Ergo Sic Tuos. Taking the first letter of each word, we are given the information that the fixed Sulphur of the alchemists is a synonym for gold: *Sulphur Fixum Sol est.*

Secret Names

This section will serve as a supplement and also as a summary of some of the points made in the preceding paragraphs regarding the oblique terminology found in alchemical literature. It is sometimes suggested that the practice of denoting chemical substances by fanciful names was a late aberration of alchemy and, as such, is not relevant to the main stream of the history of chemistry. That, however, is not so. A continuous tradition is found in alchemical literature dating back to the alchemists of Alexandria. The Greek secret names were continued and extended in Arabic alchemy and thence transmitted to Europe.

The antiquity of the secret tradition in alchemical, technical and medical writings is illustrated by the following quotation from an Egyptian papyrus:

Interpretation draws from the sacred names, which the sacred writers employ for the purpose of putting at fault the curiosity of the vulgar. The plants and other things which they make use of for the images of the gods have been designated by them in such a way that for lack of understanding they perform a vain labour in following a false path. But we have drawn the interpretation of much of the description and hidden meanings.[108]

Examples of such secret names found in another papyrus are 'blood of the dragon' for cinnabar or the red resin of the *Pterocarpus draco* and 'quicksilver' for a substance used in whitening pearls which is definitely not mercury.[109] A Greek lexicon of the art of making gold includes 'milk of the black cow' (mercury extracted from the black sulphide ore of mercury) and 'seed of Venus' (verdigris).[110]

Two historians of alchemy, Ruska and Wiedemann[111] have compiled a list of the secret names given by Arabic alchemists

---

108. Leyden Papyrus V, quoted in Berth., *A.G.*, Introdn., p. 10.

109. C. O. Lagercrantz, *Papyrus Graecus Holmiensis*, Uppsala, 1913, p. 17, l. 32; p. 7, l. 32 and p. 8, l. 33.

110. Berth., *A.G.*, tradn., pp. 6, 4.

111. 'Alchemistische Decknamen'. *Sitzungsberichte der physikalisch—medicinische Societät*, Erlangen, 56 (1924), 17–36.

to common chemical substances. Gold, silver, iron and copper were sometimes referred to as the father, mother, brother and sister respectively. Elsewhere gold is 'the day' and silver 'the night'. Metals were also referred to in a hierarchical order in which mercury was 'the second', copper 'the third' and lead 'the seventh' (i.e. the last). Realgar and orpiment were mentioned variously as 'the two brothers', 'the two kings' or the 'two friends'.

In European alchemy such fanciful names tended to multiply and in the sixteenth century one author[112] was able to give over a hundred synonyms for mercury, including such terms as 'living water', 'flying eagle', 'tail of the dragon', 'white smoke', 'runaway slave', and characteristically, 'the whole secret' (*totum secretum*). The use of terms like these continued in the seventeenth century. In Jean Beguin's *Tyrocinium Chymicum*, the later editions of which appeared in the second half of the seventeenth century, the reader is instructed in the calcination of antimony to make use of 'the venenate Scum of the two Dragons'; another chemical substance (probably calomel) is concealed by the term 'Celestial Eagle more white than Snow'.[113]

The principle of dispersion

There would be some justification for the view that alchemical literature was a conspiracy between successive generations of writers to use a maximum number of words to give a minimum of information. When one considers the vast body of alchemical literature or even the number of works by individual authors, such as are attributed to Raymond Lull or to Jabir, one cannot help questioning the motives of their authors. The Latin author Geber claimed at the beginning of his *Sum of Perfection* that in this work he had reduced the whole of alchemy to one small volume. Petrus Bonus of Ferrara went even further in his assertion that the whole secret of alchemy, to which so many tomes had been devoted, could be written down in six to twelve lines.[114]

On the one hand, therefore, there was the claim that brevity was not only desirable but possible, and on the other hand the

112. M. Toxites, *Onomasticon I*, Argentorati, 1574, pp. 11–13.
113. *Tyrocinium Chymicum*, trans. Russell, London, 1669, pp. 89, 117.
114. *Preciosa Margarita Novella*, cap. 10; *Th. Ch.*, v, p. 602.

fact that even writers who claimed to write briefly and to the point were prolix and obscure. This prolixity was often a deliberate method used to discourage the ordinary reader and might be termed more exactly 'the principle of dispersion'. Jabir admitted quite frankly that his works were written on this principle:

My books are numerous and the science in them is dispersed. Whoever reunites them, at the same time reunites the science and reaches therefore to his goal and will be successful, because I have described the whole science without keeping secret the smallest part of it; but the only enigma in them is their dispersion.[115]

In a supposed dialogue between Jabir and his master, the latter says to Jabir:

In all your works I can see no chapter which is complete in itself; all are obscure and mixed up to such an extent that one gets lost in them. . . . What you have said is true . . . but confused and mixed with other things.[116]

The application of this principle increased the difficulty of the reader in recognizing an alchemical text as such. Even a genuine theological discussion might be introduced into an alchemical work:

It is not therefore undesirable, oh my brother, to find a discourse about religion in the middle of a discourse on alchemy.[117]

The actual description of an alchemical process might only be found incidentally after reading through much irrelevant material. In the *Book of Balances* it is difficult to determine where Jabir starts the subject of the book, if indeed it can be said to have a subject. The book begins with a story about Adam, a discussion on the parts of the brain and a section on Aristotelian logic. The importance of the equilibrium of the four elements and the four humours is then touched upon; then follow a list of superstitions, mostly relating to medicine and natural history. After mentioning the properties of a few chemical substances, the latter half of the book is largely devoted to cabbalism. Before the end of the work the doctrine

115. *K. al-hawāss*, chap. 16 quoted by M. Taslimi, *A Conspectus of recent researches on Arabic chemistry*, M. Sc. Dissertation (H. & P. of S.), University of London, 1951, pp. 21, 22.

116. *The Little Book of Clemency*, Berth., M.A., iii, p. 134.

117. *K. al-mājid*, quoted by Taslimi, loc. cit.

of the four qualities is again mentioned and Jabir writes (with apparent seriousness) that he has revealed everything to the reader without using any enigmatical or obscure expressions. Incidentally, to complete the difficulties of the reader, the significance of the word 'Balance' in the title is explained only in another of Jabir's works, the *Book of Royalty*.

The principle of dispersion was used and defended by the Jewish philosopher Maimonides who, though principally concerned with theology, considered that in Natural Science too, there were topics which should not be fully explained. This might be because the author's knowledge was not complete and a systematic explanation therefore impossible, or it might be done deliberately by giving the mere headings of the discussion of a problem and scattering these throughout the book:

You must therefore not expect from me more than such heads. And even these have not been methodically and systematically arranged in this work but have been, on the contrary, scattered and are interspersed with other topics which we shall have occasion to explain.[118]

Roger Bacon made use of the principle of dispersion in connection with his alchemical writings, but in rather different circumstances. He was concerned with communicating knowledge of alchemy from England to the Pope (Clement IV) in Rome and he had to take precautions to see that no third party who might intercept his message would be able to possess all his 'secrets'. Bacon states that he has written the secrets in three separate works:[119]

(i) In the *Opus Secundum* where I have written enigmatically of practical alchemy; (ii) In the sixth sin of the *Study of Theology* where I wrote of speculative alchemy; (iii) In a separate treatise of which I sent a rough copy to your Holiness. In this, questions of natural philosophy and of medicine are treated, yet it is really about alchemy.

He says that he has done this so that only the Pope would be in a position to see these great things:

For it is scarcely possible that these four writings could fall into one

118. *Guide to the Perplexed*, London, 1947, pp. 3, 4.
119. *Part of the Opus Tertium of Roger Bacon*, ed. A. G. Little, Aberdeen, 1912, pp. 81–2. See also *Opus Tertium*, ed. J. S. Brewster, London, 1859, chap. 12, p. 42, where Bacon says that one part cannot be understood without the rest.

hand; and it does not matter to me if one or two or even three are seen by anybody, because unless a person studies all four diligently, he will be able to understand nothing of the great secrets. But because there is the possibility that by some unlucky chance all four may fall into the hands of one person, I have (following the commandment of God and the advice and example of all the sages) kept a part of the secret, and I shall only reveal this by word of mouth.

A concrete example of the application of the principle of dispersion occurs in the works of Glauber, who first prepared sodium sulphate, which to him was '*sal mirabile*'. It would have been a simple matter to state that common salt and oil of vitriol were necessary, but Glauber, no doubt mindful of the profits he had amassed by keeping the preparation of his salt secret, was not willing to publish his knowledge in so simple a fashion. On the other hand he did not wish his enemies to say that he had not a full and perfect knowledge of the preparation of the '*sal mirabile*'. He therefore adopted a compromise solution which was typical of alchemical literature. The two constituents are never clearly described together; if the name of one is stated unequivocally, the nature of the other is hidden by misleading metaphors. In the first passage to be quoted the use of common salt is described in a prolix way, but oil of vitriol is only hinted at by a reference to 'fire and water';

This, my Sal Mirabile, is prepared and separated from all vulgar Salts by the help of Art, nevertheless more easily from one than from another. For it may be elicited not only from the Salt of the kitchen, but also from other salts . . . (but) setting those salts aside, we prepare our Sal Mirabile of that common salt which is used in kitchens, separating from it by the help of Fire and Water, whatsoever is earthy and terrene.[120]

On another occasion he makes it clear that oil of vitriol must be used, but the other constituent is misleadingly described as 'white fusible Sulphur':

Now that I may, without any wandering Ambages, describe the method of preparing this Salt. . . . Know in very deed that this salt is no other than common (but rightly prepared) Oyl of Vitriol, coagulated by white fusible Sulphur into a sweet Salt. . . . But how that Oyl of Vitriol, or Universal Acidity, may be changed into such

120. *De Natura Salium*, Amsterdam, 1658, p. 80; *Works*, London, 1689, Part I, p. 261(b).

a wonderful Stone, not Corrosive, I propose not to divulge. It is enough for me positively to affirm that it may be done.[121]

Codes

Another method adopted by Glauber for concealing the necessary details of the preparation of his '*Sal mirabile*' was the use of arbitrary symbols in place of the name of a substance. One of his descriptions runs as follows:

> R of common salt two parts, dissolve it in a sufficient quantity of common water; pour A upon the solution; put the mixture into a glass Body . . . and begin to distil. . . . Dissolve the salt remaining in the Body or Retort (if neither be broke) in water, filter and evaporate the Water, let it crystallise.[122]

Glauber provides an extreme example of the steps taken to conceal the substances necessary for a chemical reaction when in one of his works[123] he persistently leaves blank spaces for the names of the substances and vessels required for the extraction of gold and silver from certain minerals.

Among seven distinct methods used to hide the secrets of alchemy which were described by Roger Bacon[124] there is one which consists of using at random different alphabets such as Hebrew, Greek and Latin, and another which consisted of using an alphabet invented arbitrarily by the author. Numerous examples of secret alphabets are given by the Neopolitan scholar Giovanni Battista Porta.[125] Despite surviving example of such alphabets, it cannot be said that their use was very common in alchemical literature.

Apart from the creation of secret alphabets, letters of the ordinary alphabet were used in such works as the *Practica* and the *De Secretis Naturae* both attributed to Raymond Lull. In the former work the letters O, P, Q, R represent the supposed composition of gold in terms of earth, water, air and fire respectively,

121. *Von den Dreyen Anfangen der Metallen*, Amsterdam, 1666, p. 89; *Works*, London, 1689, Part III, p. 17(b).

122. *Miraculum Mundi, Ander Theil*, Amsterdam, 1660, p. 12; *Works*, London, 1689, Part I, p. 225.

123. *Appendix Generalis, Prima Centuria*, Amsterdam, 1660, e.g. p. 78; *Works*, London, 1689, Part II, e.g. p. 15a.

124. *Epistola de Secretis Operibus Artis et Naturae*; Manget, i, p. 622.

125. *De Occultis Literarum Notis*, Argentorati, 1606.

although in the second of these two works these letters are used with a different meaning. A more systematic use of letters to denote substances is found in a manuscript known as the *Liber Laureatus*. The author makes a habit of using the initial letters only of the Latin names of the Aristotelian elements. Thus: I(gnis), A(qua), A(er), T(erra). Another Italian manuscript entitled *Libellus aureus* contains a list of numbers from one to sixteen, to each of which a special meaning was attached. Thus $14 = oleum$, $11 = sulphur naturae$, etc.[126]

Quite a common practice was to write down the name of a substance with its letters transposed. This method of concealment is referred to by Hoghelande in his treatise on the difficulties of Alchemy.[127] An example of this was found by Berthelot in a twelfth century manuscript of the *Mappae clavicula* in which the following passage occurs:

De commixtione puri et fortissimi xknk cum III qbsuf tbmkt cocta in ejus negocii vasis fit aqua quae accensa flammam incombustam servat materiam.[128]

Berthelot has interpreted the three barbaric words in this passage by replacing each letter by the preceding letter of the alphabet. Thus:

xknk = vini
qbsuf = parte
tbmkt = salis

In this way the passage is shown to refer to the preparation of alcohol by the distillation of a mixture of strong wine and salt, but care was taken by the author to conceal the names of the substances required.

Another instance in which there is some reason for believing that a re-arrangement of letters has been used to conceal an essential constituent in a chemical reaction is in the *Epistola de Secretis* attributed to Roger Bacon in which the making of gunpowder is described. The use of saltpetre and sulphur is stated unambiguously but there is also a jumble of letters, which, it is reasonable to suppose, refer to charcoal (without which the

126. Both MSS. are described by Carbonelli, *Sulle Fonti Storiche della Chimica e dell' Alchimia in Italia*, Rome, 1925, pp. 49ff., 31.
127. *Th. Ch.*, i, p. 156. 128. Berth., *M.A.*, i, p. 61.

mixture would not explode). The passage in question is printed in the 1542 Paris edition as follows:

Sed tamen salis petrae LVRV / Vo Po Vir Can Vtriet sulphuris et sic facies to- / nitruum. . . .[129]

By the sixteenth and seventeenth centuries it had become generally known that one of the devices used to conceal the names of substances was to form anagrams of them or to use drastic abbreviations. Thus among the hundreds of names used to describe the philosopher's stone were Xelis (=*silex*, i.e. flint by inversion) and Xidar (=*radix*, i.e. a root). It was, therefore, not an uncommon practice to study closely any uncommon word to see if it could be reduced to a familiar name. A term which attracted particular attention in this respect was *Alkahest* (the supposed universal solvent) which some had tried to reduce to '*alles Geist*' and other derivations which Kunckel effectively ridiculed.[130] Boerhaave[131] provides some interesting evidence from the writings of Paracelsus,[132] to whom he attributes the invention of the word 'alkahest':

And upon considering that it was usual with him (i.e. Paracelsus) to conceal common words by the transposition of their letters, it was imagined that this was the case here; though sometimes too he formed strange words by joining the beginnings of different words together. Thus when he would make use of *Tartarus* to resolve the Saburra in the Spleen, he says, take *Sutratar*. And again, when for diseases proper to the kidneys he prescribes *Saffron* which from its golden colour the Chemists called *Aroma Philosophorum*, he says these distempers are cured by *Aroph*. Hence, therefore, some persons have thought that *Alkahest* signified *alkali est*.

Finally the use of acrostics to convey a statement or the name of an important substance is occasionally found in the literature (see p. 34).

129. *De mirabili potestate artis et naturae*, Paris, 1542, *Epistola de Secretis* f. 52r. Steele (*Nature*, *121* (1928), 208–9) has suggested that this edition was based on a defective manuscript. The original cipher was in Greek characters but became completely transformed in the course of copying.
130. *Laboratorium Chymicum*, Hamburg and Leipzig, 1716, Part 3, p. 506.
131. *Elements of Chemistry*, trans. Dallowe, London, 1735, vol. i, p. 490.
132. *Sämtliche Werke*, ed. Sudhoff, Munich and Berlin, 1922–33, vol. 3, pp. 26, 21.

CHAPTER THREE

The Dilemma of Alchemical Literature

The Importance of the Written Word in the Alchemical Tradition

The literature of alchemy was not merely a record of the activity of alchemists and a curiosity to those attracted to the study of alchemy. It was of vital importance to every student of alchemy whether his motive was the scientific one of investigating nature, the commercial motive of making gold, or the mystical one in which chemical changes symbolized a deeper reality. Chemical reactions could not be carried out by guesswork or magic; as in other sciences, a systematic study of previous work in the same field was necessary:

There is no way by which this art can truly be found . . . except by completing your studies and understanding the words of the philosophers.[133]

In the *Turba Philosophorum* Parmenides exhorts the student to study books constantly, and this detailed examination of written texts was an important feature of alchemy. Even in the earliest Greek alchemical texts we notice that there is a notable preoccupation with finding out the meaning of the ancient authors, e.g. utterances attributed to Hermes. The allegorical style which was almost universally adopted did not lead to ready understanding, and it might be only after a passage had been read through ten times that some of its meaning might be understood. Geber at the beginning of his *Sum of Perfection* advises the reader of his works to 'labour studiously in Our Volumes, and endeavour to ponder them very often in your Mind that you may acquire the true Intention of Our Words'. A detailed study of any work was all the more necessary because even a slight error in the text might materially alter the

133. Ricardus Anglicus, *Correctorium alchymiae*, cap. ii; *Th. Ch.*, ii, p. 387.

sense of a passage. As Thomas Norton of Bristol wrote in his
Ordinall of Alchimy:

> ... chaunging of some one sillable
> May make this Boke unprofitable
> Therefore trust not to one Reading or twaine,
> But twenty tymes it would be over sayne.

It was generally agreed that reading should not be confined
to one author. The man who wished to learn the secrets of alchemy should read widely. There was some truth in the assertion of the late sixteenth-century alchemist Michael Sendivogius
that 'one writer explains another'.[134] It was on this premiss that
the editor of the *Musaeum Hermeticum* arranged a selection of
tracts by different authors in one volume, hoping that 'each
would throw light on the other's meaning'. A seventeenth-
century work contains the following advice:

> Read, and think over what you read. If you make nothing of it,
> read the same books over again, then read other books; for the last
> which you read will be able to provide you with the meaning of all
> the others in the same way that those which you read first will enable
> you to understand the later ones.[135]

A term, the meaning of which in one context was doubtful,
would be more easily understood after seeing it in other con-
texts. As Maimonides said,

> What I say in a particular passage is a key for the comprehension
> of all similar passages.[136]

Another reason why wide reading was necessary was to acquire
greater familiarity with the rich symbolism of alchemy. Finally,
there was the fundamental need to separate plain statement
from allegory and to distinguish truth from falsehood. This is
how Bernard Trevisan described his method of acquiring knowledge of alchemy:

> I looked for where most books were in agreement. Then I con-
> sidered that this was the truth. For they can only say the truth in one
> respect. And in this way I found the truth. For where they agreed
> most was the truth.[137]

134. *Concerning Sulphur*, Preface; *M.H.*, p. 601, *H.M.*, ii, p. 128.
135. *Texte D'Alchimie*, Paris, 1695, p. 39.
136. *Guide to the Perplexed*, London, 1947, p. 21.
137. *De transmutatione metallorum*, Zacaire, *Philosophie Naturelle des Métaux*,
Lyons, 1612, p. 202.

PLATE 3a. The wolf devouring the dead king. (From *Atalanta Fugiens*)

PLATE 3b. The first key of Basil Valentine. (From M. Maier, *Tripus Aureus*)

The Limitations of Alchemical Literature

Although there was a strong tradition in alchemy which attached great importance to the written word, there was for many workers a feeling that this was not enough. The principal reasons for this attitude may be considered under the following headings:

(a) Knowledge of alchemy was not intended for the casual reader.
(b) A practical craft could not be learned from books.
(c) Few alchemical authors wrote from personal experience.
(d) Alchemical literature contained many misleading or false statements.

The Greek alchemists had called their work the 'Divine Art' and throughout its history there have always been alchemists who were convinced that their art was of a divine character. In the works attributed to Jabir the author constantly invokes God and calls upon His intercession. He tells the student to ask for God's assistance in the work and he attributes failure on the part of any alchemist to lack of patience and the absence of God's help.[138] Another Moslem alchemist says that only those whose understanding has been opened by God can understand the philosopher's stone.[139] The necessity of the intervention of God to complete the alchemist's understanding was often reiterated. In the later literature in particular the continued failure of alchemists to produce practical results was one reason why it was often repeated that alchemy was a gift of God and that without His blessing the alchemist laboured in vain. This attitude is very relevant to the deliberate obscurity of alchemical texts. The writer did not usually claim to give the ordinary reader very much chemical knowledge, but only what would be sufficient if he had the necessary insight or inspiration to be successful. The authors provided a means of gaining knowledge such as the making of gold, but the burden of granting this dangerous knowledge is placed upon God. Many authors stressed the importance of careful study to obtain the necessary knowledge, but others felt that the student required not so much learning as virtue. This attitude was not unreasonable in those for whom alchemy was a spiritual exercise, but it was not

138. *Book of Mercy*; Berth., *M.A.*, iii, pp. 166, 185.
139. *Book of Ostanes*; Berth., *M.A.*, iii, p 116.

wholly absent even among practical alchemists. When all natural means have failed, a man may believe that his goal may be reached with the help of the supernatural. For others the chances of success seemed so slender in comparison with the possibilities of failure that luck or intuition might sooner lead to the secret than rational theory or experiment.

There was also the attitude that alchemy was a craft, and not even the clearest of text-books could replace the practical exercises and oral instruction which a master could provide. There were great difficulties in books and personal help would be invaluable in the interpretation of the writings of the 'Sages'. Petrus Bonus considered that, apart from divine inspiration, the only way of interpreting the enigmas of the Sages was by personal guidance by an Adept.[140] Even in the *Turba* it is suggested that book-learning alone is not enough because the alchemists' secret transcends the power of words to describe it.[141] Bernard Penotus, a follower of Paracelsus, considered that the art of chemistry was not be to gleaned from writings but by the use of one's hands.[142] Another example of a practical man who scorned the use of books in his search for the secrets of nature was Bernard Palissy. Believing that formal education was overestimated, he denied that a knowledge of Latin was necessary for a practical man of science. He had taught himself the ways in which substances react by using his hands and his eyes:

I have had no other book than the sky and the earth . . . for it is possible for everyone to know and read this fine book.[143]

An obvious but nevertheless fundamental predicament which influenced the whole of the literature of alchemy was the fact that, once words or symbols had been committed to paper and the manuscript passed out of the author's possession, he was incapable of selecting the people who subsequently read it. We may charitably assume that most writers had the intention of further enlightening those students who already had some knowledge of alchemy, but most authors had no intention of helping the common herd of mankind. For this reason an alchemical text required to be both informative and mysterious

140. *Preciosa Margarita Novella*; *Th. Ch.*, v, p. 571.
141. Op. cit., ed. Ruska, Berlin, 1931, p. 132.
142. *Praefatio*; *Th. Ch.*, ii, p. 82.
143. *Discours Admirables*, *Oeuvres*, Paris, 1844, pp. 129–30, 263–4.

according to the class to which the reader belonged. Yet there was always the danger that a work might fall into the hands of someone who was unworthy of the 'secrets' it contained. In a sixteenth-century work entitled *Dialogue between Nature and a Son of Philosophy*, 'Nature' says,

These things (i.e. knowledge of alchemy) are not to be mentioned or shown openly except to the God-fearing, and then by discourse, for what is written down can be seen by the unworthy as much as by the worthy.[144]

A compromise solution was the use of a series of symbols which would be meaningless to the uninitiated and was intended solely for the guidance of workers. Such a formula occurs in the writings of Zosimos[145] and is known as the formula of the crab—a name which refers to one of the symbols used in it. It was probably a cipher used by Egyptian craftsmen concerned with the counterfeiting of gold. 'In this formula we have the last remnant of an ancient symbolism that was quite meaningless without *viva voce* exposition. The method of working was in this manner handed down from one generation of craftsmen to another.'[146] Roger Bacon, who took the most thorough precautions against the possibility of his information reaching any one but the Pope for whom it was intended, says that he divided his explanation into parts which are found in four different works but even then he remarks,

I have (following the commandment of God and the advice and example of all the sages) kept a part of the secret and I shall only reveal this by word of mouth. For it would never be allowed to write down the secret in full, nor will this ever happen. . . .[147]

Elsewhere Bacon refers to the many obscurities which are to be found in alchemical books and he supports the oral tradition by remarking that nobody could understand these obscure passages without the help of a teacher.[148]

In spite of the large body of alchemical literature, it has been argued[149] that the alchemical tradition was largely an oral one

144. *Th. Ch.*, ii, p. 97.
145. Berth., *A.G.*, Introduction, p. 152.
146. J. C. Brown, *A History of Chemistry*, 2nd edn., London, 1920, p. 46.
147. *Part of the Opus Tertium of Roger Bacon*, ed. A. G. Little, Aberdeen, p. 82.
148. *Epistola de Secretis Operibus Naturae et Artis*; Manget, i, p. 622.
149. Ganzenmueller, *Die Alchemie im Mittelalter*, Paderborn, 1938, p. 118.

for another important reason: because of the fire and the corrosive substances found in every laboratory, most alchemists would be unlikely to work with a costly manuscript at their side, or if they did so the chances of its survival would be slight. Hence learning of recipes and the mental assimilation of metaphorical descriptions without constant reference to a text were not insignificant features of alchemy.

Among the many who believed in the feasibility of the claims of the alchemists there were a number who adopted a critical attitude towards the literature. The claims made in alchemical books became ever more extravagant and we might agree with Guibert, an opponent of alchemy, that not one alchemical book out of a thousand in circulation at the beginning of the seventeenth century would be found to be what its title claimed.[150] It must not be forgotten that many wealthy patrons were willing to pay high prices for alchemical manuscripts, and many clever but unscrupulous alchemists must have taken advantage of this ready market to increase the flood of alchemical literature with their own pseudo-science. With the invention of printing the written word became available to a larger public and thereafter it was not only the wealthy who were duped. In an age when it was customary to publish descriptions of experiments which the author had not himself carried out, there was much room for deception—and self-deception. The *Secrets of Nature*, ascribed to Arnald of Villanova, tells the story of a monk who laboured unsuccessfully for many years to prepare the philosopher's stone and finally became mad. Nevertheless, this did not prevent him publishing a book and hence increasing the flood of false knowledge which continually threatened the stream of early chemistry. For the serious student there was the greater difficulty of distinguishing the works of those who largely wrote what their imagination suggested and authors who described actual chemical changes but were unwilling to use clear language. Even the best of authors would be tempted to compensate for their ignorance of the complete process for making the philosopher's stone by quoting from the Ancients. Yet it was only too easy to quote the words used by a previous writer of repute without knowing what the words meant. The possibility of misunderstanding would be aggravated by quotation out of context. Every alchemist had his favourite authorities, recognizing, as

150. *De Interitu Alchemiae*, Tulli, 1614, Tract 2, pp. 89–90.

many did, that there were authors whose works were wholly misleading. Bernard Trevisan says that there are some authors who, far from helping the reader, lead him into positive error and in this class he cites Arnald of Villanova, Raymond Lull and others.[151]

Another reason why books could not be relied upon was the lack of consistency in the use of terms and the application of analogies. Petrus Bonus quotes from Rhazes the warning that words used figuratively were used with one signification in one place and with quite a contrary meaning in another.[152] The chaos in nomenclature in Arabic alchemy is frankly admitted in the Book of Crates:[153]

No philosopher was willing to accept the nomenclature which his predecessor used to denote the same operation. . . . Each of those who had reached the summit of the science sought to formulate a nomenclature different in origin to that of his rival.

The author goes on to say that this lack of system in nomenclature had caused many people to come to the conclusion that the whole of alchemy was a deception.

The many conflicting statements found in alchemical writings presented the student of alchemy with a tremendous difficulty, and we may ask ourselves why alchemy was not for this reason generally recognized as a misguided art. The crux of the matter is that, as the 'Sages' spoke in allegorical language, it was usually possible to reconcile assertions which, on first sight, appeared contradictory. The point was made that, although the ordinary reader might be baffled by their language, the 'philosophers' understood each other since they were speaking a more universal language than either Greek, Arabic or Latin. A second way of explaining apparently contradictory statements made by previous generations of writers was to suppose that there were several ways of reaching the same goal. It was therefore not possible to read a large number of alchemical works by different authors and learn a little from each, as many workers such as Trevisan had thought:

The Ancients have prepared this matter in different ways; some with immense Labour and with danger, others have taken a shorter

151. *De Alchemia*; *Th. Ch.*, i, p. 685.
152. *Preciosa Margarita Novella*, cap. x; *Th. Ch.*, v, p. 602.
153. Berth., *M.A.*, iii, p. 50.

and more certain route. They wish to be guided by the Ancients and believe that they can learn of the weights required in the work of Lullus; the fermentations from Avicenna; the fire from Trevisan; the projection from Paracelsus etc., but they are mistaken, for each of these has his own process; therefore if you find Geber's directions different from those of Lully, or those of Morienus different from those of Arnald of Villanova or Paracelsus, do not dispute with the one or the other; for all of them have reached the goal by different means, although they used the same matter.[154]

Quite a few alchemists recognized that contradictions occurred in the works of the 'Sages' but refused to regard this as evidence against the validity of their Art. On the other hand there were some who, having regard to the immense body of literature of alchemy, could understand why authors were not always consistent, but they were disheartened by finding contradictions in works attributed to the same author.[155]

Not only did alchemical literature contain many statements which were merely misleading. There were numerous examples of statements which were indisputably false. Even the *Rosarium Philosophorum*, written in a period when alchemy was at its height in Western Europe, admits openly that the making of false statements[156] was one of the many ways regularly used by authors to mislead the ordinary reader. The discovery that lies were plainly to be found in alchemical literature played its part in shortening the life of alchemy. It came to be recognized that lies in alchemy were the rule rather than the exception. By the beginning of the eighteenth century Kunckel could ironically suggest that the etymology of 'alkahest' was *Alles Lügen est* (It is all a lie). Elsewhere the same chemist speaks of the suggestion made by a friend that if every year one falsehood only were removed from alchemy, this science could be purged of its deceptions. Kunckel remarks that even if twenty lies were taken away every year, he doubts whether this would solve the problem because thirty more would spring up.[157]

154. Barma, *Saturnia Regna*, Paris, 1657, pp. 27–8.
155. The fact should not be overlooked that famous names like those of Geber, Roger Bacon, etc. were used by some unscrupulous alchemists to pass off their own compositions. This would help to explain some of the inconsistencies found in works attributed to the same author.
156. '*Per falsam et alienam practicam occultare*', op. cit., Frankfurt, 1550, f. 34v.
157. *Chymische Anmerkungen*, Wittenberg, 1677, p. 147. *Laboratorium Chymicum*, Hamburg and Leipzig, 1716, Part 3, p. 506.

The Reasons for Obscurity

Having discussed the fact that much alchemical literature was hopelessly obscure, it remains to ask why this should have been so. Most of the obscurity may seem at first sight to have been deliberate and hence easily avoidable. If, however, it is accepted that the science of alchemy as a method of transforming base metals into gold was based on errors in the communication of ideas from one language and culture to another, it may be considered that intentional obscurity was only a secondary factor. As far as the European alchemist is concerned, one might say that, lacking the initiative of the experimental method, he did his best to follow the garbled texts available. It would be false to say that the alchemical author had a clear idea of all the processes required to make 'gold', but that when he committed these ideas to paper he used mysterious language. This is only what the author wanted to be believed, and most authors were not lacking in their excuses for the facade which served to cover their basic ignorance.

Intentional Obscurity

Among the excuses offered for obscurity were the social and economic consequences if the method by which gold could be made became common knowledge; but, above all, authors spoke reverently of their fear of God and the repercussions such a revelation would have on the author himself.

Right up to the birth of modern chemistry the idea persisted that alchemy was a divine science and the belief that alchemy was partly supernatural affected the communication of knowledge of that science. It was repeatedly stated by alchemical authors that anyone who revealed all the secrets of alchemy would be struck down by God. (Writers apparently took a big risk when they revealed even one of two 'secrets'.) The *Book of Royalty* of Jabir gives the reader severe warnings against revealing to anyone else the secret hinted at by the author. One author quotes the pseudo-Aristotle, saying that, 'anyone revealing the secrets of nature and art would be breaking the heavenly seal' and adding that 'many evils would follow the person who disclosed the secrets'[158] A later Latin tract refers to the penalty

158. *Epistola de Secretis Operibus Artis et Naturae*, Manget, i, p. 622.

of divine anathema visited upon anyone who did not keep his knowledge to himself.[159] The *Rosarium Philosophorum* is more precise: no one was permitted to reveal the secret of the art; if he did disclose it, he would incur the indignation of the Lord and would die of apoplexy! It was generally believed that, in so far as alchemy was a gift of God, the decision as to which mortal was to receive this precious secret rested with God alone. If a mere man were to assume this divine prerogative he would be punished accordingly.[160] Even the *Mappae Clavicula*, which is more a technical than an alchemical treatise, includes an injunction to 'hide the sacred art which should be transmitted to no one'.[161]

Another reason why alchemical knowledge was kept secret was not so much that it was sacred but that it protected the livelihood of the person who owned the secret. This was something which alchemy inherited from the technical tradition. Nearly every trade and profession had its tradition of secrecy and, although notes might occasionally be written down to aid the memory, essential details of any process were handed down from father to son or from master to apprentice. More than two thousand years before the birth of Christ the workmen of ancient Egypt had their secret processes which included embalming and metallurgy. Later, when it was discovered how to make glass, the making of coloured glass for ornament seems to have been the private knowledge of a few craftsmen. No man was anxious to make it generally known how he carried out his trade as long as other people, profiting by this information, might make his own living insecure. There have been many cases in Europe even in modern times where a secret 'remedy' has made a fortune for its inventor. It was only natural for the person who invented or developed a technical process or discovered a new chemical substance with medicinal uses to establish a monopoly over his knowledge by secrecy. It is only comparatively recently that monopoly by secrecy was supplemented by the registering of patents.

Semantic Change

Quite apart from deliberate efforts made to conceal knowledge (or lack of knowledge), all later alchemy (i.e. the alchemy which bequeathed processes and chemical reagents to the science

159. Laurentius Ventura, *De Lapide Philosophico*; *Th. Ch.*, ii, p. 227.
160. *Th. Ch.*, i, p. 141.   161. Berth., *M.A.*, i, p. 36.

of chemistry) was plagued by errors in the copying and translation of texts and, more fundamentally, by semantic changes. It was naively assumed by the later alchemists, as it is by many people to-day, that one word denotes one object, as the word 'cat' denotes the animal we call by that name. This is not necessarily the case. A word may stand for an idea of an object rather than the object itself. Thus the word 'gold' is associated with the idea of yellowness, shininess, heaviness, etc. A body possessing such a finite number of physical and chemical properties is called 'gold'. It is precisely with this word 'gold' that so much of the confusion in alchemy arose.

Each time that alchemy was transplanted from one language and culture to another, there was the possibility of misunderstanding the aims of the previous workers. The fact that their predecessors had often used figurative language was often not allowed for in the translation and this explains much of the nonsense that was written. But the lack of understanding of basic vocabulary was even more important. Hopkins, who is known as the propounder of the 'colour theory' of alchemy, argues that for the Alexandrian alchemists the meaning of the word 'gold' was 'any gold-coloured metal alloy or bronze'.[162] By the time alchemy reached the Arabs the definition of gold had changed and therefore the ancient recipes for making 'gold' lost their meaning and validity. In the first place it seems that the Egyptian language, lacking a special word for gold, denoted it by the expression 'yellow metal', a term equally applicable to an alloy of the same colour.

The term 'gold' underwent an important change when it was taken over from the Egyptian craftsmen by the Alexandrian alchemists who were deeply influenced by philosophical and religious ideas. For the Alexandrian alchemists gold was not so much a substance as a quality, not really a body but rather a spirit. The process of transmutation consisted of imposing the necessary qualities on a suitable base. This could be effected by a process similar to dyeing by a suitable 'tingeing spirit'. Demokritos regarded the changing of copper into gold as a straightforward operation. The copper was to be heated for three days and then treated with a certain preparation:

and then it will be gold (ἔσται χρυσός)

162. A. J. Hopkins, *Alchemy, Child of Greek Philosophy*, New York, 1934, pp. 194, 104n.

Zosimos makes it clear that to make gold is to impart a certain quality to a substance:

> ... But our gold which possesses the desired quality is able to make gold and transmute ($\beta\alpha\pi\tau\epsilon\iota\nu$) into gold. Here is the great mystery —that the quality becomes gold then it makes gold.

This passage also throws light on the meaning of the Latin *transmutare*, which although in its ordinary sense means nothing more than 'to change', in its technical sense is derived from the Greek $\beta\alpha\pi\tau\iota\zeta\omega$ meaning literally 'to dip' as a fabric is dipped in a solution of a dye.[163] It should be clear from the above that what the Alexandrian alchemists of the third and fourth centuries A.D. understood by 'gold' was not the same as the conception of an alchemist in western Europe in mediaeval times, which in turn would have been considered inadequate by a nineteenth century chemist. This might be shown by the following scheme in which letters are used to represent Aristotelian qualities:

M = a material substance
N = the property of being yellow
O = the property of being shiny
P = the property of being heavy
Q = the property of being malleable
R = the property of being fusible
S = the property of not being corroded by exposure to the air
T = the property of giving an appropriate yellow streak on a 'touch-stone'
U = the property of withstanding the test of cupellation[164]
V = the property of withstanding the test of cementation[165]

These qualities might be refined and extended to meet the criticisms of a nineteenth-century chemist or physicist:

P* = specific gravity
R* = melting point

163. e.g. 'Demokritos' says '$\beta\acute{\alpha}\psi\eta$!' (i.e. dip the metal in some yellow material) (Berth., *A.G.*, texte grec, p. 44, l. 13). See also ibid., texte grec, p. 46, l. 11, p. 127 and tradn., p. 134.

164. The gold under test was melted on a flat dish or *cupel* formed of bone ash and air was blown over the surface of the molten metal. Any lead present would be easily oxidized.

165. This consisted of heating the gold under test with a paste of vitriol, sal ammoniac, etc. and observing whether the metal was corroded.

W* = heat conductivity

X* = electrical conductivity

Y* = forms two series of salts with valencies of one and three respectively. The latter are more stable and tend to form complexes. . . .

Thus for Zosimos the essence of gold might be denoted simply by the formula NO. A contemporary of Zosimos might have understood by the word 'gold' a substance fully represented by the formula MNOP. The term 'gold' came to be used so loosely that Geber went to some trouble to explain exactly what he meant by the word:

> We say Gold is a Metallic Body, Citrine, ponderous, mute, fulgid, equally digested in the Bowels of the Earth, and very long washed with Mineral Water; under the hammer extensible, fusible and sustaining the Tryal of the Cupel and Cement. According to this definition, you may conclude that nothing is true gold, unless it hath all the Causes and Differences of the Definition of Gold.[166]

This might be summed up by the formula MNPQRTUV. To these immediate physical and chemical tests might be added that of durability (S). Avicenna[167] recognized gold by seven tests: fusion, the touch-stone, density, taste, action of fire, solution and sublimation. These tests were later faithfully quoted by Vincent of Beauvais. An Arabic manual of the thirteenth century defines gold by fourteen essential qualities, including those relying on the five senses viz. colour, taste, smell, feel and sound (when struck).[168] Apart from empirical tests, it was very easy for an alchemist to speak of gold in terms of current theory:

> Gold is a perfect body composed of pure, fixed, clear and red Mercury and of clean, fixed, red and non-combustible Sulphur; it has no defect.[169]

Such a statement can have very little meaning for practical men. A practical chemist would judge gold entirely by physical or chemical tests such as cementation. By the nineteenth century

166. Geber, *Sum of Perfection, Works*, London, 1928, p. 63, Geber goes on to suggest that copper may be made into 'gold' agreeing with the above definition.

167. Berth., *M.A.*, i, pp. 304–5.

168. Muhammad ibn Abi Talib, *Manuel de la Cosmographie du Moyen Âge* Copenhagen, 1874.

169. *Speculum Alchemiae*, attrib. Roger Bacon, cap. 2; Manget, i, p. 613.

gold might have been practically defined by the more sophisticated properties which have been listed. More briefly gold might be defined to-day as the element of atomic number 79 and aggregate atomic weight 197.2.

Having surveyed the evolution of the use of the term 'gold' in a practical sense, we should not forget that gold was used by some writers as a symbol of perfection; such usage served only to increase the existing confusion in alchemical literature.

Errors due to faulty translation and copying

The Latin alchemical books which were published in the seventeenth century, at about the same time as the appearance of chemistry as a distinct science, were largely based upon earlier texts in Latin and many of these can be traced back to Arabic and, in some cases, even to Greek sources. In other words, there was a continuous tradition stretching back at least to the first few centuries of the Christian era, and this tradition was largely transmitted by the written word. It would be an over-simplified view to consider that there were only two stages in this translation: from Greek to Arabic and from Arabic to Latin. The Alexandrian alchemists who wrote in Greek had themselves derived much of their technique and vocabulary from Egyptian craftsmen. When translations were made from the Greek, this was often into Syriac or Hebrew. Most of the Syriac texts were later translated into Arabic. When the Arabic texts came to be translated into Latin in the twelfth and thirteenth centuries, Spain was a natural meeting place for the two cultures of East and West. The common method of translation was two-fold: one scholar would translate from Arabic into the Castilian vernacular, and a second, whose ability in Latin was more marked, would complete the process by translating from Castilian into Latin. In many cases the final stage in translation was from Latin to the vernaculars of the separate states which were slowly emerging to form modern Europe. The adventure of translation sometimes added to the attraction of a work rather than raised doubts as to its reliability. An example of this is the way in which William Salmon, an English doctor and author of the seventeenth century, introduces a translation of a text ascribed to 'Hermes' by a bold claim of its pedigree:

The Golden Work of Hermes Trismegistus; Translated out of

Hebrew into Arabick, then into Greek, afterwards into Latin; and now done out of Latin into English. . . .[170]

The translation of technical matter presented special difficulties which were increased by the widespread use of allegory. Faced with such difficulties, translators often contented themselves with a literal translation. It was safer not to translate words the meaning of which was imperfectly understood. Thus, in the translation from Arabic to Latin, such words were often transliterated e.g. alkali, alembic, camphor, borax, elixir, talc, saffron. When we find the term '*aleusanthi*' in a Latin work this is an obvious case of transliteration from the Greek: ἁλός ἄνηθ (=*flos salis*). There are numerous other examples of words which have been transliterated rather than translated. Occasionally it is evident that the copyist had no knowledge at all of the language concerned. An example of this is a passage from an early French Latin M.S. where it is quite obvious that the person who transcribed it had no knowledge of Greek beyond the alphabet. The result was a meaningless jumble of letters.[171]

A proper appreciation of the limited success of the translators can only be obtained by a detailed comparison of the manuscripts of an original text and its translation. Among such studies may be mentioned one by Ruska[172] and another by Stapleton[173] who has compared an Arabic treatise by Ibn Umail (tenth century) and its Latin translation in Zetzner's *Theatrum Chemicum* (2nd edn., 1622, vol. v, pp. 218–66) and Manget's *Bibliotheca Chemica Curiosa* (1702, vol. 2, pp. 216–35) under the title of *Tabula Chemica* by 'Senior'. Stapleton remarks that the Latin translator seems to have had considerable difficulty with the Arabic text, and in a series of footnotes he comments on discrepancies between the original text and its Latin translation. There are several instances where the failure to observe the minutiae of the Arabic script led to a divergence of meaning. Many misunderstandings and changes also arose not through copying but were due to mistakes in hearing when they were copied by dictation. Thus similar sounds as well as similar letters could be easily confused.

170. W. Salmon, *Medicina Practica*, London, 1707, p. 179.
171. L. A. Muriatori, *Antiquitates Italiae medii aevi*, Mediolani, 1738–42, vol. 2, p. 387. For a reconstruction of the original Greek and translation see Berth., *M.A.*, i, p. 9, n. 3.
172. *Das Buch der Alaune und Salze*, Berlin, 1935, espec. pp. 18–22.
173. *Mem. Bengal, 12* (1933).

It often happened that mistakes were made in the translation of the names of substances but there is one case in particular where the result of this may well have proved fatal, as well as bringing chemical medicine into disrepute. A Byzantine Greek called Nicolaus Myrepsus compiled a compendium of remedies in which he drew on Arabic sources, although his knowledge of Arabic was poor. He made the mistake of including arsenic as a remedy in certain cases.[174] This was due to his translation of the Arabic *dársini* (=cinnamon)[175] which the Arabs obtained from the island of Sina or Ceylon. The idea that arsenic had special medicinal properties as a mild remedy for internal use persisted up to the seventeenth century.

Not every translator was content with his comparatively humble task. If he thought he understood the meaning of an obscure part of the text, he often added his own commentary, so that the two parts often became fused together, the commentary being indistinguishable from the original. Such commentaries were often more obscure and confusing than the original and, had it not been for experiments made by the more practically minded alchemists, alchemical literature would have represented an uninterupted decay as it went further from its sources.

The copying of manuscripts was another important source of error. Alchemical manuscripts did not have a very long life when they were used by practical workers in their laboratories not far from furnaces and corrosive liquids. Thus, quite apart from increasing the number of copies of a text available, a great deal of copying was necessary merely to preserve texts. Every time a work was copied it was possible for errors to occur and these errors would be the more numerous if the copyist did not fully understand the meaning of the sentences he was copying, as was often the case. A very frequent mistake in copying was to write *vitrum* (glass) for *nitrum* (soda) or vice-versa. Careless writing and the use of manuscript abbreviations not generally standardized were responsible for many mistakes. Michael Sendivogius, writing in the seventeenth century, refers to the general confusion in alchemical literature:

174. *De compositione medicamentorum*—H. Estienne, *Medicae Artis Principes*, Paris, 1567, vol. 2, col. 694.

175. 'Darseni, id est cinamomum'—Serapion, *Insignium Medicarum*, Argentorati, 1531, p. 169.

The confusion is rendered worse confounded by the ill will of the Sages, . . . and by the carelessness with which some of the most important volumes are copied and printed; the sense of a whole passage is often hopelessly obscured by the addition or omission of one little word (e.g. the addition of the word 'not' in the wrong place).[176]

As Thomas Norton had said:

> chaunging of some one sillable
> May make this Boke unprofitable.

The Effect of Obscurity in Alchemical Literature

An important consequence of alchemical obscurity was the time wasted in studying texts, time which could have been devoted more profitably to practical research. The young alchemist was continually advised to read the works of the 'Ancients' with patience, and to re-read them as many times as was necessary to understand them fully. As we have seen, to read and have some understanding of an alchemical treatise might require years of study. Bernard Palissy refers disparagingly to the works of Geber, Lull and other alchemists 'the study of which has made many lose both their time and their wealth'.[177] Alchemical symbolism presented a problem to anyone who wished to read books on the subject. There is a record that Isaac Newton, whose intellectual powers can hardly be belittled, devoted more than a week in May 1681 merely to understanding the meaning of a few alchemical names and symbols[178] so that he could follow the alchemical books in his possession. These he not only read, but even copied out long passages word for word. On the other hand, the obscurity of alchemical books must sometimes have had a good effect in so far as some students were driven in desperation to do experiments for themselves and think on fresh lines.

As far as the general public was concerned, we might say that the most important consequence of alchemical obscurity was to set the prestige of alchemy and its practitioners very low indeed. The fact that many alchemists were rogues and charlatans was enough to make people view alchemy with suspicion, but if some overcame their prejudices enough to give alchemy a closer

176. *Concerning Sulphur*, Preface; *M.H.*, pp. 601–2; *H.M.*, vol. ii, p. 127.
177. *Discours Admirables*, Dédication, *Oeuvres*, Paris, 1844, p. 129.
178. *Catalogue of the Portsmouth Collection*, Cambridge, 1888, p. 23.

inspection, they were met with allegories, equivocations and barbarisms. The alchemist, when he was not persecuted for fraud, was scorned—as in Ben Jonson's play *The Alchemist* (1610). About the sixteenth century, several books were written specifically attacking alchemy such as the *Tractatus contra alchemistas* (Lyons, 1610) by Arnaudis. One of the best sellers among all alchemical books was a criticism of alchemy by C. Agrippa entitled *De incertitudine et vanitate scientiarum* (1529). Another opponent of alchemy was Guibert who wrote two works attacking it in the early years of the seventeenth century. One of these, *Alchemy impugned by Reason and Experience* (Strasbourg, 1603) prompted Libavius to write a reply. In answer to these attacks books were written defending alchemy, notably the *De veritate et antiquitate artis chemicae* (Paris, 1561) which includes a list of venerable authorities who (allegedly) wrote in favour of alchemy. Glauber, writing in the seventeenth century, cites Thomas Aquinas and Albertus Magnus among others as evidence in support of the truth of alchemical premisses. When Richard Russell translated Geber's works into English in the seventeenth century, he thought it necessary to claim that

Chymistry is a true and real art, and (when handled by prudent artists) produceth true and real effects.

Another important effect of obscurity in alchemical language was to prolong the life of alchemy so that it died only a lingering death in the seventeenth and eighteenth centuries. Alchemy did not form a clear target for its adversaries and hence it avoided the mortal blow which the science of chemistry, as its legitimate successor, should have been able to deliver. Whenever an alchemist made a sweeping statement about 'mercury' or 'sulphur' or some other general principle, more metaphysical than physical, he was able to give such terms as wide and vague a meaning as he wished in order to escape the criticism of his contemporaries. Thus 'Basil Valentine' was able to challenge the right of his critics to deny his assertions by saying that they did not understand him properly.[179] The meaning of his terms, he said, was quite different from that of his opponents.

This aspect of alchemical language was at the same time its strength and its weakness. By the seventeenth century, when alchemy was in retreat against the general onslaught of criti-

179. *Triumph Wagen Antimonii*, Leipzig, 1604, p. 192.

cism, alchemists were always able to represent themselves as people who had been misunderstood or, more arrogantly, as men who possessed wisdom far beyond that of ordinary men. The burden of proof, however, had now gone to the other side. Alchemical theory was no longer one coherent whole. Its exponents were regarded more and more as charlatans. If alchemists could not say clearly what they meant by their sulphur and their mercury, then clearly it must be because they themselves did not know. Clear ideas could be expressed in clear language. Descartes, in his *Discours de la Méthode* (1637), made it a fundamental rule for himself

> to comprise nothing more in my judgement than what was presented to my mind so clearly and distinctly as to exclude all ground of doubt.

Whilst alchemists persisted in the vague use of chemical language, seventeenth-century authors, who wrote books belonging more properly to chemistry, became more self conscious about the language they used. The French chemist Le Febure, while not renouncing metaphysical ideas took care to distinguish the meaning of the terms he used. He distinguished[180] between nitre or Saltpetre which is 'a crystalline Hexagonal salt used in the making of gunpowder' and another type of nitre which is a universal salt—'a mysterious salt, which is the soul of all physical generation, a Child and Son of Light, and the Father of all Germination and Vegetation'. Even John Mayow, whose reckless use of language is illustrated by the statement that his 'nitro-aerial spirit' 'may rightly be termed Mercury', was critical of the use of the term 'spirit' in chemistry.[181] Robert Boyle in his *Sceptical Chymist* (1661) made it clear that in a science it is to be expected that language will be used precisely and not figuratively. Thus he would have criticized Mayow's use of the term 'Mercury' in the passage quoted above. Much of the *Sceptical Chymist* is concerned with attacking, on the one hand, the idea of the four Aristotelian elements and, on the other, the three principles of Paracelsus. Boyle gives a useful (although not entirely original) definition of an element:

> And, to prevent mistakes, I must advertise you, that I now mean

---

180. *A Compendious Body of Chymistry*, London, 1664, vol. 2, p. 283.
181. *Medico-Physical Works*, A.C.R. No. 17, Edinburgh, 1907, p. 34.

by elements ... certain primitive and simple, or perfectly un-mingled bodies. ... [182]

The French chemical author, Nicolas Lemery, also attacked the terms used by his contemporaries. Whilst accepting the five principles as a working hypothesis, he was highly critical of explanations in term of salt, sulphur, etc. which he describes as 'high sounding terms which explain very little'. Similarly when dealing with 'invisible inks' he scorns a current explanation of their action in terms of 'sympathy' and 'antipathy' which he describes as 'general terms which explain nothing'.[183] The same terms 'sympathy' and 'antipathy' were criticized about the same time by the English philosopher John Locke.[184] Locke recognized the importance of language in philosophical and scientific discussions and he devotes a special chapter in his *Essay* to the abuse of words. He states, what was then coming to be realized, that on examination of the literature of philo-sophy (including 'natural philosophy') 'certain words ... will be found ... not to stand for any clear and distinct ideas'.

Thus in the seventeenth century we see the awakening of a general dissatisfaction with the current use of language. In the field of chemistry allegory and mysticism became outmoded. With the publication of clear text-books of chemistry such as Lemery's *Cours de Chymie* systematic obscurity was banished for ever. The eighteenth century was to witness a general reform in chemical nomenclature.

182. *The Sceptical Chymist*, Everyman edn., London, 1911, p. 187. It should be noted, however, that Boyle, far from advocating a chemistry based on elements, was rejecting the concept in favour of a corpuscular approach to matter.

183. *Cours de Chymie*, Paris, 1697, pp. 589, 308.

184. *Essay Concerning Human Understanding* (first publ. 1690), Bk. III. chap. 11, Everyman edn., London, 1947, p. 246. See also ibid., Bk. III. chap. 10, Everyman edn., p. 242.

Part 2

EARLY CHEMICAL TERMINOLOGY

'He who wishes to instruct others should bestow upon
each separate thing a definite name.'

Agricola; *De Natura Fossilium, (De re metallica,*
trans. Hoover, London, 1912, p. 3n.)

CHAPTER ONE

Early Terminology and Names
Based on Physical Properties

Introduction

In an examination of some of the earliest names given to chemical substances we cannot expect to find a terminology related to chemical composition, since this was largely unknown. The greatest achievement possible at first was the distinction between one substance and another and the identification of different specimens of the same substance. Such distinctions and identifications were very fallible, since they could be based only on rudimentary physical properties, particularly colour. Sometimes scientifically useless distinctions were made, as between gold found in one place and that found in another. At the other extreme, quite distinct chemical substances were sometimes grouped under one general name. These remarks apply to early civilizations such as those based on the Nile and on the Tigris and Euphrates, but the same lack of foresight led to difficulties in more modern times.

Before the science of chemistry came into being in the late seventeenth and particularly the late eighteenth century there existed a body of practical knowledge of materials based on the crafts of the smith, the dyer, the glass-maker, the distiller and several other trades. This technical knowledge, together with some ideas from alchemy (itself partly technical and partly philosophical), formed the early beginnings of chemistry. As chemistry had an origin which was both indefinite and hetero-geneous, it is understandable that its terminology shared these characteristics. If we think of some of the terms used by chemists before the reform of nomenclature, terms like *sugar of lead, butter of antimony, oil of vitriol, cream of tartar* and *milk of lime,* we see the point of Dumas' remark that chemistry had borrowed its language from the kitchen,[1] The technical origin of chemical terms applies not only to substances but equally to processes, and household terms as well as those used in metallurgical and other arts came to be applied to chemistry. Even to-day such terms as 'washing' and 'roasting' are familiar to the chemist.

The result of the development of iatrochemistry in the sixteenth century by Paracelsus and his followers was not only to benefit medicine by the use of chemical preparations but also to influence chemistry to the extent of producing several generations of distinguished pharmaceutical chemists and physicians, men like Jean Beguin (*fl.* early seventeenth century), Nicolas Lemery (1645–1715), Friedrich Hoffmann (1660–1742) and C. W. Scheele (1742–86). With chemistry and pharmacy so closely connected, another influence was added to chemical terminology.

Ancient Terminology

Native copper and gold were probably the first minerals known to man; in Egypt before 4000 B.C. iron ore and certain semi-precious stones were also known. What concerns us here is the identification, classification and naming of minerals based on their more obvious physical properties. The origins of many names in the language of the ancient world are still in dispute among philologists and we can include here only a very few of the less controversial origins of the names of minerals. The oldest Egyptian name for gold is the hieroglyphic *nub*, which is also the term meaning 'to smelt'; it may also be connected with the gold mines of Nubia. In any case there are special hieroglyphics denoting the place of origin of certain specimens of gold—'gold of the water' (alluvial gold), 'gold of the mountain', 'gold of Coptos', etc.[2] The common Egyptian word for silver, *hetch* or *ḥd* means 'white' and it is not surprising that malachite (or some other green ore of copper) was known by the term *vatch*, meaning 'to be green'.

1. J.-B. Dumas, *Leçons sur la Philosophie Chimique*, Paris, 1837, p. 325.
2. For the complicated early nomenclature of gold see R. J. Forbes, *Metallurgy in Antiquity*, London, 1950, p. 154. The Egyptian names mentioned above are taken from Sir E. A. W. Budge, *An Egyptian Hieroglyphic Dictionary*, London, 1920, pp. 353, 523a, 150b.

Turning to the civilizations of Babylonia and Assyria, we find similar tendencies in primitive terminology.[3] Thus the name for silver means 'white brilliance' and in the nomenclature of iron, lead and copper, colour plays a leading part. Other factors influencing terminology included smell (arsenic compounds), taste, fusibility, magical properties and method of preparation —copper and silver, for example, being described as 'washed' or 'refined'.

The Sumerian cuneiform language was remarkably advanced on the earlier hieroglyphics and was particularly suited for the expression of the names of minerals. In the word lists compiled by the Sumerians (about the seventh century B.C.) the first part of the word denotes an outstanding property of the group of substances (the class) and to this was added a name dependent on individual characteristics (the species). Thus similar substances are found near each other in the lists. Examples of group names are: ZA (rock, stone) and ᵃPAR (white sand). Properties were indicated by the use of suffixes, e.g.: GUG, DIR (red), GÌN (blue), SUḪ (yellow/green), TU (heavy), AŠ (hard), AŠ-AŠ (very hard), ᵃZATU (effervescent with acid, i.e. vinegar). The construction of the following words, as interpreted by Campbell Thompson, can then be understood:

ᵃZA. GÌN	'blue stone'	(lapis lazuli, etc.)
ᵃZA. GÌN. AŠ. AŠ	'very hard blue stone'	(saphire)
ᵃZA. TU	'heavy (white) stone'	(ceruse, white lead)
ᵃZA. TU. PAR. AŠ	'moderately hard white stone effervescing under acid'	(calcite)
ᵃZA. TU. PAR. AŠ. AŠ	'very hard white stone effervescing under acid'	(marble?)
ᵃZA. SUḪ	(the base of different vitriols)	
ᵃZA. SUḪ. DIR	'red vitriol'	(ferric oxide)

This excellent systematic nomenclature was not carried into any other language and it had no parallel until the development of

3. The following account of these terminologies is based entirely on R. Campbell Thomson; *Dictionary of Assyrian Chemistry and Geology*, Oxford, 1936.

the nomenclature of organic compounds in the nineteenth century of our own era.

Turning briefly to other languages, we may note that the Hebrew term for silver *Keseph* means a shiny white metal and the Greek and Latin words *argyros* and *argentum* may be derived from a root *radj* or *arg* meaning 'white, bright, shining'. Pliny said of silver that it was 'brighter and more sun-like' than even gold.[4] It would seem that colour was almost universally the basis of the name given to silver. One of the Aryan words for copper, '*roudhos* is said to mean red,[5] thus providing another example of colour terminology. The English term 'copper' from the Latin *cuprum* is based on the name of the island of Cyprus where copper was found. Pliny uses the terms *aes rubrum* and *aes cyprium* as synonyms and it seems more probable that the metal derived its name from the island than vice versa.

Methods of Naming Substances

The basis of many chemical names was the appearance of the substance or some other elementary physical property, although later a chemical or medicinal property was sometimes invoked. The physical properties might be based on any of the five senses and although sight was obviously the most important of these, taste and even sound[6] were not considered irrelevant in naming substances. Although there was very little conscious systematization in chemical terminology, a retrospective analysis shows that the following considerations were most often taken into account in naming substances: colour, taste or smell, consistency and crystalline form, a person associated with the discovery or use of the substance or the place where it was prepared or found naturally, its (supposed) medicinal properties and finally its method of preparation. This is not the historical order of principles of nomenclature, since there was no definite historical sequence. Nevertheless, colour has over a long space of time been considered of primary importance and its use in ancient civilizations has already been noted above. On the other hand,

---

4. Pliny, *Hist. Nat.*, *33*, 58.　　　　　　5. Forbes, op. cit., p. 371.
6. Tin was distinguished from lead not only by its colour but by its sonority, e.g. Geber's reference to *plumbum stridens*, *Summa Perfectionis*, Berne, 1545, Bk. 2, Part 2, p. 123. Similarly one of the essential qualities of gold was that it was sonorous.

terms based on the method of preparation of a substance were most widely used in the eighteenth century immediately preceding the introduction of systematic nomenclature. Some of the factors mentioned could only be incorporated into chemical terminology in extreme instances, as in the case of taste. To call lead acetate *sugar of lead* and magnesium sulphate *bitter salt* almost exhausted the range of possibilities.

Solubility and heaviness also played a small part in terminology. These characteristics too could only be used to distinguish extreme cases. Solubility was an essential attribute of the conception of a salt up to the end of the eighteenth century, but occasionally one salt was particularly soluble as compared with another. Thus potassium bisulphate is much more soluble than normal potassium sulphate and it is possible that the *sal enixum* of Paracelsus was the former salt. Similarly, although tartar is sparingly soluble in water, normal potassium tartrate is appreciably soluble and was therefore distinguished as *soluble tartar*. To recognize and name a mineral by its heaviness would seem obvious enough, but there are few naturally occurring substances the weight of which is sufficiently great to distinguish them immediately from other minerals. About the only cases of minerals named after their heaviness were barytes and tungsten.

Colour as a Basis for Chemical Names

We have seen how important colour was in the earliest names given to chemical substances and colour continued to be of primary importance to craftsmen, who valued elementary chemical knowledge chiefly as an aid to the preparation of decorative materials. Of the sixteen Accadian terms for gold Forbes has pointed out that no less than nine refer to its colour or shade.[7] Berthelot suggested that the references in Theophrastus to 'male blue' and 'female blue' represented blue compounds of cobalt and copper respectively, the difference in shade being marked enough to invite a distinction.[8] In the early civilizations colour was important because it was often connected with magic and in mediaeval Europe colour continued to have an

7. R. J. Forbes, 'On the Origin of Alchemy', *Chymia*, 4 (1953), 4.
8. *Introduction a l'étude de la chimie des anciens et du moyen âge*, Paris, 1889, p. 245.

important symbolical significance, of which some remains to the present day. In alchemy colour was often the basis of *Decknamen* (or 'cover-names'), so that copper was called 'the green' and 'yellow wind' stood for sulphur. Each of the various stages in the supposed preparation of gold was accompanied by an appropriate colour change.

Colour was sometimes used in names to distinguish metals. Tin and lead were sometimes referred to as *plumbum candidum* (white lead) and *plumbum nigrum* (black lead) respectively, the term *plumbum* being extended from its use to cover a particular heavy, easily fusible metal to a more general use to denote a class of such metals. Agricola distinguished bismuth by calling it *plumbum cinereum* (ash-coloured lead). Such nomenclature obviously had the disadvantage of emphasizing physical resemblances between these three metals rather than suggesting their chemical individuality. Metal sulphides too were sometimes referred to in a similar way, and we read in the alchemical lexicons that 'red sulphur' is arsenic (sulphide) and 'black sulphur' is antimony (sulphide). In the eighteenth century our magnesium carbonate and manganese dioxide were distinguished by the names *magnesia alba* and *magnesia nigra* respectively, although in this case any supposed connection was the result of a long-standing linguistic confusion.[9] The coloured compounds of certain metals like iron, copper, mercury and arsenic could easily be given characteristic names, although these were sometimes ambiguous: 'the green lion' (ferrous sulphate), 'Spanish green' (basic copper acetate, 'red precipitate of mercury' (mercuric oxide), etc. The etymologies of the words *haematite* ('blood-like stone'), *orpiment* ('gold pigment') and *verdigris* ('green of Greece') all relate to their colour. Colour terminology was not very helpful in distinguishing the many white substances known and yet in the fifteenth to the eighteenth centuries we come across references to *creta alba* (gypsum), *sal albus* (borax), *plumbum album* (basic lead carbonate or acetate), 'pearl white' (bismuth oxychloride), 'Spanish white' and even the self contradictory expression *atramentum album* ('white blacking').

9. The confusion probably dates back to the Greeks who used the expression Μαγνῆτις λίθος for a white mineral, but later, loadstone, although black in colour, was called by the same name which both derived from their place of origin, *Magnesia*, in Asia Minor (Theophrastus, *History of Stones*, trans. John Hill, London, 1746, pp. 79n., 105–6). For the use of 'magnesia' in alchemical literature see pp. 25–6.

Colours could be used directly or indirectly as a source of terminology. An important secondary use of colour was by analogy with familiar coloured substances. Such analogies were grist to the mill of the imaginative alchemists, but at present we are concerned with the non-mystical aspects of early chemistry. We are therefore less interested here in a term like *lac virginis* (usually a suspension of basic lead carbonate) than the term *milk of lime* (a suspension of calcium hydroxide), an expression which has persisted to this day. The appearance of the liver prompted the expressions *liver of sulphur* (potassium poly-sulphides) and *liver of antimony* (fused antinomy sulphide) and even influenced the terminology of gases when Bergman gave the name *aer hepaticus* to our hydrogen sulphide. Other com-pounds of antimony were known as *snow of antimony* and *kermes mineral*, so-called after the insect used to produce a red dye. Gold-coloured tin sulphide was known as *aurum mosaicum*. A popular term in seventeenth and eighteenth century chemistry was *Aethiops*, a term which had the status of classical usage; ancient Greek geographers had applied the term to all dark-skinned races south of Egypt. Seventeenth-century chemists adopted it to denote black compounds. *Ethiops mineral* was made by rubbing together equal parts of mercury and sulphur until the quicksilver was 'killed'. It therefore consisted largely of black mercuric sulphide. *Ethiops martial* was a term·used to denote black iron oxide.

Another general term associated with colour was *crocus*. In the fifteenth century *crocus* was a term applied only to yellow pig-ments.[10] Although in the following century Libavius defined *crocus* as 'the magistery of metallic bodies reduced to a yellow powder',[11] he admitted that it was applied to dark red powders like *Crocus Martis* (ferric oxide) and *Crocus Saturni* (red lead), and later even green basic copper acetate was known by the name *Crocus Veneris*. The terms *ochre* and *saffron* were used synony-mously with *crocus* to describe coloured compounds of metals in powder form.

Substances were sometimes named not after their own colours but after the colour produced in a characteristic reaction. The best example of this is the term *atramentum sutorium*, used by

10. Le Begue, *Tabula de vocabulis synonymis* (1431), Merrifield: *Original Treatises on the Arts of Painting*, London, 1849, vol. i, pp. 23–5.
11. *Alchymia*, Frankfurt, 1606, Bk. 2, tract 1, cap. 27, p. 74.

Pliny[12] and adopted by Agricola.[13] The term literally means 'shoemakers' blacking', just as *atramentum librarium* was black writing ink. Yet this name must be reconciled with the fact that it was undoubtedly a green substance, ferrous sulphate (sometimes mixed with native copper sulphate). The explanation of this is to be found in the use of this substance in blackening leather.[14] The term *calomel* might be explained on similar principles despite the difficulty which has been found with the etymology of this word. The difficulty here is that the term was used to denote the white mercurous chloride,[15] whereas the name suggests a black substance ($\mu\epsilon\lambda\alpha\varsigma$ = black). It is possible that the name was related to its remarkable property of turning black, when spirit of hartshorn (ammonium hydroxide solution) was poured on it.[16]

One of the few advantages of the early attention paid to colour was that it was sometimes possible to use this as a criterion for distinguishing pure substances from impure. In the *Liber Claritatis*, attributed to Jabir, there is the statement that nitre may be found white or yellow, but the white variety is to be preferred.[17] Another instance is the use of the name *pearl ashes*, given to the whitest (and therefore purest) form of potassium carbonate extracted from the ashes of plants. On the whole, however, the early preoccupation with colours was detrimental to the progress of chemistry since colours are uncertain, variable, accidental qualities. They have little relation

12. *Hist. Nat.*, *34*, 112, 123.

13. *De Re Metallica*, Bk. 12, transl. Hoover, London, 1912, p. 572.

14. Sir John Pettus, *Fleta Minor*, Part 2, *Containing Essays on Metallic Words*, London, 1683, Art. Copperas: 'This Copperas . . . is called Atramentum Sutorium, because shoemakers-black is made with it.' An alternative explanation is that, when the crude mixtures of copper and ferrous sulphates were found, they were so impure as to be naturally black. Hence in the *Libellus de Alchimia* (attrib. to Albertus Magnus) there is the statement: 'Atramentum is a black earth. . . . Its black colour changes to a permanent red through calcination' (op. cit., para. 22; trans. Sister V. Heines, Berkeley and Los Angeles, 1958, p. 32).

15. The name originated with Turquet de Mayerne and was referred to by Lazarus Riverius as 'calomelanos Turqueti seu mercurius dulcis sexies sublimatus' (*Observationum Medicarum et Curationum insignium*, Cent. 4, Hague, 1657, p. 60). In the posthumous works of Turquet de Mayerne it occurs in a letter dated January 1612 (*Opera Medica*, ed. J. Browne, London, 1700, Part 1, p. 101).

16. E. J. Holmyard, *A Higher School Inorganic Chemistry*, 2nd edn., London, 1952, p. 277.

17. *Liber Claritatis Totius Alkimicae Artis*, para. 71, *Archeion*, *9* (1928), 471.

to chemical constitution. This was beginning to be recognized by the end of the seventeenth century and Lemery remarks how easy it is to change black antimony to a white calx— 'which shows that colours are not fundamental'.[18] Equally plain is a warning by Kunckel that colours are only a *lusus naturae* so that the chemical nature of a substance cannot be guessed from its colour.[19] Yet, even in the time of Lavoisier, chemists thought colour of sufficient importance to group the white metals together under the name of *métaux lunaires*,[20] thus perpetuating alchemical notions on their connection with silver. Nevertheless, the remarks of Lemery and Kunckel herald the beginning of a critical attitude towards the common ideas of chemistry and its language. Until chemical science was in a position to relate compounds generally to their chemical constitution, it was convenient to distinguish many coloured compounds by reference to their most obvious characteristic. Even in the reform of nomenclature of 1787 colours were not altogether excluded from the proposed chemical terms.

Terminology based on Consistency and Crystalline Form

Another property of substances which impressed the early chemists was their consistency; for instance, they noticed whether a solid easily crumbled to a powder or if a liquid was viscous. Sometimes such observations were linked with the colour of a substance and it could be argued that expressions like *milk of lime* and *butter of antimony* were based as much on colour as consistency.

Going back to the terminology used by Dioscorides[21] and that used by Pliny in his *Natural History*, we find that the consistency of substances was not neglected. The term ἁλός ἄνθος (*flos salis*) was applied to a yellow efflorescence which occurred, for example, on the surface of the Nile marshes and was probably impure sodium carbonate. The term ἀφρὸς νίτρου (*spuma*

18. 'Ce qui montre que les couleurs n'ont rien de réel' (*Cours de Chymie*, Paris, 1697, p. 271). Lemery's example could have been more apt, but the important thing is the gradual infiltration into chemistry through Boyle and Lemery of a philosophy which regarded colours as secondary qualities.

19. *Laboratorium Chymicum*, Hamburg and Leipzig, 1716, Part 3, cap. 2, p. 196.

20. Lavoisier, *Oeuvres*, Paris, 1862–93, vol. ii, pp. 32–3.

21. *The Greek Herbal of Dioscorides*, ed. R. T. Gunther, Oxford, 1934, Bk. V, 129, 131, 88.

nitri) was probably applied also to an efflorescence of soda The χαλκοῦ ἄνθος of Dioscorides was mentioned in Pliny as *aeris squamae* or *aeris flos*, a term adopted by Agricola. It was black cupric oxide (or sometimes red cuprous oxide), although the term was later applied to verdigris.

Another term connected with consistency was 'flowers'[22] which Libavius defines as a spiritous substance extracted by sublimation.[23] *Flowers of zinc* and *flowers of phosphorus* were obvious expressions to denote the volatile oxides of these substances and the term *flowers of sulphur* is still used to-day. Cerussa, too, is a term the etymology of which seems to have been based on its consistency (Gr. κηρός =wax). Pliny mentioned that blue and green vitriol looked like glass[24] and by the eighth century this resemblance had given rise to the name *vitreolum* (Lat. *vitrum* =glass) which occurs in the *Compositiones ad Tingenda*.[25]

The compounds of antimony, which became widely known at the beginning of the seventeenth century through the works of 'Basil Valentine' provided further opportunities for a terminology based on consistency. This author described the preparation of a yellow translucent glass of antimony to which he formally gave the name *vitrum Antimonii*.[26] This term in seventeenth-century literature usually denotes the fused sulphide of antimony, although the same term was applied to the compound we should now call antimony borate. Another term used for a compound of antimony was 'butter of antimony', an apt though primitive description of the deliquescent chloride. Lemery described it as 'butter or glacial oil of antimony' and the similar compound obtained by distilling arsenic with corrosive sublimate was called 'corrosive oil of arsenic' or 'butter of arsenic'. Stannic chloride, known usually as 'fuming liquor of Libavius', was sometimes called 'butter of tin' and Sage gave the name 'butter of zinc' to zinc chloride.[27] Although such a use of the term 'butter' in chemistry was criticized by Macquer and

---

22. Several reasons for the use of the term 'flowers' are given by Angelo Sala, (*Anatomia Antimonii*, Pars II, cap. 3; *Collectanea Chimica Curiosa*, Frankfurt, 1693, pp. 342–3).

23. *Alchymia*, Frankfurt, 1606, Lib. 2, Tract 2, cap. 40, p. 180.

24. 'vitrum esse creditur' (*Hist. Nat., 34,* 124).

25. Berth., *M.A.*, i, p. 14.

26. 'Und wird dieses Vitrum von mir genandt . . .' (*Triumph Wagen Antimonii*, Leipzig, 1604, pp. 119–20).

27. *Mém. Acad., 1770,* 22.

others, it can hardly be denied that, before the introduction of a truly systematic nomenclature, it did something to associate substances of a similar composition by a common name.

When, at the beginning of the seventeenth-century, Oswald Croll prepared fused silver chloride, he saw a resemblance between the hard white solid and horn and therefore called it *luna cornea*[28] (horn silver). In the eighteenth century the chlorides of lead, tin and mercury were sometimes called 'corneous' (or 'horn') lead, 'horn tin' and 'horn mercury' respectively. Rouelle, misunderstanding the nature of the compound now known as bismuth oxychloride, called it *bismuth corné*.[29]

With regard to liquids, the physical property of viscosity was emphasized in terminology to the entire exclusion of chemical considerations. The term 'oil' was extended to describe not only natural oils but also strong acids and alkalis of oily appearance and consistency. The most important compound described under this heading was concentrated sulphuric acid. The date of the discovery of sulphuric acid is uncertain, but by the early sixteenth century several references to *oleum vitrioli* are found in contemporary medical works.[30] Dilute sulphuric acid was sometimes called *spiritus vitrioli* or *spiritus sulphuris*, according to whether it was prepared by distilling green vitriol or by condensing the fumes of burning sulphur in water.[31] The relationship between the products of these two operations was still something of a mystery in the mid-eighteenth century.[31a] The name *oleum de sulphure* in the *Luminare Maius* of 1566 was given equally to a genuine oil containing some dissolved sulphur and to sulphuric acid prepared *per campanam*.[32] Beguin in the following century gave the name *oil of sulphur* to an alkaline sulphide of ammonia.[33] He said it was improper to give this name to spirit of sulphur prepared *per campanam*, but the

28. *Basilica Chymica*, Frankfurt, 1609, p. 218.
29. *Mém. Acad.*, *1754*, 585.
30. e.g. Valerius Cordus, *De Artificiosis Extractionibus*, Pars III, Cap. 1, *De Oleo vitrioli faciundo*, *Works* (posthumous), Argentorati, 1561. Also Brasavolus, *Examen omnium simplicium medicamentorum*, Lugduni, 1537, p. 513.
31. Both would contain some sulphurous acid, the latter more than the former.
31a. e.g. Macquer; *Élémens de Chymie Théorique*, Paris, 1749, p. 43 says they are identical, but in 2nd edn. (Paris, 1756, pp. 45–6) he says that they differ because the latter contains phlogiston.
32. *Manliis de Bosco*, op. cit., Venice, 1566, f. 139.
33. *Tyrocinium Chymicum*, trans. Russell, London, 1669, p. 54.

chemists who succeeded him preferred to reverse his ideas, calling the former *spiritus fumans sulphuratus Beguini*. More important than Beguin's preparation, however, was potassium carbonate which in concentrated solution was known as *oil of tartar*. The name is found in Chaucer's *Canon Yeoman's Tale* and remained in common use for four hundred years.

An elementary physical property of minerals is their crystalline form. In classical times Dioscorides and Pliny used the term *lonchoton* (lanced-shaped) to describe crystals of blue vitriol.[34] By the seventeenth century the crystalline form of several minerals including plume alum, gypsum and talc had been frequently observed, recorded and used to describe these substances. In the seventeenth century several salts were prepared artificially and their properties investigated. A keen observation at the beginning of that century of the crystalline form of potassium acetate resulted in the name *terra foliata tartari* ('foliated earth of tartar').[35] This was a distinctive and unambiguous term which there was no cause to change until the reform of nomenclature at the end of the next century. By analogy Baumé in 1773 proposed the term *terre foliée animale* for what is now known as ammonium acetate and the desire to systematize chemical names led to other similar expressions.

By the beginning of the eighteenth century the characteristic crystalline forms of common salt, vitriol, alum and nitre were well known, although this property was not usually used in naming them. In the first half of the eighteenth century the salts of sodium and potassium were clearly distinguished by Duhamel and Marggraf. In particular, the nitrates of sodium and potassium could be readily distinguished by their crystalline form, the former being almost cubical and the latter needle-shaped. Sodium nitrate was therefore called *cubic nitre* and potassium nitrate kept its name *nitre* or *common nitre*. In Marggraf's important paper, in which he distinguished the salts of the 'mineral' and 'vegetable' alkalis, he described the nitrates as *nitre cubique* and *nitre prismatique* respectively.[36] This attention to crystalline form was important since it enabled chemists to distinguish the various salts produced by the action

34. *Herbal*, V, 114; *Hist. Nat.*, *34*, 124.
35. P. Mueller, *Miracula Chymica*, Wittenberg?, 1611, p. 66.
36. *Opuscules Chimiques*, Paris, 1762, vol. ii, pp. 386–7.

of any acid on a given alkali. This was the method adopted by Donald Munro to distinguish the sodium salts of various organic acids.[37]

Terminology based on the Senses of Taste and Smell

To analyse substances by their taste may have been primitive and occasionally dangerous, but in some cases it was very effective. Lead acetate, for example, was known as *sugar of lead* for at least two centuries before it acquired its present name at the end of the eighteenth century; and the taste of a small crystal of this substance was an easy method of identifying it.

The importance of taste in early terminology can be seen in the word στυπτηρία (=alum), which describes the astringent taste of many metal sulphates which could be classified as 'alums' on the criterion of taste alone. The term 'salt' was also closely linked with taste, the original salt (sodium chloride) being used to impart a flavour to food. Bernard Palissy used the term 'salt' in a very wide sense, setting no limit to the number of salts in nature and saying that there were as many salts as there were tastes.[38] By the eighteenth century the concept of salt had assumed more rational proportions, but taste and solubility in water were still the main criteria. When Duhamel distinguished sodium salts from potassium salts in 1736 he was able to cite their different taste as evidence.[39] At a time when it was not customary to distinguish compounds according to the proportion of their constituents, it was usual to speak of *mercurius dulcis* (or sweet sublimate)[40] to distinguish it from corrosive sublimate. Boerhaave quotes an alchemical maxim:

> Whosoever is not acquainted with the taste of Salts will never arrive at the knowledge of our arcana.[41]

It should be remembered that 'salt' at this period included not only neutral salts but also acids and alkalis. Before the use of

37. 'An Account of some neutral salts made with vegetable Acids and with the salt of Amber', *Phil. Trans.*, 57 (1767), 479–516.
38. *De l'Agriculture, Oeuvres Complètes*, Paris, 1844, pp. 506, 509.
39. 'Sur la Base du Sel Marin', *Mém. Acad., 1736*, 226.
40. Boyle says it was given this name not so much because it is sweet as because it is insipid compared with corrosive sublimate (*Works*, ed. Birch, vol. i, p. 364).
41. *Elements of Chemistry*, trans. Dallowe, London, 1737, vol. i, p. 438.

indicators in the seventeenth century[42] acids and alkalis could sometimes be distinguished by their respective sharp and bitter tastes.[43]

Taste was particularly useful in distinguishing magnesium salts. The early history of magnesium is obscured by linguistic confusion, since the same term was used to denote compounds of manganese, but there could be no mistaking *bitter salt* or *sal amarum* (magnesium sulphate). On the criterion of taste the salt from the mineral springs at Epsom was soon identified with that obtained from the mother-liquor of nitre. *Bitter spar* was a term used by Klaproth for dolomite (a double carbonate of magnesium and calcium).[44] When in 1798 Vauquelin discovered a new earth in the mineral *beryl* it was called *glucina*, meaning 'sweet', because of its characteristic property of forming salts with a sweet taste.[45] The name of the element was, however, later changed to *beryllium*.

A seventeenth-century book of mineralogy emphasizes the importance of smell as well as taste and sight in the identification of mineral ores.[46] Yet smell entered in only a small way into chemical terminology and then almost entirely in connection with gases, the properties of which were investigated in the second half of the eighteenth century. Thus Scheele referred to our hydrogen sulphide as *stinking sulphureous air*[47] and ammonia was sometimes called *aer urinosum*. The term *urinous salt* (*sel urineux*) was sometimes applied to all alkaline salts,[48] but more usually it was the smell of ammonium salts which was associated with putrified urine since they gave off a similar smell.

42. e.g. Boyle, *Experiments touching colour*, London, 1664, p. 245n. mentions the different colours of syrup of violets when added to an acid, alkali or neutral salt.

43. According to a tract ascribed to Albertus Magnus, the term 'alkali' meant 'the dregs of bitterness' (*faex amaritudinis*) (*Th. Ch.*, ii, p. 470).

44. *Schriften der Gesellschaft naturforschender Freunde zu Berlin*, *11* (1793), 51.

45. This was at the suggestion of the editors of the *Annales de Chimie* who included the reformers Guyton de Morveau, Berthollet and Fourcroy (*Annales de Chimie, 26* (1798), 169n.).

46. Barba, *El Arte de los Metales*, trans. R. E. Douglass and E. P. Mathewson, New York, 1923, pp. 4ff. This is what he says about the tasting of ores: 'The sense of taste does not give less information in determining the Purity or mixture of Earths than the Sense of Smell. Pure Earth has no taste whatsoever, while ordinarily that which has taste owes the same to a mixture with mineral Substances. Scarcely any are free from this quality when they are dry. . . .' (ibid., p. 7).

47. *Chemical Observations on Air and Fire*, trans. Foster, London, 1780, p. 186.

48. Macquer, *Dictionnaire de Chymie*, Paris, 1766, vol. ii, p. 485.

CHAPTER TWO

Terminology based on Other Considerations

The Association of Metals and Related Compounds with the Planets

The association of the sun, moon and the five nearer planets with seven metals was firmly established nearly two thousand years ago. The concept of seven planets probably dates back to the eighth or ninth centuries B.C., possibly as a result of certain Chaldean influences. In a pre-scientific attempt to read unity into the physical world the seven moving heavenly bodies were related at an uncertain date to seven common metals.[49] In relating particular planets and metals, colour was often the criterion used. Gold suggested the colour and splendour of the sun; the moon, which at night assumed the role of the sun during the day, was naturally associated with the bright colour of silver; the red tint of Mars suggested copper to some and iron to others. Saturn was always associated with lead. This was because Saturn, being (as we now know) the farthest of the then-known planets from the sun, took longest to complete its orbit and gave the impression of moving slowly. A slow-moving planet was considered the most appropriate to associate with a heavy metal. The planets were not always associated with the same metals, although there was general agreement that gold and silver (the noblest metals) were associated with the sun and moon and lead (the basest metal) was associated with Saturn. This may be seen from the following table:[50]

---

49. This connection was ascribed to the Persians by Origen (second century A.D.) and is fairly common in neoplatonic authors. See also Partington, 'The Origin of the Planetary Symbols for the Metals', *Ambix*, *1* (1937), 61–4

50. Origen, *Contra Celsum*, 6, 22; Migne, *Patriologia, Series Graecae*, vol. 11, Paris, 1857, p. 1323; Berthelot, *Introduction à la chimie des anciens*, Paris, 1889, pp. 81, 84.

Origen (2nd cent. A.D.)		Olympiodorus (6th cent. A.D.)		Stephanos of Alexandria (7th cent. A.D.)	
Lead	Saturn	Lead	Saturn	Lead	Saturn
Tin	Venus	Tin	Mercury	Tin	Jupiter
Bronze	Jupiter	Electrum	Jupiter	Mercury	Mercury
Iron	Mercury	Iron	Mars	Iron	Mars
Copper	Mars	Copper	Venus	Copper	Venus
Silver	Moon	Silver	Moon	Silver	Moon
Gold	Sun	Gold	Sun	Gold	Sun

In medieval alchemy the relationship between the metals and the planets was so intimate that the names of the planets were used as synonyms for the names of metals. From this relationship a rich pictorial symbolism developed (see for example Plate 2b). Occasionally the names of the metals were entirely replaced by the names of planets and, as has already been pointed out, the reader is left in doubt whether he is reading an alchemical or an astrological tract.

The use of the names of planets had a bad influence in early chemistry, since it perpetuated ancient superstitions of a real connection between the two. One factor which contributed to the breakdown of the one-to-one correspondence between the planets and the metals was the discovery and examination of antimony, bismuth[51] and zinc in the sixteenth century and of platinum in the mid-eighteenth century. Even if it were argued that the former were only 'semi-metals', no-one could deny the full right of platinum to be classed as a metal once its properties were investigated.[52] That the supernatural association of the metals with the planets was still accepted in the second half of the seventeenth century can be seen from the standard works of Le Febure[53] and Glaser.[54] Lemery's famous text-book, the *Cours de Chymie* (editions from 1675–1757), had the merit of ridiculing any associations between the planets and the metals,[55] although

51. The *Probierbüchlein* (early sixteenth century) got over this difficulty by saying that Jupiter controlled the ores of both tin and bismuth (*Bergwerk und Probierbüchlein*, trans. Sisco and Smith, New York, 1949, p. 77).

52. It was sometimes referred to as 'the eighth metal' (e.g. Macquer, *Mém. Acad., 1758*, 119).

53. *A Compendious Body of Chymistry*, London, 1664, vol. ii, pp. 168, 183.

54. *The Compleat Chymist*, London, 1677, pp. 68–9, 77, 86, 113.

55. Op. cit., Paris, 1697, pp. 59, 83.

Lemery continued to use the astrological names for the metals and some of their compounds.

The names of planets then were used not only in connection with metals themselves but were often extended to their compounds. Without appreciating this point it would be impossible to understand chemical terminology at the end of the seventeenth century. Looking through a standard work like that of Lemery, we encounter names such as *vitriol of the moon, magistery of jupiter, salt of saturn, spirit of venus, saffron of mars*. It is important to realize that such terms were in common use for most of the eighteenth century. In the last days of the *ancien régime* of chemical terminology Fourcroy gave the name *jovial regulus of Antimony* to an alloy of antimony containing some tin and he not only used the traditional term *lunar nitre* (silver nitrate), but proposed the new term *martial chalk* to denote a carbonate of iron.[56] In the *Méthode de Nomenclature Chimique* the astrological synonyms of the metals were abandoned, but the name 'Mercury' was retained as it seemed preferable to the popular name 'quicksilver'. When the results of Klaproth's researches suggested to him that he had discovered a new metal, he saw no danger of causing astrological prejudice when he named it *Uranium*[57] to commemorate the fact that it had been discovered in the same decade as the new planet (Herschel, 1781).

Terminology based on the Names of Persons

When a substance came to be associated with a particular person, either because he first prepared it or because he popularized its use in pharmacy, the proper name often became incorporated into the name of that substance. There was always, of course, a time-lag between the discovery and use of a substance and the adoption of a name commemorating its originator. It was not usual for a man to donate his own name to a substance; he relied on his contemporaries for this. Not even Glauber,[58] who prepared sodium sulphate and boastfully proclaimed its powers as an almost universal medicine, could give his name directly to this salt. To him it was *sal mirabile*;

56. *Elements of Natural History and Chemistry*, London, 1788, vol. iii, pp. 64, 340, 238.
57. *Mémoires de l'Académie Royale des Sciences de Berlin, 1786–7*, 172.
58. *Works*, trans. Packe, London, 1689, Part 1, p. 224; Part 2, p. 178.

posterity preferred 'Glauber's salt'. Glauber also prepared ammonium sulphate which he called *secret sal ammoniac*, but the obscurity of this expression was lessened by calling it *Glauber's secret sal ammoniac*. Again, to call any substance the *alkahest* or 'universal solvent' was indeed presumptuous, although van Helmont often used this name for what may have been a concentrated aqueous solution of potassium carbonate.[59] It became known as *Alkahest of van Helmont*, although Boerhaave referred to it as *Glauber's Alkahest*.[60] There was also *Respour's Alkahest* which was probably a zinc compound.

According to Gren,[61] the expressions *liquor (spiritus) fumans Boylei* and *spiritus Beguini* both denoted the same substance (ammonium polysulphide), which affords another example of how different chemists could be credited with the same preparation, thus confusing the student who might think of these as different substances. While on the one hand the use of personal names tended to increase the number of chemical terms in relation to the number of chemical substances, it did sometimes have the effect of distinguishing different substances which otherwise could have been easily confused. Thus the *fuming liquor of Boyle* (see above) was distinguished from the *fuming liquor of Libavius* (stannic chloride). The salt which Christophe Glaser called *sel polychreste*[62] (potassium sulphate) was named *Sal Polychrestum Glaseri* in honour of the chemist generally associated with its discovery. Unfortunately this was not the only salt which was claimed to have many (medicinal) uses. Such properties were also claimed for sodium potassium tartrate which was prepared by Seignette, an apothecary of La Rochelle. The latter was therefore called *Sel polychreste de Seignette* or more simply *Seignette's salt* and hence confusion was avoided.

The following are a few other examples from the seventeenth and early eighteenth century of chemical terms based on personal names:

59. This was suggested by W. Johnson, *Lexicon Chymicum*, Frankfurt and Leipzig, 1678, p. 262, and Supplement, p. 9. The relevant passage from Helmont is in *De Febribus*, cap. 15. (*Opuscula Medica Inaudita*, Amsterdam, 1648, *De Febribus*, p. 58a.)

60. *Elements of Chemistry*, trans. Dallowe, London, 1735, vol. ii, p. 278, since Glauber describes its preparation without any reference to van Helmont (*Works*, Part 1, p. 153).

61. *Neues Journal der Physik*, 1795, II, 199.

62. 'Salt of many uses', *The Compleat Chymist*, London, 1677, p. 159.

offa Helmontii	J. B. van Helmont (1579–1644)	potassium carbonate
(*digestive*) *salt of Sylvius*	François Sylvius (1614–72) (Prof. of medicine at Leyden)	potassium chloride
Homberg's (*sedative*) *salt*	Wilhelm Homberg (1652–1715) (member of Paris *Académie des Sciences*)	boric acid
Glauber's spirit of nitre	J. R. Glauber (1604–70)	fuming nitric acid
praecipitatus Vigonis	Giovanni de Vigo (*b. c.* 1460) (famous Italian surgeon)	mercuric oxide
spirit of Mindererus	Raymond Minderer (*d.* 1621) (practised medicine in Augsburg)	ammonium acetate solution
powder of Algaroth	Vittorio Algarotto (*d.* 1604) (President College of Physicians, Verona)	antimony oxychloride
neutral arsenical salt of Macquer	P-J. Macquer (1718–84)	potassium dihydrogen arsenate

After Guyton de Morveau in 1782 had condemned the use of proper names in chemistry and this view was endorsed in the *Méthode de Nomenclature Chimique* (1787), the use of such names was largely abandoned in pure chemistry.[63] In mineralogy, however, chemical constitution was not the only consideration in nomenclature. It was still considered appropriate to name minerals after the leading mineralogists and Berzelius, for example, had three minerals and a supposed new element named after him. What is more, the old terminology was perpetuated in such names as *Sylvine* and *Glaserite*.

Terminology based on Place Names

The incorporation of the names of towns and countries in chemical terminology was in some ways parallel with the use of personal names. Thus the names of places were sometimes used merely to commemorate a particular discovery. The use of the term *Rochelle salt* was similar to the use of the name *Seignette's*

63. In several cases, particularly when the systematic chemical name was complex, the names of discoveries continued to be used, or new expressions were deliberately coined. Thus we have not only *Scheele's green* (cupric hydrogen arsenite) but *Berthollet's salt* (potassium chlorate), *Mohr's salt* (ferrous ammonium sulphate), etc.

salt, the former commemorating the town in which the originator of this salt lived.

The use of place names properly applied also imposed a certain standard in chemistry. In the days before analysis it gave a certain precision to chemical preparations if the source of the reagents was accurately specified. It was usual to describe the vitriols in terms of their place of origin. In the sixteenth and seventeenth centuries white vitriol (zinc sulphate) was known as *vitriol of Goslar*. Before the discovery of this substance two other kinds of vitriols mentioned in the early chemical books were *Roman vitriol* and *Hungarian vitriol*, both of which were highly prized. One of these names denoted our copper sulphate and the other ferrous sulphate, but it was not always clear which was which and it is a pity that they were not clearly distinguished as *blue vitriol* and *green vitriol*. According to Lemery[64] and other chemical writers on the continent of Europe, *vitriolum Romanum* was green vitriol and *vitriolum Hungaricum* was blue vitriol, but this was not necessarily how these terms were understood in Britain. Pemberton, a British medical and chemical writer, remarked on this in the mid-eighteenth century:

> It is not improbable, that as we have in this country given the game of *Roman* to blue vitriol, by which the writers of other countries intend a green; so we might call some other kind of vitriol by the name of *Hungarian*, which foreign authors apply to the blue.[65]

Cyprian vitriol was obviously copper sulphate and the name *German vitriol* was sometimes applied to the bluish-green mineral which contained both copper and iron. Vitriol was also sometimes associated with France and was occasionally called *terra francisca*.[66] It is interesting to note that, when the names of countries were involved, they were usually foreign countries, so that in France vitriol was sometimes described as 'Spanish earth'[67] and was also, and more rationally, described as coming from England and Germany.

We may take England and Spain (two countries on the periphery of Europe) as examples of how the remainder of Europe used predominantly the names of foreign countries

64. *Traité Universel*, Paris, 1698, pp. 818–19.
65. *The Dispensatory of the Royal College of Physicians*, *London*, transl. with remarks by H. Pemberton, London, 1746, p. 66n.
66. Simon Ianuensis, *Clavis Sanationis*, Venice, 1514, f. 11r.
67. Planis Campy, *Bouquet*, Paris, 1623, *Dictionnaire*, pp. 924–76.

when they were qualifying substances geographically. It is true that for many of these names there was a rational basis, yet it is surprising that a central European country like Germany, which was rich in mines and minerals, should not have contributed more local names to chemical terminology. We may take a few examples of names involving England. There was, of course, *stannum Anglici* based on the fame of the Cornish tin mines. From the vitriol manufactured in England from the iron pyrites in the Isle of Wight came the names *vitriolum Anglicum*[68] (ferrous sulphate), *terra anglica rubra*[69] (ferric oxide) and *oleum vitrioli Anglicum*.[70] Also based on chemical industry was the term *phosphorum Anglicum*,[71] based on the fact that a considerable quantity of phosphorus was prepared in England in the eighteenth century and exported abroad. The mineral which Boyle referred to as *Creta Bathensis* became known in eighteenth century France as *craie blanc d'Angleterre*. Similarly what was known in this country as *Epsom salts* was sometimes referred to more vaguely as *sal anglicum*[72] and, to complicate matters, Macquer gave the same name (*sel d'Angleterre*) to what we now call ammonium carbonate.[73] It seems that what in Britain was called *sal polychrestum Glaseri* was sometimes called *sal polychrestum Anglorum* by the Germans.[74] If the substances described as 'Spanish' had a logical foundation for their names, this may have depended partly on the fact that it was through Spain that the alchemy of the Arabs came to Europe. The term *Spanish green* occurs in Theophilus[75] (fl. *c.* A.D. 1000) and Agricola says that a knowledge of this substance (basic copper carbonate or acetate) had come to Germany from Spain.[76] Other coloured substances described as 'Spanish' were *Spanish white* (bismuth oxychloride) and *Spanish black* (burnt cork). Washing soda was occasionally described as *Soda Hispanica*[77]

68. Neumann, *Chymiae Medicae Dogmatico-Experimentalis, Züllichau*, 1749–1755, Part 2, pp. 789ff.
69. Gren, *Neues Journal der Physik 1795*, II, 232.
70. Remler, *Neues Chemisches Wörterbuch*, Erfurt, 1793, p. 24.
71. e.g. Stahl, *Fundamenta Chymiae*, Nuremberg, 1723, Bk. 2, p. 58.
72. Gren, op. cit., p. 245.
73. *Dictionnaire de Chymie*, Paris, 1766, vol. ii, p. 449, vol. i, p. 100.
74. Gellert, *Anfangsgründe zur metallurgischen Chymie*, 2nd edn., Leipzig, 1776, p. 37.
75. *De Diversis Artibus*, trans. R. Hendrie, London, 1847, Book 1, cap. 27.
76. Agricola, *Interpretatio, Works*, Basle, 1558, p. 461.
77. Gellert, op. cit., p. 28.

and in the eighteenth century Buffon[78] complained that the term *craie d'Espagne* was improperly applied to talc.

If the arbitrary nature of these geographical names has not already been sufficiently demonstrated, it might perhaps be seen in the various names given to magnesium sulphate in England, Germany and Italy. It was known in these respective countries as *Epsom salt, Sedlitz Salz* and *Sal di Modena*.[79] We can see here the disadvantages such names had of obscuring the possible chemical identity of a substance obtained from different sources. The advantage of a terminology based on place names was that it did serve to distinguish different substances of the same class such as the vitriols. Its use was inevitable at a time when the purity of many substances was questionable, but in the eighteenth century, when the identity and purity of substances were less in doubt, place names were inappropriate to the science of chemistry. Such names as the *Swedish acid*[80] and *Prussian blue*[81] need not have been anything more than temporary labels which could be replaced when the composition of these compounds had been investigated.

Terminology based on Medicinal Properties

The influence of Paracelsus in the sixteenth century did much to bring about the use of inorganic chemical substances in medicine in addition to the many traditional vegetable drugs. Gradually there spread an appreciation of the ancilliary role which chemistry could play in medicine, so that much of the chemistry of the seventeenth and early eighteenth centuries was pharmaceutical chemistry. The value set on the medicinal properties of chemical substances by the pharmaceutical chemists of this period was naturally reflected in the terminology employed.

Unfortunately this had the bad effect, as far as pure chemistry was concerned, of turning away attention from the composition of a substance to its properties (real or supposed) in the field of

78. *Histoire Naturelle des Minéraux*, Paris, 1783–8, vol. i, p. 61.

79. Brugnatelli, *Elementi di Chimica*, Pavia, 1795–8, vol. i, p. 87. In France the term *Epsom salt* was often used, but did not always denote magnesium sulphate. See Baumé, '*Comparaison du Sel d'Epsom d'Angleterre avec le sel d'Epsom, préparé en France*', *Chymie Expérimentale*, Paris, 1773, vol. iii, pp. 564ff.

80. Hydrofluoric acid (Priestley, *Experiments . . . on air*, London, 1774–7, vol. ii, p. 187).

81. Also called Berlin blue (*Miscellanea Berolinensis, 1710*, 380–1).

medicine. Glauber called the sodium sulphate he had prepared *sal mirabile*, because he thought its medicinal possibilities were boundless. A similar lack of scientific humility led Glaser to call his salt *sal polychrestum*, as which it found favour in the public eye for a few years, until it was largely supplanted by Seignette's salt which also went on the market under the name of *sal polychrestum*. The term *Panacea* was used very liberally in the seventeenth and early eighteenth centuries; it was applied to various preparations including antimony compounds. The following is a list of some of the more common inorganic compounds which, at the beginning of the eighteenth century, were known by names related to their medicinal properties:

Specificum purgans Paracelsi ⎫	
Sal polychrestum Glaseri ⎬	potassium sulphate
Febrifugal salt ⎭	
Anodinum minerale	potassium sulphate *or* nitre deflagrated with antimony
Diaphoretic antimony	a mixture of antimony oxide and potassium antimonate
Febrifugal salt of Sylvius ⎫	
Digestive salt of Sylvius ⎬	potassium chloride
Sal prunellae[82]	potassium nitrate + sulphate
Diuretic salt	potassium acetate
Cathartic salt of Glauber	sodium sulphate
Bitter cathartic salt	magnesium sulphate
Emetic powder ⎫	
Tartar emetic ⎬	potassium antimonyl tartrate
Homberg's sedative salt	boric acid

Many of these names were unsatisfactory because of their ambiguity, and confusion was likely to arise when the same property (e.g. a purgative) was incorporated in the name of more than one substance. Also the medicinal virtues might themselves be called in question. Macquer was sceptical as to whether the 'febrifugal salt' could be relied upon, as its name suggests, to cure fevers.[83] A committee of the Royal College of Physicians of London, meeting in 1745, considered that '*anti-*

---

82. So called because it was believed to be a specific remedy for a certain plum-coloured quinsy (R. James, *Medical Dictionary*, London, 1743–5, art. *Nitrum*).

83. *Dictionnaire de Chymie*, Paris, 1766, vol. ii, p. 543.

monium diaphoreticum, till its medical properties shall be better agreed, may more unexceptionally be called *antimonii calx*.[84] Yet such names continued to be used generally until the reform of terminology in 1787.

Terminology based on the Method of Preparation of a Substance

Probably what might seem to be the most inoffensive method of naming substances, before their composition was known, was by their method of preparation. If this could be summarized in two or three words it would seem ideally suited to the early stages of chemistry, and yet probably more confusion was caused by this method of naming than by any other.

There were many cases where the name of a substance, representing an attempt to indicate its method of preparation, was definitely misleading by falsely suggesting its composition. For example, the term *cinnabar of antimony* suggests a compound of antimony, whereas the name was applied to red mercuric sulphide prepared from antimony sulphide and mercuric chloride. It was clearly appreciated by several chemists in the eighteenth century that *cinnabar of antimony* did not differ essentially from ordinary cinnabar; and even before then Friedrich Hoffmann had pointed out in 1689 that 'Cinnabar of antimony is nothing but mercury joined (*amalgamatus*) with the sulphur of antimony'.[85] Other striking examples of misleading names for compounds based on their method of preparation were *sal ammoniacum fixum* (calcium chloride) and the much criticized *mercurius vitae* (a mixture of antimony oxychloride and oxide). Boerhaave was at least taking a step in the right direction when he called the latter *mercurius vitae antimonii*.[86] In all these cases the name seems to have been given to a compound before its composition was understood. In the three cases cited above a knowledge of the process of double decomposition would have

84. *The Dispensatory of the Royal College of Physicians*, London, transl. H. Pemberton, London, 1746, p. 64.

85. *Exercitatio Medico-Chymica de Cinnabari Antimonii*, Frankfurt, 1689, p. 57. See also: Neumann, *Lectiones Publicae*, Berlin, 1732, p. 334; Macquer, op. cit., vol. i, p. 262; *Essay for the Reformation of the London Pharmacopoeia*. London, 1744, p. 82; 'the substance from which it takes its name [i.e. Antimony] has no share in its composition'.

86. Boerhaave, *Elements of Chemistry*, trans. Dallowe, London, 1735, vol. ii, p. 366.

resulted in a less misleading terminology. These names were originally given usually with the intention of describing the composition of a substance, although in the light of subsequent analysis their only rational justification is that they relate to the method of preparation.

Another pair of terms which caused some confusion were *Spirit of Saturn* and *Spirit of Venus*, names suggesting compounds of lead and copper respectively. Jean Beguin described the preparation from minium and distilled vinegar of a liquid he called *burning spirit of Saturn*, because it was inflammable and he thought it was a compound of lead.[87] Actually the lead takes no part in the reaction and the product of distilling lead acetate is impure acetone. Beguin's terminology did not go without comment however, for Christophe Glaser later referred to 'A burning Spirit of Saturn (as it is called) but rather, a Spirit of the Volatile Salt of Vinegar'.[88] Tachenius referred to the product of distillation of copper acetate as 'pretended spirit of Venus'[89] because it was really only distilled vinegar—the meaning which Macquer gave to the expression. It is typical of the confusion of terminology in early chemistry that the *London Pharmacopoeia* of 1721 gave the name *Spiritus Veneris* to sulphuric acid obtained by the distillation of copper sulphate.

Two general terms used in the seventeenth and eighteenth centuries and relating to the preparation of substances were *flowers* and *precipitate*. *Flowers* were prepared by condensing the fumes of a solid which was being burned or distilled. This explains the meaning of *flowers of sulphur*, an expression still used to-day. The term *precipitate* would seem to be unambiguous and yet it was sometimes applied to substances not obtained by precipitation. An outstanding example of this abuse was the famous so-called *red mercury precipitate*. This was made by dissolving mercury in *aqua fortis*, evaporating the solution (mercuric nitrate) to dryness and then gently heating the solid, leaving a substance which was mostly mercuric oxide. Obviously no precipitation was involved. Yet despite criticisms by Lemery, Neumann and Macquer and others, the term 'precipitate' was misused for most of the eighteenth century. It will be remembered that Priestley first obtained his *dephlogisticated air*

87. *Tyrocinium Chymicum*, trans. Russell, London, 1669, p. 58.
88. *The Compleat Chymist*, London, 1677, p. 84.
89. *Hippocraticae Medicinae Clavis*, Frankfurt, 1669, pp. 114–16.

(oxygen) by heating the same red powder, 'common red precipitate'.[90]

Where terminology based on methods of preparation was not misapplied or used in a misleading way, it often obscured the fact that two or more substances prepared by different methods were identical. We may take three important instances of this concerned with sulphuric acid, potassium carbonate and potassium salts generally.

The product of the distillation of green vitriol was called *spirit of vitriol* (or, if more concentrated, *oil of vitriol*). When sulphur was burned in a large bell and the fumes condensed in water the product was a mixture of sulphuric and sulphurous acids and was called *spirit of sulphur*. As normally prepared, it was identical in composition with *spirit of vitriol*, which also consisted of sulphuric acid with some sulphurous acid. Some of the more discerning chemists of the seventeenth century appreciated the similarity between the acids,[91] yet they did not suggest the unification of terminology and text books continued to mention the two acids as separate preparations unrelated to each other.

Another artificial distinction was made between *spirit of nitre* and *aqua fortis*. The preparation of the former as described by Beguin was by distilling saltpetre with three parts of common Bolus, while in the preparation of *aqua fortis* the essential reagents were saltpetre and vitriol (hydrated ferrous sulphate).[92] In both cases the product was nitric acid (more or less concentrated), yet this identity was not generally appreciated. Lemery commented that *aqua fortis* fumed more than *spirit of nitre* and said that this was because the former acid was really a mixture of spirit of nitre and spirit of vitriol.[93] In the mid-eighteenth century Cullen complained of the misleading duplication of terms:

90. Priestley was concerned with the 'air' given off by heating *common red precipitate*. At first he suspected that this air came from the 'nitrous acid' (i.e. nitric acid) used to prepare the *red precipitate*, since the latter was produced 'by a solution of mercury in spirit of nitre'. He therefore repeated his experiment with *mercurius calcinatus* which was 'produced by exposing mercury to a certain degree of heat, where common air has access to it'. (*Experiments and Observations on Different Kinds of Air*, London, 1774-7, vol. ii, p. 35.)

91. e.g. A. Sala, *Anatomia Vitrioli*, 3rd edn., Leyden, 1617, p. 92. Libavius, *Syntagmatis Arcanorum*, Frankfurt, 1660, vol. i, p. 437.

92. e.g. Beguin, *Tyrocinium Chymicum*, transl. Russell, London, 1669, pp. 50, 58.

93. *Cours de Chymie*, Paris, 1697, pp. 355, 347.

It is certainly improper to support, as it were by authority, a difference of names where there is no real difference of the thing. How readily these different names mislead may be observed from hence that in almost every table of specific gravities there occur in two distinct articles the specific gravities of *spirit of nitre* and *aqua fortis*.[94]

In the *Pharmacopoeia Augustana* of 1653 there is a list of some thirty salts extracted from the ashes of different plants. Prominent here and in current chemical works were *sal absinthii* (salt of wormwood), *sal juniperi, sal gentianae, sal guaiaci ex ligno*, etc. These salts were supposed to have virtues dependent upon the particular plants from which they were obtained. The majority of pharmaceutical chemists of the seventeenth and early eighteenth centuries did not appreciate that all these substances owed any qualities they might possess to their chief ingredient, potassium carbonate, which was already available to them as *sal tartari*. Had they been less concerned with the origin of any particular specimen of salt and more concerned with its chemical properties, they might have realized that by strongly heating cream of tartar they had the purest form of this substance. Yet Kunckel in 1676 stated quite plainly that *Salt of Wormwood, Salt of Tartar, Salt of Cinnamon* and *Potash* were identical and any one of them could be used in an experiment with the same results.[95] Nevertheless the separate names continued to be used in the eighteenth century, although Cullen about 1750 proposed the term *vegetable alkali* to describe the salts extracted from the ashes of plants.[96] Macquer complained in his *Dictionary* of 1766 that, as the salts obtained by the lixiviation of the ashes of various plants yielded the same substance when purified, it was useless to distinguish the name of the plant from which it was extracted. The salts should be called *alkali of tartar* or *alkali of soda* as was appropriate. This is a striking example of how only a change in nomenclature could overcome deep rooted prejudices.

The useless multiplication of names was not confined to potassium carbonate; it applied also to the whole group of substances

94. L. Dobbin, 'A Cullen Chemical Manuscript of 1753', *Annals of Science, 1* (1936), 147–8.
95. *Nützliche Observationes*, Hamburg, 1676, cap. 1, cap. 7.
96. But not sea-weed, etc. which yielded sodium salts (L. Dobbin, loc. cit., pp. 149–51).

which we now recognize as salts of potassium. The two main sources of potassium salts in the seventeenth and eighteenth centuries were tartar (potassium hydrogen tartrate) and nitre (potassium nitrate). According to the contemporary classification into animal, vegetable and mineral, tartar was of vegetable origin (the *vegetable alkali* of Cullen), whereas nitre was considered as a mineral.[97] In the famous text-books of Lemery and Boerhaave, for example, the preparations from tartar are separate from those from nitre. When tartar was strongly heated to yield *salt of tartar* (potassium carbonate) the product could be readily acted upon by acids to form salts. With spirit of vitriol the *tartarus vitriolatus* produced was often quite a pure form of potassium sulphate. If, on the other hand, nitre was strongly heated with oil of vitriol the product was called *nitrum vitriolatum*. This was sometimes potassium sulphate, although under less forcing conditions the main product would be the bisulphate.[98] Alternatively, by the favourite method of deflagration, using a mixture of nitre and sulphur, impure potassium sulphate could be formed. Thus, whether tartar or nitre was the starting point, it was possible to arrive at the same product. If this identity was appreciated by leading eighteenth-century chemists, there were certainly many others who considered salts derived from tartar and those prepared from nitre as distinct substances. It is strange that, although Caspar Neumann considered that *nitrum vitriolatum* was the same as *tartarus vitriolatus*, yet he described the preparation of, e.g. *terra foliata nitri* as if it were quite different from *terra foliata tartari*; in modern eyes both were potassium acetate.[99] The revised *London Pharmacopoeia* of 1746 still included the preparations *tartarus vitriolatus* and *nitrum vitriolatum* with no hint as to their identity, although a critic two years previously had said about *nitrum vitriolatum*, 'It differs very little, if at all, from the *Tartarus*

97. Even the enlightened Macquer argued that nitre could never be considered to be of vegetable origin (*Dictionnaire de Chymie*, Paris, 1766, vol. ii, p. 138).

98. Until chemists had some idea of sulphuric acid as dibasic, the salts we now call the sulphate and bisulphate were likely to be identified. Thus a discussion in 1724 (*Mém. Acad., 1724*, 129), as to whether *tartarus vitriolatus* yielded *vitriolic acid* on distillation, is resolved if it is appreciated that some chemists were using the neutral salt for this experiment while others were using the acid salt under the same name.

99. *Lectiones Publicae von Salpeter*, etc., Berlin, 1732, pp. 88, 108.

Vitriolatus for which it has long been substituted in the shops.'[100]
The German medical and chemical author, Rudolph Vogel,
was one of those who was convinced that the salts prepared
from tartar and from nitre were distinct substances and in his
enumeration of the neutral salts he listed the combination of the
three mineral acids with the alkali of nitre and also with the
vegetable alkali.[101]

In spite of the disadvantages, there were many terms like
spiritus sulphuris per campanam and *oleum tartari per deliquium* which
were used unambiguously in the seventeenth century to describe
substances by their method of preparation. An important criticism, however, which could be levelled against such names was
that they stressed the method and the substances used in the
preparation at the expense of any indication of the chemical
composition of the product. Another disadvantage was the
cumbersome nature of such names. Some of Scheele's letters
provide us with good examples of these: *spiritus salis ammoniaci
cum sale alkali parata* (ammonium carbonate) and *vitriolum
veneris cum alkali fixo praecipitatum* (basic copper acetate).[102] The
use of these phrases became obsolete with the introduction of
systematic nomenclature. Even then Cavendish considered that
some salts, such as corrosive sublimate and calomel, had
different properties according to their method of preparation
and therefore thought it 'very wrong to attempt to give them
names expressive of their composition'.[103] When Pearson tried
to popularize the reformed chemical nomenclature in England
he argued that the name sulphuric acid was more appropriate
than vitriolic acid, because its method of preparation from
vitriol had been largely replaced by the method in which sulphur was used.[104]

100. *An Essay for the Reformation of the London Pharmacopoeia*, London, 1744,
p. 59.
101. *Lehrsätze der Chemie*, trans. Wiegleb, Weimar, 1775, pp. 479–80.
102. *Nachgelassene Briefe*, ed. Nordenskiöld, Stockholm, 1892, pp. 33, 261.
103. *The Scientific Papers of the Hon. Henry Cavendish*, ed. Sir E. Thorpe,
Cambridge, 1921, vol. ii, p. 326. This opinion is also found in the pharmacopoeias which used the terms *mercurius dulcis sublimatus* and *mercurius
dulcis praecipitatus* to describe mercurous chloride prepared by sublimation
and precipitation respectively.
104. *A Translation of the Table of Chemical Nomenclature*, London, 1794, p.
19.

CHAPTER THREE

The Growth of Chemistry

Chemical Terminology in the Pharmacopoeias

In the sixteenth, seventeenth and eighteenth centuries, before the establishment of a systematic nomenclature which had the authority of its joint authors as well as its logical coherence to recommend it, the terminology found in books on chemistry was a matter of personal choice of the author. Apart from the avoidance of the most obvious examples of absurd or misleading terms, there was no criterion for accepting one description of a substance in preference to another. In this respect the pharmacopoeias were able, at least potentially, to play a unique role. Pharmacy and chemistry were, of course, closely related in this period and many of the so-called chemists of the seventeenth century, like Beguin and Lemery, were really pharmaceutical chemists. By considering the standard texts of the pharmacists, the pharmacopoeias, it is possible to take a cross-section of pharmaceutical chemistry in the hope of finding some general principles of terminology. The establishment of many of the national pharmacopoeias had to wait till the nineteenth century, but before then the pharmacopoeias issued under the authority of important towns were capable of acting as a standard not without influence on pharmacy and chemistry.

One of the earliest pharmacopoeias in Europe was that published at Augsburg under the aegis of the Medical College of that city. The first edition of the *Pharmacopoeia Augustana* was issued about the year 1564 and contains a few inorganic chemicals such as *aqua fortis, oleum ex tartaro, sal Hammoniacum* [sic], *alumen rochae, vitriolum Romanum* and *sal nitrum*.[105] A decree of the Augsburg Senate in 1582 admonished apothecaries not to prepare nor offer for sale substances known to be dangerous including all preparations of mercury and antimony. This dis-

---

105. *A Facsimile of the first edition of the Pharmacopoeia Augustana*, with introductory essays by Theodor Husemann, Madison, Wisconsin, 1927.

trust of 'mercurials' and 'antimonials' was almost universal among the established authorities of the sixteenth century and lasted well into the seventeenth century. The sixth issue of the *Augsburg Pharmacopoeia*, however, included *flores ac Vitrum Antimonii, Antimonium diaphoreticum* and *turpethum minerale*, as well as *sal Saturni* (lead acetate), *sal vitrioli* (ferrous sulphate), *nitrum sulphure purgatum* (a mixture of potassium nitrate and sulphate), *crocus martis* (ferric oxide), *flores sulphuris* (sublimed sulphur) *lapis septicus* (potassium hydroxide) and fourteen '*sales artificiosi*' from plants.

The Royal College of Physicians of London issued their pharmacopoeia in 1618 and there is little doubt that it was influenced by the Augsburg publications. The second issue of the *Pharmacopoeia Londinensis* of December 1618, which represented the considered opinion of its sponsors including Turquet de Mayerne, contains most of the chemicals mentioned in the *Augsburg Pharmacopoeia* with a few additions, notably the so-called *mercurius vitae* (antimony oxychloride), *mercurius dulcis* (mercurous chloride) and *tartarus vitriolatus* (potassium sulphate).

Although many of the pharmacopoeias had no more than a local influence, the *London Pharmacopoeia* in its eighteenth-century editions was particularly well known not only in Britain (where it was rivalled by the *Edinburgh Pharmacopoeia*) but also on the continent of Europe. Some editions were printed on the continent and the French translation of the *London Pharmacopoeia* of 1746 was known to Macquer,[106] Guyton de Morveau,[107] and Berthollet,[108] each of whom contributed to the reform of chemical nomenclature in the second half of the eighteenth century. If there is any justification in the claim that pharmacopoeias set a standard and influenced chemical terminology, it is the 1746 edition of the *London Pharmacopoeia* which shows it. The deliberations by a committee of the Royal College of Physicians, which led to a complete revision of the previous edition of the pharmacopoeia, were continued over a period of nearly eight years and the final publication naturally benefited by the criticisms offered during this time. The *London*

106. The translation under the title *Pharmacopée du Collège Royal des Médecins de Londres*, Paris, 1761, was officially read by Macquer before it was given the *Approbation* (dated Oct. 1758 and signed: Macquer).

107. Bergman, *Opuscules*, trans. Guyton de Morveau, vol. i, Dijon, 1780, p. 385n.

108. *Mém. Acad., 1782*, 617.

Pharmacopoeia of 1746 represented a deliberate and authoritative reform of the abuses which had crept into chemical terminology. The details of this reform are considered, together with other criticisms, in Chapter 4 (pp. 116–18).

The Admission of New Substances into Chemistry

In the acquisition of knowledge we proceed from the known to the unknown, and when investigating new substances, there is a natural tendency to describe them in terms of substances already known. This tendency is all the more marked when evidence of the distinct nature of the substances concerned is lacking. As important examples of this habit of nomenclature, we may cite the early names given to the metals tin, antimony, bismuth, platinum and manganese.

Tin was sometimes referred to by Pliny as *plumbum candidum* in contrast to lead, which was *plumbum nigrum*. For Geber too, tin was a kind of lead, distinguished as *plumbum stridens* from the creaking noise sometimes made when tin is bent. Another metal or 'semi-metal', considered to be of the nature of lead, was antimony. which was sometimes referred to by the alchemists as *marcasita plumbea*[109] and Neumann in the eighteenth century gave a list of ten synonyms of antinomy, which can be divided into the allegorical (e.g. 'wolf') and those based on its similarity to lead.[110]

Bismuth was recognized as a distinct mineral by Agricola in the sixteenth century,[111] but unfortunately the term *plumbum cinereum*, which he sometimes used to describe it, did little to make men appreciate that this was a new 'semi-metal'.[112] According to the German chemist, Pott,[113] bismuth had been variously described before the eighteenth century as white or female antimony, a kind of lead, and imperfect silver. Indeed miners sometimes called it *tectum argenti*, regarding it as silver not yet completed in the earth.[114] The most common opinion in

109. e.g. Ruland, *Lexicon Alchemiae*, Prague, 1612, p. 318. The connection made by the Ancients between antimony and 'lead' was taken literally by Giovanni Baptista della Porta, who related how antimony might be turned into lead (*Magia Naturalis*, Amsterdam, 1664, lib. 5, cap. 2, p. 245).
110. *Lectiones Publicae von . . . Salpeter, etc.*, Berlin, 1732, pp. 255–6.
111. *Bermannus, Works*, Basle, 1558, p. 439.
112. *De re metallica*, transl. Hoover, London, 1912, p. 3.
113. *Dissertations Chymiques*, Paris, 1759, vol. ii, pp. 267–78.
114. According to Hellot, *Mém. Acad., 1737*, 231.

the seventeenth century, however, was that bismuth was a kind of tin and this is shown in the Latin term *stannum glaciale* or its French equivalent *étain de glace*. Lemery naïvely stated the opinion that bismuth is a derivative of tin 'prepared artificially by the English'.[115]

A metal which came to the attention of chemists in Europe in the middle of the eighteenth century was platinum. It had been given the Spanish name *Platina*, meaning 'little silver' from its silvery colour rather than from a mistaken identity with silver. It was, however, compared with gold because of several similarities including its resistance to attack by acids. Macquer mentioned the name 'white gold'[116] to describe the metal and the Swedish chemist, Scheffer, who had also studied the properties of platinum said that its close similarity to gold justified such a description.[117]

In the early eighteenth century native manganese dioxide, the *Braunstein* of the German and Swedish mineralogists, was regarded as a poor ore of iron. In 1740, however, Pott showed that it contained no iron and, after unsuccessful attempts by Bergman and Scheele to reduce the ore to a metal, Gahn finally succeeded in 1774 in isolating the metal. The fact that manganese was sometimes called a 'modification' of iron irritated the Irish chemist Kirwan:

The word *modification* has been strangely abused. . . . Cobalt, nickel and manganese have been said to be only modifications of iron; but as long as it is not known wherein that modification consists, this word presents no idea whatever. . . .[118]

Eighteenth-century chemistry was characterized not so much by the discovery of new minerals as by the more careful examination of minerals already known and the process of distinguishing new substances associated with them. What in the seventeenth century was described as a 'calcareous earth' may have consisted largely of chalk, but on the other hand it is possible that it comprised any of the earths later called *magnesia*, *alumina* and *baryta*. It was an important landmark in the history of chemistry

115. *Cours de Chymie*, Paris, 1697, p. 115.
116. *Mém. Acad.*, *1758*, 119ff.
117. '*Das weisse Gold, oder siebente Metall*', *Königlich Swedischen Akademie der Wissenschaften, Abhandlungen*, *14* (1752), 275ff.
118. *Elements of Mineralogy*, London, 1784, p. 371.

when Black demonstrated that the word 'air' had a plural, and
the recognition that the word 'earth' included several similar
but distinct substances was hardly less important. That this
lesson was learned only slowly is demonstrated by the fact that
in 1781 the vague use of the term 'absorbent earth' by contemporary writers was the subject of criticism by Guyton de
Morveau.[119]

The distinct nature of new substances was not always easy to
demonstrate by elementary analytical methods and the scep-
tics could always maintain that any apparent discovery was
really a substance previously known containing various impurities which 'disguised' it. This was the view taken by
Neumann in 1732 about *magnesia* which he thought was merely
lime combined with a little spirit of nitre and spirit of salt.[120]
Indeed when Martin Lister described it in hot English mineral
springs, he referred to it as 'calcareous nitre' (*nitrum cal-
carium*).[121] At the turn of the century it was sold in Rome as
'powder of Count Palma' or *Magnesia*. In 1708 Friedrich Hoffmann referred to it as 'a certain neutral salt without any special
name and which is almost unknown'[122] and he later distinguished it experimentally from quicklime.[123] Alumina was
discovered as a result of the researches of Marggraf who isolated
a substance which he called *Alaunerde*, which was distinct from
lime. In France it was known as *argille* until Guyton de Morveau suggested *alumine*, a name derived from what was then its
commonest source. A fourth 'earth' was discovered in Sweden
by Gahn and Scheele. Although the first specimens of it they
examined were associated with *magnesia nigra*, further analysis
revealed its presence in heavy spar and they therefore referred
to it as *Schwerspatherde*.[124] It was later called barytes.

What we now call the salts of sodium and potassium were
distinguished in 1736 by Duhamel who showed that the base
was different, although the acid was the same in the following
pairs of salts: sea salt, digestive salt; Glauber's salt, vitriolated

119. *Observations sur la Physique*, 17 (1781), 216–31.
120. *Lectiones Publicae von . . . Salpeter, etc.*, Berlin, 1732, p. 102.
121. *Exercitationes et Descriptiones Thermarum ac Fontium Medicatorum Angliae*,
Leyden, 1686, pp. 1, 6–7.
122. *Dissertationes Physico-Medicae*, Leyden, 1708, Pars Altera, p. 200.
123. *Observationum Physico-Chymicarum*, Halle, 1722, p. 117.
124. C. W. Scheele, *Nachgelassene Briefe*, ed. Nordenskiöld, Stockholm,
1892, pp. 115, 121.

tartar; cubic nitre, nitre.[125] Duhamel did not, however, distinguish the two bases by particular names and confusion between the two alkalis was not uncommon in the mid-eighteenth century. Marggraf later confirmed the results of Duhamel's experiments and in his collected works the alkalis are usually referred to respectively as *the alkali salt of common salt* and *the alkali salt of the vegetable kingdom*. They were distinguished by Cullen as *fossil alkali* and *vegetable alkali* respectively and in the second half of the eighteenth century until the reform of chemical nomenclature the two alkalis were known most commonly as the mineral and vegetable alkalis.

Obscure, Mystical and Contradictory Terminology

We have examined in some detail terminology with a rational origin in the properties of the substance concerned, but we must also turn our attention to another group of terms more poetical than scientific. The limits of this group of names is not easy to define and on the borderline there are names like *sulphur album fixum* ('fixed white sulphur') for potassium nitrate and 'snow of antimony' for an oxide of antimony. There were a large number of *Decknamen* or 'cover names' for substances in Greek, Arabic and European alchemy, but most of these were mystical names which had been abandoned by chemists by the end of the seventeenth century. Such names have therefore been discussed in the section dealing with alchemical language.

Typical of the unnecessary mystery attached to the names of many chemicals was the widespread use of the adjective *philosophic*. The phrases 'gold of the philosophers', 'mercury of the philosophers' were commonplace in alchemical literature and it is regrettable that early chemistry continued to be influenced by this tradition. The examples quoted below are all taken from seventeenth and eighteenth-century chemical works:

'philosophical spirit of vitriol'	(hydrochloric acid)
'philosophical spirit of wine'	(spirit of wine concentrated by freezing)
'philosophical spirit of tartar'	(spirit of tartar distilled with wine)

125. *Mém. Acad., 1736*, 215–32.

'philosophical spirit of nitre'	(spirit of nitre prepared by distilling saltpetre with oil of vitriol)
'philosophical water'	(aqua regia)
'philosophical flowers of vitriol'	(boric acid)
'philosophical foliated earth'	(potassium acetate)
'philosopher's wool'	(zinc oxide)
'secret or philosophical sal ammoniac'	(ammonium sulphate)
'secret fixed sulphur of the philosophers'	(the calcined residue when sulphur is distilled with linseed oil)

Another term occurring in seventeenth and early eighteenth-century chemical literature and which requires some explanation is *magistery*. 'Magistery' originally meant 'the work of the master', a preparation which required some special skill or knowledge. As the term involved a certain prestige there was a tendency for pharmacists and chemists to use it to describe preparations which they especially esteemed or which they wished the public to consider of particular value.

Libavius at the beginning of the seventeenth century defined the term *magistery* as a preparation 'separated to a certain extent from external impurities, elaborated and exalted'.[126] Unfortunately *magistery* came to have the widest possible connotation and it was admitted at the end of the seventeenth century that this term could be applied to all preparations of metals. Boyle complained of the wide and conflicting use of *magistery* by various authors, but nevertheless tries to define it as

a preparation whereby there is not an analysis made of the body assigned, nor an extraction of this or that principle, but the whole or very nearly the whole body by the help of some additament . . . is turned into a body of another kind. As when iron or copper by an acid menstruum . . . is turned into vitriol of Mars or of Venus . . . or . . . when quicksilver . . . is by lasting operation of the fire, without external additaments . . . turned into a red powder that chymists call *Praecipitate per se*.[127]

The term magistery was often used to denote a precipitate and, as it came to be appreciated that these terms were synonyms, the more rationally minded chemists of the eighteenth century pre-

126. *Alchymia*, Frankfurt, 1606, Lib. 2, Tract 1, pp. 41ff.
127. Boyle, *Works*, ed. Birch, London, 1744, vol. i, pp. 403–4.

ferred to speak of 'precipitate' than 'magistery'. Towards the end of the century the term *magistery* was used only in conservative circles and then only to denote two or three preparations such as *magistery of bismuth* (bismuth oxychloride), *magistery of coral* (calcium carbonate) and *magistery of sulphur*—preparations which had borne these names for more than a century.

Two other pretentious terms occurring in early chemical literature are *alkahest* and *arcanum*. The former term was sometimes applied optimistically to corrosive liquids such as oil of tartar or spirit of nitre. The term *arcanum* was introduced by Paracelsus to denote a medicine which acted in a certain way.[128] Its literal meaning of 'secret preparation' was, however, the generally accepted sense in the seventeenth century. Two important substances were often referred to as arcana, namely potassium sulphate (*arcanum duplicatum*) and mercuric oxide (*arcanum coralinum*). The use of high-sounding terms was criticised by Lemery who challenged the concept of a superior chemical medicine implied by the term 'potable gold':

> The very name of *potable gold* imposes on many people and it provides a means by which charlatans can deceive the public with impunity. By giving a preparation the colour of gold it is not difficult to deceive people who judge by superficial appearances and by great names.[129]

Some non-systematic names were not only vague but definitely misleading. An example of this is the use of the term 'regenerated'. In the eighteenth century the name *nitrum regeneratum* was very properly given to the nitre obtained by the action of nitric acid on potassium carbonate. Yet the term *tartarus regeneratus* was used by many chemists to denote not potassium tartrate as might be expected, but other potassium salts such as the chloride and acetate; Boerhaave among others meant by *sal marinus regeneratus* not sodium but potassium chloride.

In the absence of systematic nomenclature it was natural that the existing terms were modified in an *ad hoc* manner to meet new requirements. An unfortunate consequence of this was the

128. Like the majority of Paracelsian terms the exact meaning of *arcanum* is obscure. On one occasion however Paracelsus tried to explain the difference between his conception of a medicine and an arcanum; he says the latter, by its essence (*Wesen*) acts directly, as opposed to a medicine (*Arznei*) which achieves its object by a balancing of the 'elements' (*Paragranum, Sämtliche Werke*, ed. Sudhoff, Munich and Berlin, 1922–33, vol. viii, p. 106).

129. *Traité Universel*, Paris, 1698, p. 790.

introduction of obviously contradictory expressions. If zinc oxide were called *nihil* ('nothing') or *nihil album*, this might be excused as an example of metaphor. More striking, perhaps, was the occurrence in the literature of double terms involving a contradiction. When the term *atramentum* ('blacking') was given to green vitriol it was probably because of the black colour it was capable of producing with tannin in leather, but in Ruland's alchemical lexicon we find the phrase *atramentum album* ('white blacking'). The term 'white lead' was an obvious description for basic lead carbonate, but we find plumbago described as *schwartz blei weiss* ('black white-lead').[130] Green vitriol was often referred to in commerce as *copperas*, a word which came to denote the class of vitriols, so that zinc sulphate could be thoughtlessly described as 'white copperas', though containing no iron. Finally, when Caspar Neumann described the product of reacting *sal volatile* with vitriolic acid (i.e. ammonium sulphate), he chose to denote it by the unfortunate expression 'fixed volatile salt' (*sal volatile fixatum*).[131] One conclusion, at least, which can be drawn from the use of such expressions is that to practical chemists the original literal meaning of a term was very soon forgotten.

The Confusion caused by the Use of the Same Name for Different Substances or Different Names for the Same Substance

Before the introduction of a systematic nomenclature into chemistry, confusion was often caused by the use of the same (or similar) names for unrelated substances or of completely different names for the same (or a similar) substance.

It sometimes happened that a name used to denote one thing was equally applicable to another quite unrelated substance. Thus *electrum* was used to denote both amber and gold-silver alloy. There is no question here of any practical confusion between the two substances, yet the equivocal nature of the term was unfortunate, based, no doubt, on the similarity in colour of the two substances. The term *chrysocolla* had several different meanings in classical times, but usually denoted copper compounds. The etymology of the term (*chrysos* = gold, *colla* = solder) explains its meaning as a substance used in soldering and in this

130. Pott, *Dissertations Chymiques*, Paris, 1759, vol. iv, p. 2.
131. *Chymiae Medicae Dogmatico-Experimentalis*, Züllichau, 1749–55, vol. iii, p. 182.

sense it came to include borax, which was used as a flux as well as the copper minerals which were used as solder. In the sixteenth century the term was still ambiguous, and Agricola, referring to *chrysocolla*, avoids confusion with the copper ore by referring to it as '*Chrysocolla* which the Moors call Borax'.[132] Another example is the term *aqua fortis* (strong waters, *eau forte*, etc.) which at various times was used to denote not only concentrated nitric acid but also spirit of wine and caustic soda solution. *Infernal stone* was another equivocal term, metaphorically suggesting a caustic substance used in medicine. In England this name was applied in the early eighteenth century to an alkali hydroxide, but unfortunately in France the term *pierre infernale* was applied to fused silver nitrate. The French translator of the *London Pharmacopoeia* (Paris, 1761) was careful to avoid confusing the two substances.

Although the use of ambiguous names led to some confusion, this was minimised by the use of a distinguishing adjective or phrase or merely by judging the meaning according to the context. More serious perhaps was the use of completely different names for substantially the same substance. This usually depended on the origin of the substance, whether it came from one place or another, whether it was natural or artificial.[133] Often the multiplying of names depended on different methods of preparation of the compound concerned.

The composition of a salt could often be regarded in two ways as is suggested by the term *fusible sulphur* and *fixed nitre* which might both claim a certain degree of aptness as descriptions of potassium sulphate. A good example of how the various considerations involved in pre-systematic terminology might conflict is provided by what we now call magnesium sulphate. In the early eighteenth century it was variously referred to as:

Sal Epsom, anglicum	(place)
Sal amarum	(taste)
Sal catharticum	(medicinal property)

132. *De re metallica*, trans. Hoover, London, 1912, p. 560n. See also Biringuccio, *De la Pirotechnia*, trans. C. S. Smith and M. T. Gnudi, New York, 1942, p. 117n.

133. e.g. Mercury which occurs naturally was called *argentum vivum* by Pliny, but that which was prepared artificially from cinnabar was called *hydrargyrum* (*Hist. Nat.*, *33*, 99, 123). Quite often substances prepared by the early chemists were labelled 'artificial' as if they were essentially different from the (identical) substance which was found in nature.

Another example of this multiplicity of names is provided by what we now call potassium acetate. It used to be called:

Terra foliata tartari	(crystalline form)
Sal Sennerti	(name of supposed discoverer)
Tartarus regeneratus	(composition—but mistaken)
Arcanum tartari	(mystical name)
Sal diureticus	(medicinal property)

An important dichotomy in terminology was based on the difference between a solid and its aqueous solution. The following examples illustrate the divergence that sometimes existed:

MODERN NAME	SALT IN SOLID STATE	SOLUTION OF SALT
potassium carbonate	*fixed alkali salt*	
	vegetable alkali etc.	*oil of tartar*
ammonium acetate	*vegetable ammoniacal salt*	
		Spirit of Mindererus
calcium chloride	*fixed sal ammoniac*	*Oil of Chalk*
ferrous tartrate	*extract of Mars*	*tartarised tincture of Mars*

There was also the special case of silver nitrate usually known as *Crystals of Silver* or *lunar nitre*, but when fused was known as *lunar caustic* or *the infernal stone*.

The Confusion resulting from Semantic Change

An eighteenth-century writer on the natural sciences re-marked:

> Errors about names are what alone have given more than half the confusion we have in regard to the Works of the Ancients.[134]

If we survey the history of chemistry from Dioscorides and Pliny to Macquer and Lavoisier, we observe that certain terms changed their meaning. One of the greatest sources of confusion in terminology was the original ignorance of writers as to the nature of substances named. Names like *aes, minium, nitrum,* and *molybdaena* were used before there was any very definite idea of what was meant by these terms. If the term *aes* was given to a

---

134. Theophrastus, *History of Stones*, trans., John Hill, London, 1746, p. 111n.

bright, heavy metal of a certain colour, then anything which satisfied these simple conditions could be described as *aes*.[135] It would be a grave historical fault to criticize the classical civilizations for not distinguishing alloys from pure metals, since the concept of a pure substance and any means of identifying one had not yet been developed. The copper found in Cyprus was called *aes cyprium* or *cuprum* by the Romans and when this term was established with its present meaning, *aes* (bronze, etc.) came to be used to denote the alloy.

Colour played a large part in the identification of substances and it is not surprising therefore that the red oxide of lead and the red sulphides of mercury and arsenic were confused with one another. This confusion was all the more acute as Pliny, whose *Historia Naturalis* was later looked upon as an authoritative work, had only a very superficial knowledge of the substances he described. When Pliny refers to *minium* he is speaking of red mercuric sulphide,[136] although he also mentions a *minium secundarium* which was red lead. This 'second-rate minium' was a substitute for the more expensive cinnabar and was used to adulterate it even in Roman times. Eventually *minium* was so commonly associated with the lead compound that it ceased to have any connection with mercury. It seems that to Pliny *minium* was any red powder and this is confirmed by his remark that copper may be heated in a furnace 'till it becomes a kind of minium',[137] which is the modern cuprous oxide. In the works of Geber *minium* is definitely red lead and this became the accepted usage. Probably the first writer to describe clearly the manufacture of red lead was Vitruvius, who unhappily chose the name *sandaraca* to describe it.[138] Most writers including Dioscorides and Pliny, however, understood *sandaraca* to mean realgar or red arsenic sulphide and so the circle of confusion was complete.[139]

135. Bailey says that *aes* was any metal in which the predominant constituent was copper. In Pliny's *Historia Naturalis* it included: (*a*) pure copper, (*b*) bronze (mainly copper and tin), (*c*) brass (mainly copper and zinc), (*d*) a copper-lead alloy, (*e*) a copper-lead-tin alloy (K. C. Bailey, *The Elder Pliny's Chapters on Chemical Subjects*, London, 1932, vol. ii, pp. 159–61).

136. *Hist. Nat.*, *33*, 123. Pliny states that mercury is obtained from *minium*. See also ibid., *33*, 120.

137. '*donec ad speciem minii redeat*', *Hist. Nat.*, *34*, 106.

138. *De Architectura*, 7, 12.

139. Pliny says that the Greeks called minium *cinnabar* and this led to further confusion, since *cinnabar* was used not only to denote the modern

The term *nitrum* (*nitron, nitri*, etc.) is quite common in many ancient writings. It occurs in the Old Testament,[140] in the works of Aristotle[141] and Pliny[142] and in many other places besides. As Hoover has remarked, 'A review of the disputations on what salts this term comprised among the Ancients would itself fill a volume.'[143] There are many difficulties in identifying it since, as taken from the earth, it was often very impure and therefore did not have constant properties. Another difficulty is that it was undoubtedly used to refer to more than one substance. It is, nevertheless, possible to make the generalisation that it was usually soda and occasionally potash. From its use as a detergent, its use in making glass and other properties mentioned there is little doubt that it was not the modern nitre (potassium nitrate). If the lexicons are consulted to find the meaning of *nitrum* in the late sixteenth and early seventeenth centuries, a variety of white substances are mentioned including rock salt, talc and 'borax', which is indicative of the general confusion on the meaning of the term. Nevertheless, the expression *sal nitri* was usually used to denote saltpetre, particularly when the latter had been purified.

Another term describing a white salt which changed its meaning between the time of Pliny and early European chemistry was *sal ammoniac*. Pliny's *sal armoniacum* is probably a superior kind of common salt,[144] but another white substance (our ammonium chloride) is meant by the *sal armoniac* of Geber and the early chemists of Western Europe.

The confusion in the meaning of terms was probably at its worst in the late sixteenth century when technical workers were trying to reconcile their own practical knowledge with the writings of the Ancients. This confusion is exemplified in the work of Agricola, who did not appreciate that 'the Ancients'

mercuric sulphide, but also the so-called 'dragon's blood', which was probably the resin of certain trees, notably the *Pterocarpus draco* (Bailey, op. cit., vol. i, p. 219).

140. e.g. Proverbs xxv. 20. See also Jeremiah ii. 22: 'For though thou washest thee with nitre. . . .'

141. e.g. *On Marvellous Things Heard*, 53.

142. *Hist. Nat., 31*, 107. (*Nitrum* can be made from wood ashes.) See also ibid., *36*, 191, 194.

143. Agricola, *De re metallica*, trans. Hoover, London, 1912, p. 558n. See also J. Beckmann, *A History of Inventions*, 4th edn., London, 1846, vol. ii, pp. 482ff.

144. *Hist. Nat., 31*, 39 see also Bailey, op. cit., vol. i, p. 163.

were themselves confused. Despite the fact that Agricola had discussed the terminology of classical writers at some length,[145] he managed to use terms such as *cadmia* and *molybdaena* in various senses. In fact, by trying to adopt the terms used by Pliny, Agricola merely added to the confusion. Hoover has remarked on the stream of wasted ink caused by the misapplication of the derivatives of the Greek term μόλυβδος for lead,[146] and only the briefest summary need be repeated here. Pliny had used the term in various senses, usually to mean argentiferous lead, but also lead sulphide and possibly even litharge.[147] From his interpretation of Pliny, Agricola usually used the term *molybdaena* for hearth lead,[148] but he also applied it to lead carbonates.[149] The term *molybdaena* was sometimes applied to substances resembling lead such as graphite. Finally towards the end of the eighteenth century an element was isolated from a black substance resembling lead (molybdenite) and the same name was used to describe it and so we have the modern name *molybdenum*.

The variations of usage of most of the terms so far discussed were brought about by similarity in appearance which caused one substance to be mistaken for another similar to it. With an increase in knowledge a term could be used more rigidly to denote one particular substance and in modern technical chemistry the terms minium, nitre and molybdenum have a definite restricted meaning, in each case at variance with Pliny's usage of these terms.

There are other terms where it is easier to see a gradual development of meaning over a long period of time. Such terms include *alcohol*, *calx*, *salt* and *vitriol*. That the change of meaning was a very slow process can be illustrated by the history of the word *alcohol*. Originally alcohol (*al kohl*) meant a fine black powder, particularly black antimony sulphide. This meaning was generalized so that *alcohol* came to mean any very fine powder. Finally there arose the meaning of an impalpable spiritous substance as exemplified by spirit of wine. Of these four meanings the last was common by the sixteenth century and yet the other meanings still persisted. Even in the eigh-

145. *Bermannus, De Natura Fossilium*, Lib. 3; *Works, Basle*, 1558, pp. 427–434, pp. 206ff.
146. *Op. cit.*, p. 476n.   147. *Hist. Nat.*, 34, 173; 33, 108, 95.
148. *Interpretatio = plumbago, Works*, pp. 466–7.
149. Hoover, *op. cit.*, p. 408.

teenth century Baumé gave the meaning 'powders of the finest tenuity' as the first definition of alcohol and 'spirit of wine rectified to the utmost degree' as the second.[150]

The development of meaning of the terms *calx*, *salt* and *vitriol* also depended largely on a generalization of the original concept. The term *calx* was used in Roman times to denote the product of lime burning; and *calx* and *calx viva* ('quicklime') are referred to by Isidorus and Bartholomew the Englishman in the same sense.[151] By generalization *calx* came to mean any powder made by strongly heating a substance. The products obtained by heating tin and lead in air could not unnaturally be compared with quicklime. Libavius says that a calx is something produced by calcination; it is sometimes synonymous with 'ash'.[152] He does not specify the colour of calces, but there is the implication that they are usually white since the term *crocus* was applied to coloured powders like rust. In fact, however, *calx* was also used to denote solids which were not obtained primarily by heating. Paracelsus, for example, referred to basic copper acetate as *calx veneris*.[153] In the next century Glauber gave the name *calx of lune* to silver chloride prepared by precipitation.[154] Such misuse of the term *calx* was condemned by Macquer, who in common with most other eighteenth-century chemists gave the name *calx* to what we should now call the oxides of metals of whatever colour they might be.[155]

The first development of the meaning of the term 'salt' was one of generalization, so that, although originally it had denoted one particular substance (sodium chloride), by the sixteenth century it had come to include a whole group of substances characterized primarily by physical properties like taste and solubility. In the seventeenth century the products of the action of various acids on metals were described as 'salts', so that what we now call acetates and sulphates were included in this term.[156]

---

150. *Chymie Expérimentale*, Paris, 1773, vol. i, p. cxlviii.
151. *Isidori Etymologiarum*, Lib. XVI, iii, 10. *De Proprietatibus Rerum*, Lib. XVI, cap. 24.
152. *Alchymia*, Bk. 2, Tract 1, cap. 25, 26, Frankfurt, 1606, pp. 70, 74.
153. *Sämtliche Werke*, ed. Sudhoff, Munich and Berlin, 1922–33, vol. 4, p. 105.
154. *The Spagyrical Pharmacopoeia*, Part 6, cap. 27; *Works*, trans. Packe, London, Part 2, p. 170a.
155. *Dictionnaire de Chymie*, Paris, 1766, vol. i, pp. 236, 256.
156. e.g. *sel de Jupiter, sel de Saturne, sel ou vitriol de Mars*, Lemery, *Cours de Chymie*, Paris, 1697, pp. 104, 122, 162.

Nor was the term 'salt' confined to what we now call 'salts', since it included acids and alkalis. It was Bergman who pointed out that the word 'salt' was unnecessary to describe acids and alkalis.[157] An interesting restriction in meaning of the term was implied by Macquer's suggestion that it should be used to describe what we now call chlorides.[158]

The term 'vitriol' originated from the glass-like appearance of what had previously been called *atramentum*. When in medieval times these two terms for the same substance were co-existent, the word 'vitriol' was probably applied to the purified *atramentum*.[159] These names originally represented copper and ferrous sulphates, but in the seventeenth century the term 'vitriol' was applied to many other salts. The works of 'Basil Valentine' contain a reference to *vitriol of Saturn* and *Jupiter* by which are meant the acetates of lead and tin.[160] In Lemery's *Cours de Chymie* the nitrates of silver and copper are referred to as 'vitriols'. For Kunckel 'vitriol' was a general term for a salt composed of a metal and an acid.[161] This vague use of the term[162] led to some confusion and in 1766 the French chemists Demachy and Macquer both independently suggested that *vitriol* should be used only to denote the salts of vitriol acid.[163]

A certain group of terms the meaning of which changed in the eighteenth century included *antimony* and *arsenic*, which had previously denoted the minerals containing these elements (i.e. antimony sulphide and arsenious oxide). Although in the seventeenth century chemists recognized that both these minerals were compound bodies and that the former consisted mainly of a semi-metal and sulphur, the minerals continued to be given names which gave no hint of their compound nature. The 'semi-metals', antimony and arsenic, were distinguished from

157. *Nova Acta Reg. Soc. Scient. Upsaliensis*, 4 (1784), 120.
158. *Dictionnaire de Chymie*, vol. ii, pp. 432–4. Thus for Macquer *sel de fer* and *sel de plomb* were the chlorides of iron and lead (cf. Lemery).
159. 'Átramentum terra quaedam cuius nobilior species est vitriolum', *Sinonoma Bartholomei*, ed. J. L. G. Mowat, Oxford, 1882.
160. *Letztes Testament, Schluss Reden*, Strasburg, 1651, page indicated by the double letters 'oo'.
161. *Laboratorium Chymicum*, Hamburg and Leipzig, 1716, pp. 204, 250.
162. Ettmueller (*Chimia rationalis*, 1684, transl. *Nouvelle Chymie Raisonée*, Lyon, 1693, p. 60) says the word 'vitriol' should be applied only to the relevant salts of iron or copper. Names like *vitriol of Saturn* and *vitriol of Lune* are examples of improper use of the term *vitriol*.
163. J. F. Demachy, *Instituts de Chymie*, Paris, 1766, vol. ii, pp. 414–15. Macquer, *Dictionnaire de Chymie*, Paris, 1766, vol. i, p. 27, vol. ii, p. 431.

their ores by the additional term *Regulus*, a diminutive of the
Latin word *Rex* meaning 'king' and implying a substance of
special value. The German equivalent *König* makes this even
plainer. *Cobalt* and *manganese* were other terms applied traditionally to the crude ores, so that when Brandt and Gahn
respectively succeeded in extracting these 'semi-metals' from
their ores they had to use the circumlocution *regulus of cobalt*
and *regulus of manganese* to describe them.

Summing up, we may conclude that terms changed their
meaning when originally they had been used for a variety of
substances and were later restricted in meaning or, alternatively, they developed by a process of generalization to describe
a class of substance rather than one particular substance. The
meaning of terms developed as chemical knowledge increased,
but terminology often lagged far behind the practical achievements of chemists.

Simple Terminology Not Adaptable in an Expanding Science

Much of the chemical terminology in use in the sixteenth,
seventeenth and eighteenth centuries was too general to be
useful for very long. It was not usually appreciated that if a
substance were to be denoted by a simple term, the latter
should not be equally applicable to other compounds which
might be prepared in the future. Examples of this are the use
of *salt* and *crystals* as part of a proper name. Among the names
given to the product of deflagrating sulphur with nitre (to
form impure potassium sulphate) was that of *salt of sulphur*.
Whereas this might well have been an excellent forerunner of
the modern term *sulphate*, it was intended to denote one particular sulphate, a function for which it was unfitted. Similarly
the name *Salt of Mars* was given by some authors to what we
call ferrous sulphate, but it was equally applicable to any other
iron salt and was also used for the acetate. In a similar way the
terms *Crystals of Venus*, *Crystals of Saturn*[164] and *Mercury Precipitate*
could be applied respectively to more than one substance, although in the latter case there was some room for development as
in the expressions *sweet mercury precipitate, red mercury precipitate*, etc.

164. Wallerius noted without comment the fact that the term *Crystalli
Saturni* was applied to two preparations made by dissolving lead in aqua
fortis and oil of vitriol respectively (*Minéralogie*, trans., Paris, 1753, vol. ii,
p. 182).

Other names too, revealed, at best, the identity of only one of the constituents in a compound. *Fixed nitre*, for example, could be a preparation in which either sulphur or charcoal was used to 'fix' the nitre.[165] The name *fixed sal ammoniac* gave even less correct information.[166] Probably the most naïve terms of all were the expressions *sal de duobus*, *sal duplicatum*, *arcanum duplicatum* for what we now call potassium sulphate. These names commemorate one of the first syntheses of salts in the laboratory. When *Glauber's salt* (sodium sulphate) or *foliated earth of tartar* (potassium acetate) were prepared in the early seventeenth century, they could just as appropriately have been described as a salt of two constituents or a 'double salt'.

Finally there was the idea found in Germany in the mid-seventeenth century[167] that a solid prepared from an acid spirit could be described as a 'coagulated acid spirit'. This terminology was in practice confined to salts prepared from *Sal Absinthii*, nitre or tartar (i.e. the potassium salts). Thus:

> *Spiritus Nitri Coagulatus*   = potassium nitrate
> *Spiritus Salis Coagulatus*   = potassium chloride
> *Spiritus Vitrioli Coagulatus* = potassium sulphate

It is strange that this system was applied only to what were later recognized to be potassium salts, so that the corresponding sodium salts, for example, continued to be described as *cubic nitre*, *sea salt* and *Glauber's salt* respectively. The term *Spiritus salis marini coagulatus* was one of the anomalies left in the revised *Pharmacopoeia Londinensis* of 1746, but the French translator of this work did not neglect to point out that the term could apply equally well to a whole series of neutral salts.[168]

The Growth in Knowledge of the Constituent Parts of Compounds

It was natural that in the early civilizations the names given to substances should be based entirely on their physical

165. In the late seventeenth century *fixed nitre* was usually potassium carbonate, but the same name had been used to describe the sulphate (Lemery, *Cours de Chymie*, Paris, 1697, pp. 355–9, 378).

166. The residue when sal ammoniac is heated with lime is calcium chloride.

167. Mynsicht, *Thesaurus et Armamentarium Medico-Chymicum*, Rothomagi, 1651, pp. 31, 32; *Augsburg Pharmacopoeia*, 1653, pp. 787–8; *Nuremberg Pharmacopoeia*, 1666, pp. 172–3.

168. *Pharmacopée du Collège Royal des Médecins de Londres*, Paris, 1771, vol. ii, p. 348n.

properties since practically all chemical knowledge of them was lacking. Yet at the end of the seventeenth century, although the composition of many compounds was known, no serious attempt had been made to express this knowledge in the terminology used. At the end of the eighteenth century Fourcroy complains of the impossibility of finding out exactly when an accurate knowledge of the constituents of particular compounds was obtained.[169] Probably a substance like cinnabar, which is a simple compound of a well-investigated metal, was among the first compounds to be analysed and synthesized,[170] so establishing its composition. Certainly at the beginning of the seventeenth century Angelo Sala had synthesized sal ammoniac and had established the composition of blue vitriol by analysis and synthesis.[171] He prepared the former from spirit of salt and the volatile salt of urine and the latter from copper, spirit of sulphur and water. Jean Beguin appreciated that corrosive sublimate consisted of mercury together with an acid spirit and also that 'antimony' contained the regulus of antimony and sulphur.[172] When these two substances react together he considered that the regulus of antimony was 'calcined' by the acid spirit to form butter of antimony and the mercury and sulphur came together to form ordinary cinnabar (mercuric sulphide). In the seventeenth century it was known that sweet sublimate and corrosive sublimate were both 'mixt bodies' containing mercury and an acid and chemists also appreciated that the former contained a greater proportion of mercury.[173]

There was then, towards the end of the seventeenth century, a fair amount of knowledge about the nature of compound bodies and it would have been possible to have indicated the composition of a few compounds in their names. The number of these compounds, however, was small and the need for systematization was not felt until the second half of the eighteenth century. We should not forget that until about 1750 the dis-

169. *Elements of Natural History and Chemistry*, 3rd edn., London, 1790, vol. iii, p. 466.

170. e.g. Theophilus, *De Diversis Artibus* (*c.* 1100), Lib. I, cap. 32.

171. *Aphorisms*, (1620), no. *38* (*Collectanea Chimica Curiosa*, Frankfurt, 1693, p. 252). *Anatomia Vitrioli*, 3rd edn., Leyden, 1617, p. 73.

172. *Élémens de Chymie*, Paris, 1615, p. 168.

173. Lemery, op. cit., pp. 203–5. Lemery explained the difference in physiological properties of the two compounds by saying that the additional mercury caused the points of acid present in corrosive sublimate to be blunted.

tinct nature of the common substances, soda and potash, was not generally appreciated.[174] Also we should not forget that the chemists of the early eighteenth century who accepted the phlogiston theory had a quite mistaken idea of the chemical composition of several important substances. For them sulphur was a compound of vitriolic acid and phlogiston and a metal calx was a simpler substance than a metal. Another reason why a systematic nomenclature would have been inopportune at the beginning of the eighteenth century was the lack of practical ability to identify a compound prepared in different ways, as is illustrated by the number of current names for what is now recognized as the same substance, e.g. potassium carbonate.

174. e.g. Stahl thought the difference between *nitrum vitriolatum* and *sal Glauberi* lay in the proportions of acid they contained (*Fundamenta Chymiae*, Nuremberg, 1732, p. 167).

The Move towards Reform

Criticisms of Terminology

As the major reform of chemical nomenclature took place in 1787, it would be easy to assume that discontent with the nomenclature dates from the eighteenth century. An examination of chemical literature of the seventeenth century (and even earlier), however, reveals a persistent critical attitude to certain examples of current terminology. Even in the sixteenth century Agricola criticized the term *litharge*[175] ($\lambda i\theta os$ =stone + $\check{a}\rho\gamma\nu\rho os$ = silver) and its Latin equivalent *spuma argenti* on the grounds that it is derived from lead and not silver—'Wherefore it might more rightly be called spuma of lead than of silver'.[176] Libavius was also critical of the use of certain terms.[177]

A term to which several seventeenth-century chemists took exception was Paracelsus' *mercurius vitae* ('mercury of life'), used in pharmacy and chemistry to denote the poisonous antimony oxychloride. The term was criticized at least as early as 1630.[178] Robert Boyle, who had no great respect for the terminology used by chemists,[179] spoke slightingly of the substance 'which Vulgar Chymists are pleased to call *Mercurius Vitae*'. Friedrich Hoffmann said that it was a misnomer[180] and Nicolas Lemery said the same. Lemery also criticized the use of the term *red precipitate of mercury* to describe mercuric oxide, pointing out that no precipitation was involved in its preparation. In one of the notebooks of Isaac Newton is found a scornful reference to the

175. Hoefer remarked: 'This name contributed in no small measure to extend the doctrine of the transmutation of metals.' (*Histoire de la Chimie*, 2nd edn., Paris, 1866, vol. i, p. 260n.)

176. *De re metallica*, Bk. 10; trans. Hoover, London, 1912, p. 475.

177. *Alchymia*, Bk. 2, tract 2, chap. 40, Frankfurt, 1606, p. 184.

178. J. Freitag, *Aurora Medicorum Galeno-Chymicorum*, Frankfurt, 1630, p. 606.

179. 'I think it fitter to alter a terme of art than reject a new truth' (*The Sceptical Chymist*, Everyman edn., London, 1911, p. 91. *Experiments touching Colours*, 1664; *Works*, ed. Birch, London, 1774, vol. 2, p. 16).

180. *Exercitatio de Cinnabari Antimonii*, Frankfurt, 1689, p. 45.

term *magisterium tartari vitriolati* to denote a compound which was probably our potassium sulphate.[181] Newton saw clearly that the term 'magistery' added nothing constructive to the name of this substance and only introduced needless mystery.

The earliest persistent criticism of the old chemical terminology was probably in connection with the use of the word 'oil'. The misuse of this term was remarked upon for over 150 years before it was finally abandoned. In a book published in 1608[182] G. B. della Porta expressed criticism of the term 'oil of vitriol' although this term had been in general use in the preceding century. In 1626 Verbezius[183] insisted that the term *spirit of vitriol* should be used instead of *oil of vitriol*, because a substance could only be called an oil if it had an oily consistency, was 'fatty' (*pinguis*) and inflammable. As spirit of vitriol did not have all these properties, 'oil' was an improper name to describe it. Boyle commented that *oil of sulphur* was an improper name for *spirit of sulphur*.[184] His French contemporary Christophe Glaser said of *spirit of vitriol*.

This last Spirit is improperly called the Oil of Vitriol and is no other than the weightier and more Caustique part of the Acid Spirit.[185]

The term *oil of tartar* did not escape the attention of the critics either, and Sala pointed out that the word *oil* was misused in this expression.[186]

Apart from criticisms of the names of particular substances, there was some dissatisfaction in the late seventeenth and early eighteenth century with the abuse of terms like *sulphur* and *spirit*. In 1661 Boyle was complaining that it was ridiculous to use the word 'sulphur' to describe an incombustible body[187] and Kunckel later complained that some chemists used the word 'sulphur' equally to denote a dry or a moist principle and

181. *Catalogue of the Portsmouth Collection*, Cambridge, 1888, p. 22.
182. *De Distillatione*, Rome, 1608, p. 116.
183. *Disquisitione iatrochymica de calcantho*, Augustae Vindelicorum, 1626, p. 24.
184. *Works*, ed. Birch, vol. 3, p. 596.
185. *The Compleat Chymist*, London, 1677, p. 182. In the early eighteenth century the terms *spirit of vitriol* and *oil of vitriol* were often used deliberately to denote dilute and concentrated sulphuric acid respectively.
186. A. Sala, *Tartarologiae* (1632), Sect. 1, cap. 11, *Collectanea Chimica Curiosa*, Frankfurt, 1693, p. 139.
187. *Sceptical Chymist*, Everyman edn., London, 1911, p. 101.

a volatile or a fixed principle.[188] Neumann denied that the term 'sulphur' could validly be used to describe the inflammable principle in oils, fats, etc.; the only true sulphur was the one related to vitriolic acid.[189] Georg Ernst Stahl was, of course, a leading figure in the general reaction against the abuses of the word 'sulphur'.[190] Stahl brought into common use the term *phlogiston*, which, in turn, came to be used to explain so much that it really explained nothing. In time, *phlogiston* was subjected to precisely the same criticism which had justly been levelled at 'sulphur' half a century previously.[191] Another word very loosely used by the chemists was 'spirit'. Boerhaave made some important criticisms of the use of this term and his criticism bears some resemblance to Macquer's detailed criticism of the use of 'oil' some thirty years later. Boerhaave complained that the term 'spirit' was used indifferently to describe acids and alkalis, despite the opposite nature of these substances.[192] Any terminology which did not make a fundamental distinction between acids and alkalis was misleading.

The Royal College of Physicians of London made a notable contribution to the reform of chemical terminology when it appointed a committee to suggest reforms for the *London Pharmacopoeia*. A draught of the committee's report was published in 1742 and a critical account of this draught appeared two years later. Although both those publications were concerned with the reform of the *Pharmacopoeia* generally—the omission of drugs of doubtful effect, the introduction of new chemical medicines, the classification of drugs and the standardization of weights and measures—it was natural that they should also discuss terminology. The committee was rather conservative regarding terminology, their main criticism in this connection being the use of the term 'oil' to comprise a wide variety of chemical preparations.

The *Essay for the Reformation of the London Pharmacopoeia*, published anonymously in 1744, was more critical of terminology. After criticizing the committee for allowing the term *oleum sulphuris per campanam* to remain in the *Pharmacopoeia*, the author

---

188. *Laboratorium Chymicum*, Hamburg and Leipzig, 1716, Part 3, p. 263.

189. *Lectiones Publicae von . . . Salpeter, etc.*, Berlin, 1732, pp. 157, 161–2, 163.

190. *Nützliche Bedencken . . . von dem so genannten Sulphure, etc.* (1718), trans. *Traité du Soufre*, Paris, 1766, e.g. pp. 21, 113.

191. Lavoisier, 'Réflexions sur le phlogistique', *Mém. Acad., 1783*, 505ff.

192. *Elements of Chemistry*, trans. Dallowe, London, 1735, p. 438.

went on to criticize the terms *mercurius praecipitatus per se* and *mercurius praecipitatus ruber* (both mercuric oxide) because 'the term precipitate is improperly fixed to a medicine prepared by calcination only'. The use of the word *calomelas* to describe *mercurius sublimatus dulcis* was considered inappropriate for a white compound since the name suggests something black in colour. The author also pointed out that the so-called *Sal Martis* was only vitriol of iron and that *Nitrum vitriolatum* was no different to *Tartarus vitriolatus*. He further remarked that *Cerussa Antimonii* was 'a meer metalline calx' and that the term *Arcanum Corallinum* was a 'pompous title'.

The influence of such criticisms can be seen in a further report of the committee[193] which announced that it had resolved upon a general correction of the impropriety in names:

It has been proposed to the committee to change the name of *mercurius praecipitatus per se* to *mercurius calcinatus*, which they cannot but approve. *Mercurius praecipitatus ruber* is with equal impropriety stiled a precipitate. This they have named *mercurius corrosivus ruber.* . . . The name *calomelas* they have now omitted. . . . The appellation *arcanum corallinum* may also very fitly be changed, for some other less affected, suppose *mercurius corallinus.* . . . *Turpethum minerale*[194] is a phantastical title of a medicine, which may with propriety be called *mercurius emeticus flavus*. Among the antimonials *crocus metallorum* were more fitly stiled *crocus antimonii*, *oleum antimonii* more properly *causticum antimoniale*, and *antimonium diaphoreticum*, till its medical qualities shall be better agreed upon, may more unexceptionally be called *antimonii calx*.

The *oleum vitrioli* which had survived the first revision, but had come under fire in the *Essay* of 1744, was to be called *spiritus vitrioli* and the acid spirit made from sulphur now became *spiritus sulphuris*.

193. *A narrative of the proceedings of the Committee appointed by the College of Physicians to review their Pharmacopoeia.* This was first published (with the proposed Pharmacopoeia) in 1745 as *The Plan of a New London Pharmacopoeia*. The quotations used here are taken from a second edition of this: *The Dispensatory of the Royal College of Physicians, London*, trans. with remarks by H. Pemberton, M.D., London, 1746. See especially pp. 57ff and 62–4.

194. This term, like *Bezoar mineral* and *Kermes mineral*, originates from an analogy with products from the vegetable and animal kingdoms. The Arabs used the root of ipomea (*turpethum*) 'turpith' to treat worms. When Paracelsus obtained a substance by digesting mercury with oil of vitriol and distilling it with spirit of wine, he was successful in treating syphilis with it; he gave it the name *turpith* because of its tradition. (E. Farber, *The Evolution of Chemistry*, New York, 1952, p. 81.)

It should be appreciated that this reform began as an attempt to abolish certain drugs and to introduce new ones of proven efficacy together with an idea of rendering weights and measures unequivocal and making one or two minor changes in the names of substances and the order of their presentation in the *Pharmacopoeia*. It was the *Essay* of 1744 which particularly drew attention to the need for a wider reform and it may be significant that Bergman was familiar with this publication and quoted from it.[195] The committee of the Royal College of Physicians had expressed the hope that the *Pharmacopoeia* (publ. 1746) resulting from their labours would be 'a true pattern to the other people of Europe and to after times'. The influence of the revised *London Pharmacopoeia* was certainly very wide. The fact that it was reprinted several times on the Continent and known to the leading French chemists has already been pointed out.

One of the earliest chemical authors of the eighteenth century who consistently criticized the current chemical terminology was Caspar Neumann. In 1727 he made some references to names which were badly chosen or wrongly applied and five years later he criticized such synonyms as *Panacea*, *Sal catholicum* and *Sal sapientiae* for what we now call potassium sulphate. A further example of mystical and misleading terminology which he ridiculed was the term *philosophical spirit of vitriol*; this name was absurd, since the substance denoted contained not the slightest part of vitriol and was simply dilute spirit of salt.[196]

Caspar Neumann also criticized certain aspects of nomenclature,[197] such as the use of 'oil' applied to compounds of tartar, antimony, arsenic, etc. and also to acids. The chapter headed *Von den falschen Magisteriis* in Neumann's posthumously-published works can be compared with the article *Faux Précipités* in Macquer's dictionary published two decades later. Neumann repeated the criticism of the use of the terms 'magistery' or 'precipitate' in certain preparations where no precipi-

195. *Königl. Swedischen Akademie der Wissenschaften, Abhandlungen*, trans. Kästner, *33* (1771), 292, 295 also *34* (1772), 192.

196. *Lectiones Chymiae von Salibus Alkalino-Fixis und von Camphor*, Berlin, 1727, pp. 105-7, 78. *Lectiones Publicae von Salpeter, etc.*, Berlin, 1732, pp. 2, 89, 329.

197. *Chymiae medicae dogmatico-experimentalis*, Züllichau, 1749, vol. i, Part 2, p. 324; Part 3, pp. 445-6.

tation was involved. Yet, despite all these valid criticisms there are many examples of misleading terms used by Neumann in his own writings.

William Cullen, professor of medicine and lecturer on chemistry at Glasgow University, was another critic of the terminology accepted in the mid-eighteenth century. We may consider some of his criticisms contained in a manuscript of 1753[198] and also some constructive suggestions. Considering the union of four acids (*vitriolic, nitrous, muriatic, vegetable acids*) with the three common alkalis (*vegetable, fossil* and *volatile*)[199] and assuming that 'each acid can be joined with each alkali only in one given proportion', he wrote down the names of the twelve possible neutral salts and suggested that

the most part of the seeming great diversity of saline substances which are to be found in chemical writings may be either referred to the species above mentioned or may be properly considered as variations of these.

This is rather a sweeping statement since it excluded salts then available such as bisulphates[200] and completely ignored phosphoric and tartaric acids and calcium salts, yet the idea behind this enumeration was valuable. Cullen wished to reduce the number of synonyms which were used as alternatives by different authors or repeated in frequent parentheses by the same author, in order that it should be clearly understood about which salt he was writing.[201] Cullen criticized Boerhaave and Hoffmann, the former because he distinguished identical substances according to their method of preparation and the latter because he made a distinction between *common spirit of nitre* and *Glauber's spirit of nitre*. Cullen insisted that both these names stood for essentially the same thing as *aqua fortis*. Particularly bad examples of multiplication of names

198. L. Dobbin, 'A Cullen Chemical Manuscript of 1753', *Annals of Science, 1* (1936), 138–56.

199. In modern terms the acids are respectively sulphuric, nitric, hydrochloric and acetic; the alkalis are potassium, sodium and ammonium.

200. The existence of acid salts as definite compounds was proclaimed by Rouelle in 1754 (*Mém. Acad., 1754*, 574).

201. Writing of common salt Cullen says: 'It is to be wished that we had some name proper for this salt that might be understood to comprehend its several varieties which would have saved Dr Boerhaave the trouble of repeating the different names *sal gemmae, maris, fontium* almost every time he has occasion to mention this salt.'

which he criticized were the variety of names given to vitriolic acid, common salt and vegetable alkali. This latter term, *vegetable alkali*, was suggested by Cullen to include the various preparations of what we call potassium carbonate, known variously as *cineres clavellati*, *salt of tartar*, *alkali of wine lees* (*cendres gravellées*) and *fixed nitre*.

Probably the greatest and most influential critic of the eighteenth century was Pierre Joseph Macquer. His *Élémens de Chymie Théorique*, published in 1749 when the author was thirty-one, contains the now familiar criticisms of the term *oil* to describe acids and alkalis, *mercurius vitae* to denote a poisonous compound of antimony and *regenerated tartar* for a salt which was not tartar.[202] In his *Élémens de Chymie Pratique*, published two years later, Macquer made several more criticisms of the current chemical terms. He considered that *fixed sal ammoniac* was an improper name for the compound we now call calcium chloride and he criticized the term *philosophical spirit of vitriol* for an acid which was nothing more than spirit of salt. He was doubtful whether the so-called *sel febrifuge de Sylvius* could be relied upon, as its name suggested, to cure fevers. He was also careful to explain that *Cinnabar of Antimony* was only ordinary cinnabar and contained no antimony and he discussed whether *mercury precipitate* was a suitable name to give to a substance (again mercuric oxide) obtained without precipitation.[203]

Such criticisms were praiseworthy, but so far they did not reveal much originality. Neglecting the question of originality, however, Macquer's criticisms of current chemical terminology and his constructive suggestions for a simple nomenclature for salts are both of considerable importance, since they were repeated and amplified in his *Dictionnaire de Chymie*,[204] first published in 1766 and later translated into English, German and Italian. The form of a dictionary gave Macquer a splendid opportunity to include between the covers of a book all the substances then known to chemistry. Under the heading *Faux Précipités* he included *precipitate per se* (mercuric oxide) as an improper name and he devoted several pages in the appropriate

202. Op. cit., Paris, 1749, pp. 38–9, 148, 218.
203. *Élémens de Chymie Pratique*, Paris, 1751, vol. i, pp. 329, 411, 419; vol. ii, pp. 543, 560.
204. Op. cit., Paris, 1766, vol. i, pp. 149, 176, 185, 233, 236, 311, 481, 598ff.; vol. ii, pp. 35–6, 39, 433, 447–8, 484, 499.

place not only to *Huiles* (combustible organic oils) but also to *Huiles Improprement Dites*, where he condemned the use of the term oil to describe concentrated acids and alkalis and solutions of certain metal salts. Macquer warned the reader that 'Calx of gold' was really the metal and that the so-called 'arsenic' was really the calx (i.e. oxide) of arsenic. He criticized Lemery's use of the term *vitriol of silver* for a compound (silver nitrate) which contains no vitriolic acid and the careless use of the term *regenerated sea salt* for a kind of salt (potassium chloride) with a different base from sea salt. He pointed out the futility of using the names of plants from which salts were extracted, since when purified they were all identical and might well be called *alkali of tartar*. Macquer could not resist a jibe at *arcanum duplicatum* ('double secret') which had become one of the best known salts in chemistry (potassium sulphate).

Words should be used with a precise meaning. Thus the term *magnesia* (used to describe our magnesium carbonate) could not be properly used to denote the compound of this earth with vitriolic acid. The term *fixed sulphur of antimony* was inappropriate for ·a white calx of antimony which contained no sulphur. Macquer welcomed the suggestion by Wallerius that the term *marcasite* should be used in a more restricted sense than hitherto:

This would seem much wiser than to leave it with a vague and indeterminate meaning, because this always results in ambiguity and obscurity in nomenclature.

Macquer complained of the use of place names in chemical terminology and remarked that this practice could not but lead to unnecessary multiplication of terms. He criticized the use of the term *volatile salt* which was given to substances having little in common, saying:

They ought to be distinguished by some more particular name. The volatility of salts is a very indeterminate quality. For of those that are considered as such some are much more and some much less volatile than others.

Macquer also criticized the use of *cadmia* which had a long history of confusion and was applied to several distinct substances including cobalt. He suggested that the use of the word *cobalt* would avoid any further ambiguity. In general, Macquer complained that badly chosen names were the result of ignorance on the part of earlier chemists and alchemists. Unless there was some reform in terminology the progress of chemistry would be gravely hindered. Macquer contributed to solving this problem not only by cutting away much of the dead wood, but also by planting for the future.

The suggestions of Macquer were followed to a certain extent by his younger colleague and demonstrator, Antoine Baumé. In his *Chymie Expérimentale et Raisonée* of 1773 Baumé followed Macquer's example with criticisms of many terms, including 'fixed sal ammoniac' and 'butter of antimony'. In the latter case Baumé took the progressive step of suggesting that it might be called by the systematic name *sel marin antimonié*.[205]

Despite the criticisms of those features of the old terminology most open to objection, many chemists still continued to use these terms and even the terminology of Macquer and Baumé was not beyond reproach. Jean-Baptiste Bucquet, a close friend of Lavoisier, was one of the many chemists who continued to speak of 'oil of tartar', 'butter of antimony', etc. and yet he made at least one important criticism of current terminology. Bucquet suggested that the name 'antimony', which was commonly used to describe the ore of that metal (antimony sulphide) should be reserved for the metal itself, thus making it unnecessary to distinguish the latter as 'regulus of antimony'. A similar suggestion had already been made by Baron d'Holbach in an article in Diderot's *Encyclopaedia* and it was finally accepted in the reform of 1787.[206]

The Superiority of Names based on Composition

An important principle of a systematic nomenclature in chemistry is that the names of compounds should be related to their constituents. Thus when Angelo Sala suggested that the residue after the calcination of green vitriol (i.e. ferric oxide) might be called *Substantia Ferrea Vitrioli*,[207] this was a move towards modern nomenclature and an improvement on the Paracelsan *colcothar*. Again, the term *mercurius vitae* for what to-day is called antimony oxychloride was obviously a misnomer and was often criticized as such in the early eighteenth

205. Op. cit., vol. i, pp. 216, 320; vol. ii, pp. 13, 120, 441, 445.
206. Bucquet, *Introduction à l'étude du règne minérale*, Paris, 1771, vol. ii, pp. 108–9. *Encyclopédie*, vol. 14, Neufchastel, 1765, p. 38b.
207. *Anatomia Vitrioli*, 3rd edn., Leyden, 1617, p. 105.

century. When Boerhaave referred to it as *mercurius vitae anti-monii*[208] the relation of the compound to antimony was implicit in the name. The term *arcanum coralinum* ('coralline secret') is an example of the worst kind of early chemical terminology, since the only hint in the name as to the identity of the substance was the comparison with the red colour of coral. When the name was changed to *mercurius coralinus* in the 1746 *London Pharmacopoeia*, this gave more of an indication of the composition of the substance. It was also an improvement when chemists began to refer to salts of *ammoniac* rather than *volatile urinous salts*. What Stahl had called *Sal nitriforme inflammabile* Rouelle called *sel ammoniacal nitreux*, a name indicating completely the constituents of the salt.[209] Macquer suggested that certain terms such as *vitriol* should be used in a strict sense to indicate the salts of vitriolic acid. With the adoption of such terms systematic nomenclature may be said to have begun.

Yet in the mid-eighteenth century many chemists were still using names which suggested quite falsely the composition of substances. The examples *mercurius vitae* and *sal ammoniacum fixum* have already been mentioned. In the latter case there was some excuse originally for giving the name to the residue when sal ammoniac was heated with lime. It did, however, introduce a ludicrous element into the science when a chemical writer says that acid of common salt dissolves calcareous earth to form *sal ammoniacum fixum*![210] The lack of an established connection between a chemical substance and its name is illustrated by the cases of sodium and magnesium sulphates. The *British Dispensatory* of 1747 describes the widespread practice of substituting *sal catharticum amarum* for *Glauber's salt* because of the comparative cheapness of the former which

is called by the name of Glauber's salt, in distinction from the true salt of his invention, which being robbed of his name, is distinguished by that of *sal mirabile*, from this counterfeit.[211]

In France Fourcroy relates that a false Epsom salt was sold which was really only Glauber's salt.[212] He appreciated the

---

208. *Elements of Chemistry*, trans. Dallowe, London, 1735, vol. ii, p. 366.
209. Stahl, *Fundamenta Chymiae*, Nuremberg, 1732, p. 52. Rouelle, *Mém. Acad.*, *1744*, 362.
210. Cronstedt, *System of Mineralogy*, trans., London, 1770, p. 137.
211. Op. cit., London, 1747, pp. 39–40.
212. *Mémoires de Chymie*, Paris, 1784, p. 382.

advantage to be gained by adopting Bergman's suggestion of calling Epsom salt *vitriol de magnésie*. When the nature of a substance was indicated by its name no confusion would result.

Nomenclature by Definition

We have already seen that the worst abuses of the old chemical terminology were criticized for a very long time before they were finally discarded. The natural means of avoiding improper terms before the introduction of a systematic nomenclature was to use a descriptive phrase which was really more of a definition than a name. A descriptive phrase might indicate the method of preparation of a compound, although ideally it would in-dicate its composition. The *London Pharmacopoeia* of 1650 described a preparation as *antimonium cum nitro calcinatum* (anti-mony calcined with nitre) and further explanation seems hardly necessary. Another pharmacopoeia referred to potassium sulphate as *Sal Polychrestum e nitro et sulphure*.[213] This was unquestionably a cumbersome expression, but it did clearly dis-tinguish this substance from *Sal Polychrestum de Seignette* (potas-sium sodium tartrate). Similarly the phrase *chalybs cum sulphure preparatus*[214] (ferrous sulphide) was an improvement on Lemery's ambiguous *Saffron de Mars apperitif*.

When in 1744 Guillaume-François Rouelle presented a paper to the *Académie des Sciences* in which he suggested a classification of neutral salts, he was faced with the difficulty that many of the salts he wished to consider had not been assigned names. Whereas he usually retained the traditional names where they existed, in the case of the less familiar salts he used descriptive phrases like 'the acid of vinegar joined with chalk' and 'the salt formed by the union of nitrous acid with bismuth.'[215] Some-times such a phrase was used as a synonym as when he referred to 'sugar of Saturn or the acid of vinegar joined with lead'. The most common group of salts to have nothing approaching a systematic name were, in modern language, the chlorides. He often referred to these in an unequivocal but cumbersome man-ner by mentioning the constituents of the salt. When Macquer

213. *Pharmacopoeia Helvetica*, Basle, 1771, Part II, p. 190.
214. H. Pemberton, *A Course of Chemistry*, London, 1771, p. 269.
215. '*L'acide du vinaigre uni à la craie*', '*le sel formé par l'union de l'acide nitreux au bismuth*' (*Mém. Acad., 1744*, 360–3).

was compiling his *Dictionary* some twenty years later, he improved on Rouelle's work by referring to general classes, which he called *vitriols, nitres, sel marins,* etc. In some instances, particularly in the case of the salts of *marine acid,* Macquer used systematic descriptions in which the name of the acid was followed by the name of the base,[216] e.g.

sel commun à base d'alkali végétal	=potassium chloride
sel à base terreuse calcaire	=calcium chloride
sel acéteux à base d'alkali marin	=sodium acetate
sel vitriolique à base de terre argilleuse	=aluminium sulphate

Meanwhile in Sweden Cronstedt had published anonymously his *Försök til mineralogie* (1758). Although he was obviously interested in the nomenclature of mineral substances, he was very cautious about coining new names for minerals which he had not fully investigated.[217] Cronstedt described all minerals by a Swedish name followed by a Latin translation or description,[218] e.g.

terra calcarea Acido Vitrioli saturata seu mixta	=calcium sulphate
Ferrum Sulphure saturatum	=ferrous sulphide
Acidum Salis Communis Argento saturatum *Argentum Acido Salis solutum et mineralisatum*	}=silver chloride

It seems likely that Cronstedt had some influence on Bergman, who in 1775 used expressions of the type: *Acidum Salis saturated with Magnesia, Magnesia saturated with the aerial acid.*[219] In his Latin writings, however, Bergman preferred to use abbreviated phrases involving the use of the past participle and he referred to the same two compounds (magnesium chloride and carbonate) as *magnesia salita* and *magnesia aerata* respectively.[220]

Cronstedt's book was translated into French in 1771 by Monnet who appears to have been impressed[221] by Cronstedt's insistence on the enumeration of the constituent parts of salts and

---

216. *Dictionnaire de Chymie,* Paris, 1766, vol. ii, pp. 430–6.
217. *System of Mineralogy,* trans., London, 1770, pp. xx–xxi.
218. *Försök til mineralogie,* Stockholm, 1758, pp. 18, 184, 123, 159.
219. *Königl. Schwedischen Akademie der Wissenschaften, Abhandlungen,* 37 (1775), 19, 21.
220. *Nova Acta Reg. Societatis Scientiarum Upsaliensis,* 2 (1775), 118–35.
221. Monnet refers to Cronstedt frequently in his *Nouveau Système de Minéralogie,* Bouillon, 1779. See also ibid., pp. 438, 293.

he describes many salts by two names, the first being its common name and the second relating to its constitution, e.g. *sel de glauber, ou combinaison de l'acide vitriolique avec l'alkali minéral; mine d'argent corné, ou combinaison de l'argent avec l'acide marin.* The same method of nomenclature was adopted by Antoine Brongniart in his *Tableau Analytique des combinaisons . . . de différentes substances* (Paris, 1778).

Some insight into the development of chemical nomenclature is gained by a study of Guyton de Morveau's early terminology. Whereas in 1782 he declared that the first principle of the reform of chemical language was that 'a phrase cannot be regarded as a name',[222] in 1776 he spoke of *le nitre qui a pour base l'alkali volatil*[223] and in his translation of Bergman in 1780 he had been unwilling to coin French terms equivalent to Bergman's expressions and therefore used such phrases as *le sel marin à base de terre pesante* and *alkali végétal uni à l'acide marin.*[224] Lavoisier too, in order to denote newly investigated salts with precision was obliged to have recourse to these long descriptive phrases. In his investigation of the salts of phosphoric acid he used such expressions as *sel phosphorique à base de sel d'Epsom* and *sel phosphorique à base d'alkali fixe végétal* and later he preferred such phrases as *alkali fixe végétal saturé d'air fixe* to Bergman's more compact expression *alkali vegetabile aeratum.*[225]

The Need for Reform

The need for a systematic chemical nomenclature made itself felt in various ways in the seventeenth and particularly the eighteenth century. One pressing need for the reform of chemical terminology was brought about by the great increase in the number of substances known. This increase is especially noticeable in the second half of the eighteenth century when several new elements were discovered, many compounds were prepared for the first time and the experiments of Black, Cavendish and Priestley were opening up a whole new field of 'pneumatic' chemistry. Perhaps, in 1734, Peter Shaw was right to remark in connection with the 'Mineral Spirit' contained in spa waters

---

222. *Observations sur la Physique, 19* (1782), 373.
223. Diderot and D'Alembert, *Encyclopédie, Supplément,* Amsterdam, 1776, vol. ii, p. 726.
224. *Opuscules,* Dijon, 1780, vol. i, pp. 110, 189, 149.
225. *Oeuvres,* Paris, 1862–93, vol. ii, pp. 148, 150, 490.

that 'Just philosophical Names can never be given to Things, till their Natures are known'. Yet when, after Black's experiments, chemists became more familiar with the chemical properties of what we now call carbon dioxide, they vied with each other to give it a name appropriate to its most significant property, so that in the ten years 1772–81 there were as many names given to this one gas. Over the same period Lavoisier alone described the gas oxygen by a succession of descriptive phrases numbering more than a dozen. The importance attached by Bergman, Lavoisier and their contemporaries to the terms *acidum aereum* (1773–4) and *principe oxigine* (1778) to denote carbon dioxide and oxygen respectively, show that chemical terminology was discussed by the leading chemists of Europe before Guyton de Morveau thought seriously about a systematic nomenclature. In the late 1770's there was immense progress made in pneumatic chemistry, but there was little agreement as to what the gaseous substances should be called. As a general term Macquer preferred *gas*, but for Priestley, the 'father of pneumatic chemistry', these substances were all different kinds of *air*. The diversity in terminology was magnified by the emergence of Lavoisier's school of thought which was hostile to the current phlogiston theory. The problem of a unified terminology of gases was tackled by Condorcet, the secretary of the French *Académie Royale des Sciences*. In the history of the Academy for 1777 (printed 1780) Condorcet stated the problem:

Chemists are not in agreement among themselves as to the names they give to different kinds of aeriform fluids. Being obliged to give an account of memoirs where a single substance often receives different names, we have thought ourselves obliged to adopt a standard nomenclature; we have named each substance according to one of its characteristic properties and the name we have given it is not related to any system, so that it can be adopted by all scientists (*Savants*), however different may be their opinion on the nature of these fluids.[226]

Condorcet was optimistic about his influence on chemists as a whole and the names *air gaseux* and *air réduit* which he suggested for carbon dioxide and nitrogen respectively were still-born.

226. *Hist. Acad.*, *1777*, 22. The philosophy of Condorcet probably had some influence on the 1787 reform of nomenclature; see e.g. Condorcet's views on the importance of the language of a science to the progress of that science (*Esquisse d'un tableau historique des progrès de l'esprit humain*, [Paris], 1795, p. 342).

His suggestion of *air vital* (oxygen) was, however, accepted by Bergman,[227] and with reservations by Lavoisier.[228]

It was in the second half of the eighteenth century that the metals, cobalt, nickel, platinum and manganese became known. Before about 1750 the term *calcareous earth* had a very wide meaning, but the investigations of Black, Marggraf and Scheele revealed the existence of other earths later to be known as magnesia, alumina and baryta. The distinction between the alkalis of the mineral and vegetable kingdoms (i.e. sodium and potassium) was not generally known before this time. To speak of a substance as an *earth* or a *fixed alkali* now required further precision. Nor should the field of organic chemistry be forgotten. All these discoveries multiplied the number of substances in the chemists world. When reactions between acids and bases were carried out systematically there resulted a large number of salts for which the seventeenth century had no name. If we consider that between the years 1771–81 in the field of inorganic chemistry alone, Scheele prepared the compounds now known as oxides of barium and manganese, silicon fluoride, hydrofluoric acid, molybdic acid, tungstic acid as well as various compounds of arsenic, we have some idea of the expansion which was taking place in chemistry in the second half of the eighteenth century. Whereas in a paper compiled in 1771 by the young Lavoisier,[229] this chemist could limit the number of salts in the mineral kingdom to six (derived from two mineral acids and three mineral alkalis and earths), some ten years later Guyton de Morveau in his *Tableau de Nomenclature Chimique*[230] trebled this number of mineral acids, added six vegetable acids and four acids of animal origin and indicated a method of naming some five hundred different chemical substances.

Names were required for the new elements and compounds. When at the beginning of the eighteenth century Hoffmann examined what we now call magnesium sulphate, he described it as 'a certain neutral salt which has no special name (*sal quoddam neutrum innominatum*) and is almost unknown. . . . Authors commonly call it nitre, but it has nothing in common with

227. *Opuscula*, Uppsala, 1779–90, vol. iii, p. 401.
228. Lavoisier took some pains to stress that the term *air vital* was not of his own choosing (*Mém. Acad.*, *1780*, 336; *1782*, 459, 476, 486; *1783*, 563).
229. *Oeuvres*, vol. ii, p. 33.
230. *Observations sur la Physique*, *19* (1782), folding plate opp. p. 382.

nitre'.[231] Unfortunately it acquired the name *magnesia* which led to some confusion with pyrolusite which was also called *magnesia*. A similar confusion might have arisen between the two 'heavy earths' if Guyton had not suggested the use of the terms *barote* and *tungstène* to distinguish them.

One indication of the need for a systematic nomenclature was the increasing use in the second half of the eighteenth century of long descriptive phrases which many of the leading chemists used in order to avoid the ambiguity of some of the current terms. Another indication of the need for new terms is provided by what might be termed the 'double terminology' in which a general term is repeated to indicate one particular substance. Passing over the 'sulphur of sulphur' and 'mercury of mercury' of the alchemists, we come to Lemery at the end of the seventeenth century who used the phrase 'the truly sulphureous part of sulphur'[232] to express the idea of inflammability. A better example is the means chemists used in the late seventeenth and eighteenth centuries to indicate what we now call a salt. At this time the term *salt* included acids and alkalis. Neutral salts were sometimes described as *sal salsum*[233] or 'salted salt'—something which was doubly a salt as opposed to *sal acidum* and *sal alkalinum*. A further example of 'double terminology' is provided by the term *tartarus tartarisatus*, although here the explanation is rather different. It is an early example of a systematic nomenclature, in which the noun *tartarus* was used to denote the base of the salt and the adjective *tartarisatus* indicated the acid constituent. The same word was therefore fulfilling two functions and in the re-formed nomenclature the name became *potassium tartrate*. A final example of 'double terminology' is provided by Lavoisier in his attempt to express the qualities of the gas he was later to call 'oxygen'. In the year 1777 he referred to it variously as *pure air, the best and most respirable part of the air, the salubrious part of the air* and on one occasion he expressed these sentiments by referring to it as *a pure air . . . which is more air than ordinary air (air pur . . . plus air que l'air commun)*.[234] This expression was seized upon by

231. *Dissertationum Physico-Medicarum*, Pars Altera, Leyden, 1708, p. 200.
232. *Cours de Chymie*, Paris, 1697, p. 419.
233. e.g. M. Ettmueller, *Nouvelle Chymie Raisonnée*, Lyon, 1693, pp. 6, 18. 'L'Acide et l'Alkali . . . unis ensemble composent un troisième sel, nommé le sel salé, qui n'est ni l'un ni l'autre et participe de tous les deux.'
234. *Mém. Acad.*, *1777*, 593, 187. *Mém. Acad.*, *1774*, 366 (May 1777). *Mém. Acad.*, *1776*, 676 (Dec. 1777).

one of his critics[235] as a basis for ridicule, but for us it is an indication of the inadequacy of ordinary language on the frontiers of knowledge.

The enormous increase in the number of substances which presented themselves to the investigation of chemists in the second half of the eighteenth century was quite beyond the capacity of the chemical worker who gave names casually to substances, names which were usually based on one of the attributes mentioned in this section. The most satisfactory names given to chemical compounds were usually long descriptive phrases which could not be tolerated by chemists indefinitely. The way lay open by which these phrases could be abbreviated into a manageable systematic nomenclature. If the seventeenth-century chemist with a knowledge of less than a dozen neutral salts was able to express himself without using a systematic nomenclature, this was clearly not possible when, about 1770–80, the number of possible neutral salts had increased to several hundred. It was the necessity to establish a systematic nomenclature of chemical compounds in general and of salts in particular which led eventually to the work of Bergman and Guyton de Morveau on the reform of chemical nomenclature. Many chemists had previously criticized the current chemical terms, but Bergman and Guyton went further by showing that it was possible to name compounds systematically according to their constituents.

235. Sigaud de la Fond, *Essai sur différentes espèces d'air fixe ou de Gaz,* nouvelle edn., Paris, 1785, p. 196.

Part 3

THE INTRODUCTION OF SYSTEMATIC NOMENCLATURE INTO CHEMISTRY AND THE ACCEPTANCE OF THE 1787 REFORM

'It is time to rid chemistry of obstacles of every kind which retard its progress and to introduce in it a true spirit of analysis; we have proved sufficiently that this reform must be brought about by perfecting the language.'

LAVOISIER, *Méthode de nomenclature chimique*, Paris, 1787, p. 16

CHAPTER ONE

Early Examples of Systematic Nomenclature

Similar Names for Compounds of Similar Chemical Constitution

Although a complete method of systematic nomenclature had to wait for the work of Torbern Bergman and Guyton de Morveau in the last quarter of the eighteenth century, the beginnings of a systematic nomenclature appear in chemistry much earlier. The phrase 'systematic nomenclature' is used here to mean a terminology in which chemically similar substances were given similar names or in which the names of compounds bore some relation to the names of their constituents.

In the first place, some chemical terms which originally had been applied only to individual substances were, in the early eighteenth century, used as general terms to describe classes of substances. An example of this is the use of the adjective *horn* (Latin: *corneus*). At the beginning of the seventeenth century Oswald Croll had used the expression *luna cornea* ('horn silver') to describe fused silver chloride. This name soon became accepted generally and the similar compound of lead was called *plumbum corneum*. Occasionally the terms 'horn mercury', 'horn tin' and 'horn bismuth' were also used. Although the term was originally based on a physical characteristic, and the substances mentioned are all white solids, there is also some chemical justification for grouping them together. Baumé explained that 'corneus metals' (*métaux cornés*) was a description applied to metals combined with the marine acid (hydrochloric acid).[1] Yet the term chosen hardly made this meaning obvious and, moreover, it could not logically be applied to coloured chlorides; also by common usage, the familiar chlorides of sodium, potassium, ammonium, and calcium were described by other quite unrelated names.

1. Baumé, *Chymie Expérimentale*, Paris, 1773, vol. ii, p. 380.

Although the term 'butter' was often criticized because it introduced an irrelevant analogy into a chemical name, in several cases its use was related to chemical composition. By itself, 'butter of antimony' may have been a misleading chemical term to describe what we now call antimony trichloride, but when one appreciates that the chloride of arsenic was referred to as 'butter of arsenic' and zinc chloride was later called 'butter of zinc', it might be admitted that the use of the term 'butter' did fulfil the function of relating the deliquescent chlorides.[2] Another example of terminology which brought together similar compounds is provided by one of the names of the salts we now call acetates. In the seventeenth century the least objectionable name for potassium acetate was *terra foliata tartari*. In the eighteenth century Baumé, despite the criticism of his colleague Macquer, used the term *terre foliée* as a general term to denote the salts which vinegar formed with the alkalis. Ammonium acetate was *terre foliée animale* and Baumé called sodium acetate *terre foliée crystallisée*.[3]

Latin Binomial Terms

There was another and more important way in which a systematic nomenclature was foreshadowed and this was by the use of binomial terms related to the composition of salts. This method of great potential value, was implied in the term *tartarus vitriolatus* ('vitriolated tartar') found, for example, in Croll's *Basilica Chymica* of 1609 and used throughout the seventeenth and eighteenth centuries to describe potassium sulphate. This simple but important method of nomenclature is implicit in several seventeenth and eighteenth-century works[4] and may be exemplified by a work of Caspar Neumann, who in 1727 was

---

2. The relative merits of the expressions *Beurres* and *Métaux cornés* as general terms to denote the salts of spirit of salt are discussed by Demachy, *Recueil de Dissertations Physico-Chimiques*, Amsterdam and Paris, 1774, p. 186.

3. *Chymie Expérimentale*, Paris, 1773, vol. ii, pp. 90, 72.

4. e.g. *tartarus nitratus, nitrum vitriolatum* (Mynsicht, *Thesaurus et Armamentarium Medico-Chymicum*, Rothomagi, 1651, pp. 18, 28); *nitrum sulphuratum* (W. Clarke, *The natural history of nitre*, London, 1670, p. 66); *chalybs tartarisatus, tartarus chalybeatus* (G. Bate, *Pharmacopoeia Bateana*, 2nd edn., London, 1691, pp. 41, 170); *mars sulphuratus*—ferrous sulphide, not the sulphate (Stahl, *Fundamenta Chymiae*, Nuremberg, 1723, p. 101); *tartarus tartarisatus* (Boerhaave, *Elementa chemiae*, Leyden, 1732, vol. ii, p. 263).

not only using the term *tartarus vitriolatus*, but also *tartarus citratus* (potassium citrate), *tartarus tartarisatus* (potassium tartrate) and *tartarus nitratus* (potassium nitrate).[5] The difficulties in appreciating the composition of a salt[6] as well as the elementary state of chemical terminology is reflected in Neumann's use of 'nitre' to denote either what we now call a potassium salt, or a nitrate, as in the expressions *nitrum vitriolatum* and *nitrum ammoniacale* respectively.[7] Not everyone realized that the terms *tartarus vitriolatus* and *nitrum vitriolatum* were synonyms. Johann Heinrich Pott suggested that this difficulty might be overcome by the use of the term *sal alkali vitriolatum*.[8] Usually these terms were introduced informally in chemical works. Most of the systematic terms, however, did not enjoy very wide popularity and probably the only term to be almost universally known was *tartarus vitriolatus* (with its variants *nitrum* or *alkali vitriolatum*). It was this term which was used by Bergman in 1775 as a precedent for the use of the past participle *Aeratum* to denote the salts of what he called *Acidum Aereum* (i.e. carbonates).[9]

It is significant that the terms quoted have all been in Latin. The structure of this language and in particular, the ease with which adjectives can be made from nouns, lent itself readily to a binomial nomenclature. It is true that in English it was later possible to speak of *magnesian vitriol* and *barytic nitre*[10] and in French Macquer[11] used the terms *tartre stybié* and *argent sulphuré* to denote tartar emetic and silver sulphide respectively, but in a living language these expressions sound forced. The fact that the French chemists generally avoided coining such expressions, preferring to make use of long descriptive phrases, has already been noted. Probably the most convincing proof that our modern chemical binomial nomenclature of chemical compounds owes its existence largely to the suitability of such a nomenclature in Latin is provided by Bergman. When writing

5. *Lectiones Publicae von Salibus Alkalino-Fixis*, Berlin, 1727, pp. 78–9.
6. e.g. the product of a futile experiment in which spirit of nitre was heated with ordinary nitre was called *nitrum nitratum* (R. James, *Medical Dictionary*, London, 1743–5, art. 'Nitrum').
7. *Lectiones Publicae von Salpeter, etc.*, Berlin, 1732, pp. 88, 108.
8. *Dissertations Chimiques*, Paris, 1759, vol. iii, p. 219.
9. *Nova Acta Regiae Societatis Scientiarum Upsaliensis*, 2 (1775), 118.
10. Fourcroy, *Elements of Natural History and Chemistry*, London, 1788, vol. ii, pp. 283, 285.
11. *Élémens de Chymie Pratique*, Paris, 1751, vol. ii, p. 364. *Dictionnaire de Chymie*, Paris, 1766, vol. i, p. 164.

in Latin in 1775 Bergman referred to magnesium chloride and carbonate as *magnesia salita* and *magnesia aerata*, but when writing in Swedish he described these compounds respectively by phrases like: *acidum salis saturated with magnesia* and *magnesia saturated with the aerial acid.*[12] In the years 1775–84 Bergman developed his ideas on the Latin nomenclature but made no attempt to translate it into his native language. In his publications in Latin in 1782 and 1784 Bergman perfected his ideas on a binomial chemical nomenclature, but in the last two papers of his life concerned with chemistry and printed in Swedish in these same two years in the *Transactions of the Swedish Academy of Sciences*, Bergman made no use at all of his nomenclature and, indeed, avoided using it by drawing on the usual descriptive phrases.[13]

Macquer's Proposals

Before a binomial nomenclature was introduced, however, a few primitive systematic names were used. Some examples have already been quoted. Another and perhaps more fruitful instance was brought about by the generalization of the term *sal ammoniac* in the mid-eighteenth century. This term had been used for several hundred years for ammonium chloride and when chemists wished to describe other related salts which had been prepared, it is not surprising that they described them as various kinds of *sal ammoniac*. In 1744 Rouelle, demonstrator at the *Jardin du Roi*, was using the terms *sel ammoniac, sel ammoniacal vitriolique* and *sel ammoniacal nitreux*[14] to denote the compounds now called ammonium chloride, sulphate and nitrate respectively. On the same principle Macquer spoke of *sel phosphorique ammoniacal*[15] and Baumé described the corresponding salt of the 'vegetable acid' (i.e. acetic acid) as *sel ammoniacal végétal.*[16]

An important contribution towards a systematic nomenclature was provided by Macquer in his *Dictionnaire de Chymie* of

12. *Nova Acta Upsaliensis, 2* (1755), 118–35. Also *Dissertatio de Magnesia alba*, Uppsala, 1775, pp. 15, 8. *Kunliga Svenska Vetenskaps Akademien Handlingar, 36* (1775), 17, 20.
13. e.g. *Järn uplöst i luftsyra, kalk förenad med saltsyra, tungjord mättad med vitriol-syra* (*Kunliga Svenska Vetenskaps Akademien Nya Handlingar, 3* (1782), 292; *5* (1784), 112).
14. *Mém. Acad., 1744*, 362.
15. *Dictionnaire de Chymie*, Paris, 1766, vol. ii, p. 438.
16. *Chymie Expérimentale*, Paris, 1773, vol. ii, p. 82.

1766. For example, Macquer took the term *vitriol*, which had been used by earlier authors to denote a variety of crystalline salts and suggested that this term should be applied to all salts of vitriolic acid:[17]

It would be fitting to give the same name *vitriol* to all vitriolic salts with a metallic base, and to name, for example, *vitriol d'or* the vitriolic salt composed of vitriolic acid and gold; *vitriol d'argent* or *vitriol de lune* the salt resulting from the union of the same acid with silver, and similarly for the others. Perhaps it would even be appropriate to include under the general name of vitriol all vitriolic salts whatever.

He adopted the phrase '*vitriol de —*' in the cases of the metals gold, silver, copper, iron, tin, antimony, bismuth and zinc and also for lead, mercury, cobalt and arsenic, admitting that the last four had still not been carefully studied by chemists.

Extending this scheme, Macquer proposed the use of the following terms in the general sense to denote salts of the respective acids. We may abbreviate his scheme as follows:

NAME OF ACID	NAME OF SALT	EXAMPLE OF SALT
acide nitreux (nitric acid)	*nitre* or *sel nitreux*	*nitre de cuivre*
acide du sel marin (hydrochloric acid)	*sel marin* or *sel*	*sel d'argent*
acide tartreux (tartaric acid)	*sel tartreux* or *tartre soluble*	*tartre soluble martial*
acide du vinaigre (acetic acid)	*sel acéteux*	*sel acéteux de plomb*
acide phosphorique (phosphoric acid)	*sel phosphorique*	*sel phosphorique am-noniacal*
(not mentioned)	*sel de borax* or *borax*	*borax ammoniacal*

It should be noted that Macquer included in this scheme not only familiar salts but also salts which were unknown at the time. Among the *nitres* which he listed as unknown were those of gold, tin, zinc and antimony. Although Macquer found it easy to express the names of the salts of familiar metals, he was less fortunate with respect to the salts of sodium, potassium, calcium and aluminium, since the metals themselves had not

17. Op. cit., vol. ii, pp. 673–4, 430–9.

been isolated and named. Thus in the case of sodium and potassium sulphates, which were common substances with well established trivial names, he made no attempt even to refer to them as 'vitriols' and he called sodium nitrate by its usual name of *nitre cubique*. In other instances Macquer adopted the use of descriptive phrases, introducing the terms 'alkali' and 'earth' which he described as 'bases', e.g.

sel acéteux à base d'alkali marin	(sodium acetate)
sel commun à base d'alkali végétal	(potassium chloride)
nitre à base terreuse calcaire	(calcium nitrate)
sel vitriolique à base de terre argilleuse	(aluminium sulphate)

Not all Macquer's suggestions were apposite, however, and as a zealous supporter of the phlogiston theory he suggested the use of the term *sulphur* as 'a general name for all the compounds of acid and pure phlogiston'.[18]

In these beginnings of a systematic nomenclature Macquer was, in general, followed by Antoine Baumé. Baumé made use[19] of such expressions as *nitre à base terreuse* and *sel acéteux calcaire* and he also followed Macquer in the naming of ammonium salts. Baumé used the term *vitriol* to describe the sulphates of various metals and *sel marin* to describe their chlorides, Further systematic expressions are to be found in the publications of other French chemists in the same decade—men such as Jean-Baptiste Bucquet[20] and Antoine Brongniart.[21]

18. Ibid., p. 507.
19. *Chymie Expérimentale*, Paris, 1773, vol. i, pp. 287, 315; vol. ii, pp. 360ff., 384, 441, 489.
20. *Introduction à l'étude du règne minéral*, Paris, 1771, e.g., vol. i, pp. 416–40.
21. *Tableau analytique*, Paris, 1778, e.g. pp. 47–74.

The Reform of Nomenclature
in Botany

Before going on to consider the details of the systematic nomenclature proposed by Bergman and by Guyton, it may be worth while pausing to consider another reform of nomenclature in the eighteenth century, the reform of botanical terms. Not only were there certain similarities between the confusion in botany and that in chemistry before the reform of nomenclature in these respective sciences, but there is also evidence that the reform by Linnaeus in botany[22] greatly influenced the attitude of Bergman towards a reform of chemical terminology.

Early Botanical Nomenclature

Since the time of Theophrastus (*c.* 300 B.C.) the number of botanical terms had been steadily growing and by the seventeenth century all but the most persistent students of botany were likely to be overwhelmed by its terminology. The Swiss botanist Gaspard Bauhin in his *Pinax theatri botanici* (1623), did something to help stem the tide which was threatening to submerge the science of botany. After a great deal of research Bauhin assembled the names which had been used to describe particular plants and constructed a descriptive phrase for each plant. The use of these long descriptive phrases became generally accepted. One of these phrases used by the French botanist Tournefort, at the beginning of the eighteenth century was: *Gramen Xerampelinum, Miliacea, praetenui, ramosaque sparsa panicula, sive Xerampelino congener, arvense, aestivum, Gramen*

---

22. Linnaeus was, of course, also responsible for a systematic classification and nomenclature of the animal kingdom. It is generally agreed, however, that the Linnaean reform was more adapted to vegetables than animals and Linnaeus' zoological classification has had to be extensively revised. It is clear that Linnaeus' first concern was with plants and this chapter is concerned exclusively with botanical nomenclature.

minutissimo semine.[23] Linnaeus later described the state of affairs at the close of the seventeenth century by saying that internal strife was prevalent in the Commonwealth of Botany under the triumvirate of Ray, Tournefort and Rivinus. The latter two botanists differed so far as to give different names to each genus, but eventually the Frenchman's terminology became the most generally accepted.

Linnaeus' Reform

Such was the state of botany when Carl Linnaeus was born in 1707. When he was pursuing his botanical studies, Linnaeus found that there was a great confusion of terminology and he later complained that a botanist was not respected unless he published long lists of synonyms.[24] At the age of thirty, Linnaeus published his *Critica Botanica* in which he set out to establish the principles on which a satisfactory botanical nomenclature could be founded.[25] Linnaeus could not, of course, pretend to have any special authority. His only excuse for taking it upon himself to suggest a complete reform of botanical terms was that a start had to be made somewhere. Linnaeus had to establish some elementary principles which, although obvious to the modern reader, were by no means agreed upon in the early eighteenth century, e.g. that all plants of the same genus should have the same generic name. Linnaeus was uncompromising in proscribing all botanical names of sentimental association, like *Noli me tangere*, *Spina Christi* and *Pater noster*. He also ruthlessly expunged what he called 'barbaric' names; he expressed a preference for Latin names but he was also willing to include words of Greek origin, since the Greeks had largely contributed to founding the science of botany. Linnaeus did not wish to sever all links with the current terminology and said, for example, that he regarded it as a 'religious duty' to preserve in generic terms the names of famous botanists. He quoted as a precedent for this the terminologies of geography, medicine, pharmacy and chemistry.

23. J. Pitton de Tournefort, *Institutiones Rei Herbariae*, 2nd edn., Paris, 1700, vol. i, p. 522. Using his binomial nomenclature, Linnaeus described the plant simply as *Poa bulbosa* (*Systema Naturae*, 10th edn., Holmiae, 1758, 59, vol. ii, p. 874).

24. Linnaeus, *Critica Botanica*, Leyden, 1737 (trans. Sir A. Hort, Ray Society, London, 1938), para. 318.

25. Op. cit., see especially paragraphs 210, 211, 229, 239, 227.

Linnaeus, though convinced of the correctness of his own views, was aware that other botanists would only accept them slowly. Many botanists would continue to use the old names:

I do not demand that you who have assimilated these names with the mother's milk of your botanical studies should forgo them. But your grandsons shall be my judges and I can answer for it that they will abandon them.

The new nomenclature did meet with some hostility and to one critic Linnaeus wrote in the following terms:

. . . I know that you are hostile to all changes of names . . . [but] . . . Botanists seem to me never to have touched upon nomenclature as a subject of study, and therefore this path of their science remains still unexplored . . . there have been no laws laid down by which names could either be made or defended.[26]

Linnaeus' claim to universal fame depends not so much on his general attitude to nomenclature, and still less on his system of classification which was largely arbitrary, but almost entirely on the system of binomial nomenclature which he was the first to use to any extent.[27] In this system of nomenclature, the full name of a plant is made up of a generic name followed by a specific name. Thus Linnaeus described the garden pea as *Pisum sativum* and common beet as *Beta vulgaris*,[28] etc. The binomial nomenclature was used by Linnaeus in his *Species Plantarum* of 1753 and was fully set out in the tenth edition of the *Systema Naturae* (1758, 59). Botanists soon began to find that this system of nomenclature, and particularly the use of trivial specific names, was a great improvement. As Lamarck said,

the accomplishment of Linnaeus, which was of great value to nomenclature, was to add to the generic name of each species of plant, a trivial name which is simple and can easily be remembered. In this way one achieves the object of naming any plant without being obliged to recite for the purpose a long, cumbersome and ridiculous phrase.[29]

26. *Correspondence of Linnaeus and other naturalists*, ed. Sir J. E. Smith, London, 1821, vol. ii, pp. 256–8.
27. Bauhin had used a few such terms, e.g. *Brassica spinosa, Alsine aquatica, Brunella Italica*, etc. (*Phytopinax seu enumeratio plantarum*, Basle, 1596, pp. 178, 481, 504).
28. *Systema naturae*, 10th edn., Holmiae, 1758, 59, vol. ii, pp. 948, 1163.
29. *Encyclopédie Méthodique, Botanique*, vol. i, Paris, 1789, p. xxiv.

Linnaeus' Influence on Bergman

Linnaeus in his later years became an international figure, as can be judged by his correspondence and his election to membership of scientific societies in most of the countries of Europe. Yet it was on his fellow-countryman Bergman, who had come into personal contact with him, that Linnaeus exerted the most fruitful influence as regards chemical nomenclature. In what ways Bergman's proposed chemical nomenclature resembled the botanical nomenclature of Linnaeus will be seen in the following chapter. Meanwhile we may summarize ten points of resemblance or factors which make some influence seem probable:

(i) Bergman had been a student of Linnaeus. Before he established himself as a chemist, Bergman had attracted the attention of Linnaeus for his work in natural history.[30]

(ii) Linnaeus had demonstrated the possibility of constructing a scheme to reform the nomenclature of one of the sciences. The reform had been accepted[31] in his lifetime and the resulting advantages to the study of botany were obvious to all.

(iii) Linnaeus had classified plants according to their parts; this analytical method excluded considerations based on colour, medicinal properties or country of origin.

(iv) Nevertheless, particularly in the case of specific names, Linnaeus allowed 'trivial' names established by custom or expressing an appropriate characteristic.

(v) Linnaean nomenclature was essentially binomial.[32]

(vi) Linnaeus proposed that the name of the genus should be expressed by one word only.

(vii) Linnaeus insisted that the name of the genus should precede that of the species.

(viii) The Linnaean reform involved the abbreviation of the long descriptive phrases previously used in botany.

30. See especially Bergman's paper on the '*cocus aquaticus*' (*Königl. Schwed. Akad. der Wissenschaften, Abhandlungen, 18* (1756), 187–92) and later his classification of larvae (*Nova Acta Reg. Soc. Scient. Upsaliensis, 1* (1773), 58–65).

31. In France Buffon's influence delayed the acceptance of the Linnaean classification.

32. Linnaeus insisted that two words should be used to describe each plant. The words should not be of unreasonable length (*sesquipedalia*) and they should not be joined together (*Critica Botanica,* para. 249, 287).

(ix) Linnaeus approved of the principle that similar word endings should be used for similar substances. Bergman applied this principle by suggesting, for example, that the Latin names of all metals should end in *-um*.

(x) Linnaeus insisted that the nomenclature of botany should be expressed in Latin.

The relevance of each of these points will be shown in the following chapter.

Bergman's Chemical Nomenclature

Torbern Bergman (1735–84) took a wide interest in the sciences and there seems to have been hardly any branch of science which escaped his attention. As a young man he was brought into personal contact with Linnaeus by his own observations of the 'insect', *cocus aquaticus* (a leech's egg). Bergman was also interested in mathematics, astronomy, physics and geography and did successful work in each of these fields. The death of the mineralogist Wallerius enabled him to attain the position of professor of chemistry at Uppsala University, and when he was appointed to this post in 1767, despite his lack of qualifications in that subject, he soon amply justified his appointment both as a teacher and as an original investigator in chemistry.

Bergman's Nomenclature up to 1775

One of the first criticisms of chemical terminology published by Bergman was in 1772 when he agreed with the author of the *Essay for the Reformation of the London Pharmacopoeia* that the term *Calomel* (which suggests a black substance) was an unsuitable name for *mercurius sublimatus dulcis*. Three years later in a paper on mineral waters Bergman referred to the 'so-called Salt ash' (magnesium chloride) which he preferred to describe by the phrase *acidum salis saturated with magnesia*.[33]

Bergman probably formed some ideas on systematic chemical nomenclature in his early years as professor of chemistry at Uppsala. He was familiar with Macquer's *Dictionnaire de Chimie* (with its suggestions for the general use of the terms *vitriol, sel, nitre*, etc.) and he sometimes quoted from it.[34] It was not until about 1775, however, that Bergman made any extensive use of

33. *Königl. Schwed. Akad. der Wissenschaften, Abhandlungen, 34* (1772), 192; *37* (1775), 19.
34. *Abhandlungen, 32* (1770), 87 and *34* (1772), 197.

systematic nomenclature. Bergman had coined the term *acidum aereum* in 1773 to denote the gas previously known as 'fixed air'[35] and it was not long before he was using the term *aeratum* to describe the salts of this acid. In his paper *On the Aerial Acid* he said that, just as the alkali of tartar saturated with vitriolic acid was called *alkali vitriolatum*,

> In the same way I shall, for the sake of brevity, call *aerata* those substances which are saturated with the acid which is always present in the ordinary air.[36]

He then applied the expression very widely to denote the salts formed by the *acidum aereum* with alkalis, earths and metals, e.g.:

alkali vegetabile aeratum	*magnesia aerata*
alkali minerale aeratum	*argilla aerata*
alkali volatile aeratum	*ferrum aeratum*
terra ponderosa aerata	*zincum aeratum*
calx aerata	*magnesium aeratum*

In his paper *On Elective Attractions* (1775) Bergman had a further occasion to use systematic nomenclature, and among the terms he used were:[37]

tartarus vitriolatus	*calx nitrata*
magnesia vitriolata	*argentum nitratum*
cuprum salitum	

Unfortunately, however, these expressions were not representative of the whole, for Bergman also referred to 'Glauber's salt', 'secret sal ammoniac', etc. Bergman made use of different word-endings to distinguish between what he called *magnesia* (our magnesium oxide) and *magnesium*[38] (our manganese). This distinction could hardly be used except in Latin and, in any case, was too slight to be acceptable to his contemporaries, especially as the word *manganèse* already existed in French. A further example of the extent to which Bergman had systematized the nomenclature he used with his students is provided in a dissertation on 'magnesia alba' published in December 1775.[39] Whereas the

35. *Kungliga Svenska Vetenskaps Akademiens Handlingar, 34* II (1773), 181.
36. *Nova Acta Reg. Soc. Scient. Upsaliensis, 2* (1775), 118.
37. Ibid., pp. 175–205.
38. '*Ita voco ne cum magnesia confundatur*' (ibid., p. 246; see also pp. 135, 225).
39. *Dissertatio Chemica de Magnesia Alba*, Praeses Prof. T. Bergman, sistit C. Norell, Dec. 1775.

paper on the 'aerial acid' had included a full range of compounds of one acid with various bases, this dissertation shows us that Bergman had also developed a nomenclature to describe the compounds of a base with most of the acids then known. A dozen different magnesium salts were included, in which the name *magnesia* was followed by the name of the acid used adjectivally: *aerata, vitriolata, nitrata, salita, fluorata, arsenicata, boraxata, saccharata, tartarisata, acetata, formicata* and *phosphorata*.

From the above, it is clear that by the end of 1775 Bergman used, at least implicitly, a comprehensive systematic nomenclature. In the remaining nine years of his life he built on this foundation, latterly with the encouragement of Guyton de Morveau.

The Development of Bergman's Nomenclature

Bergman set down some reflections on chemical nomenclature in an introductory essay to his collected works. In this essay entitled *On the Investigation of Truth* Bergman outlined what he considered to be the main aspects of experimental method. He concluded by saying,

Finally, I aim at giving denominations to things, as agreeable with the truth as possible.

I am not ignorant that words, like money, possess an ideal value, and that great danger of confusion may be apprehended from a change of names; in the meantime it cannot be denied that chemistry, like the other sciences, was formerly filled with improper names. In different branches of knowledge we see those matters long since reformed; why then should chemistry, which examines the real nature of things, still adopt vague names, which suggest false ideas, and savour strongly of ignorance and imposition? Besides, there is no doubt that many corrections may be made without any inconvenience; if instead of oil of vitriol and spirit of vitriol, we used the terms *concentrated vitriolic acid* and *diluted vitriolic acid*, I think that no-one would be thereby either confounded or misled.[40]

This rather conservative apology for reform was followed by the use of reformed terms more extensive and consistent than in 1775. What we now call the sulphates, nitrates and chlorides of metals, earths and alkalis were named by adding *vitriolatum*,

40. *Opuscula Physica et Chemica*, vol. i, Uppsala, 1779, p. xiv, trans. Cullen, London, 1784, pp. xxxvii–xxxviii.

nitratum, salitum respectively to the name of the base. In cases where another name for a substance was established by tradition, Bergman mentioned this name as well to make his nomenclature more readily understood, e.g.:

calx salita	vulgo	*sal ammoniacus fixus*
argilla vitriolata	vulgo	*alumen*
magnesia aerata	vulgo	*magnesia alba*
alkali vegetabile vitriolatum	vulgo	*tartarus vitriolatus*
alkali minerale vitriolatum	vulgo	*Sal mirabile Glauberi*[41]

In 1782 Bergman published his *Sciagraphia Regni Mineralis* in which he classified minerals into salts, earths, metals and inflammable bodies. In this work, Bergman enumerated twelve acids: *acidum vitrioli, acidum vitrioli phlogisticatum,*[42] *acidum nitrosum, acidum muriaticum* and the acids *fluoris mineralis, arsenici, molybdaenum, phosphori, boracis, succini, aereum* as well as the supposed *acidum calci ponderosae.* The three alkalis were described as before as well as their compounds with the most important mineral acids. The five 'simple earths' were called: *terra ponderosa, calx, magnesia, argilla* and *terra silicea.*

Although in the past Bergman had sometimes referred to our hydrochloric acid variously as *acidum muriaticum, acidum marinum* and *acidum salis,* he had now decided to use the first term,[43] with the inconsistency of applying the adjective *salitum* to its salts. Despite the fact that he now decribed simple metal salts consistently by expressions of the type *ferrum vitriolatum,* this rule was not always adhered to in the descriptive phrases he used to describe mixtures and compounds of three constituents, e.g. *Vitriolum Ferri niccolino contaminatum* and if a mineral contained half a dozen constituents, Bergman's descriptive phrase was necessarily a long one.[44] As he had set himself the task of describing naturally occuring minerals rather than pure chemicals, Bergman was at a disadvantage compared with Guyton de Morveau who was only concerned at that time with comparatively simple substances. In the latter half of the *Sciagraphia* Bergman often refers to Cronstedt's names, sometimes by way of

41. *Opuscula*, vol. i, pp. 29, 100, 133, 135.
42. i.e. sulphurous acid.
43. Linnaeus used the term *muria* (= sodium chloride) in his *Systema Naturae*, 1st edn., Leyden, 1735.
44. e.g. *terra silicea magnesiae, calci aeratae et fluoratae, nec non cupro ferroque calcinatis adunata* (op. cit., pp. 56, 89).

contrast or else to show that he had adopted the same terminology. Both Swedes, for instance, described the naturally occurring sulphides of lead, copper, mercury and antimony by the name of the metal followed by the expression *sulphure mineralisatum* ('mineralized by sulphur'). Bergman, however, also referred to sulphides more systematically, as when he reported the existence of two kinds of *stannum sulphuratum*.[45]

Bergman's Scheme of 1784

The revised version of Bergman's system of mineralogy appeared in 1784[46] under the title *Meditationes de Systemate Fossilium Naturali*.[47] Bergman gave special consideration to the subject of nomenclature in a section entitled *De Fossilibus Denominandis*, where he pointed out that nomenclature was as important as classification in the study of minerals. He remarked that the secretive attitude of the early chemists and their lack of knowledge of the substances they dealt with had been reflected in chemical terminology. More recently a few more rational names had been given but even these were not based on general principles of nomenclature. He pointed out that, although the nations of Europe had given much care and attention to their individual languages, the sciences might well become notorious for the barbarity and incongruity of their languages in which new names were added on an *ad hoc* basis without reference to any general plan. Botany, however, had already been reformed; why could this not happen equally well in other sciences?

The greatest difficulty in the way of a systematic nomenclature would be the contradictory opinions of individuals. But if absolute agreement were impossible, perhaps the majority of chemists would be able to agree on a system. Bergman then indicated his approval for the scheme which Guyton de Morveau had proposed in 1782.[48] Bergman set an example of cooperation by agreeing to use Guyton's term *acidum mephiticum* in preference to his own *acidum aereum* for fixed air—'or else there will be no end to the various changes'. Having rejected absurd

45. Op. cit., Preface. In his *Opuscula*, vol. ii, Uppsala, 1780, p. 11 he had referred to '*galena seu plumbum sulphuratum*'.
46. The year of Bergman's death at the age of 49.
47. *Nova Acta. Reg. Soc. Scient. Upsaliensis*, 4 (1784), 63–128.
48. See p. 156.

and useless names like *sal polychrestum* and *arcanum duplicatum* as well as misleading names like 'butter of antimony' and 'foliated earth of tartar' he discussed the principles on which a nomenclature should be based.

In the first place, names should neither have too wide a meaning,[49] nor, if there was any choice, should their sense be too limited. Realizing that these principles were rather difficult to apply in practice, Bergman concluded,

we should adopt such names as, having no determinate meaning, may have their sense fixed by definition.

Guyton de Morveau had proposed that the names of people should be banned from any part of chemical nomenclature, but Bergman did not agree with him. He referred to the use of such names in botany and anatomy, and he said he was prepared to use personal names in chemistry in cases where a systematic name was not readily available.[50]

Bergman then went on to describe the details of his proposed nomenclature. Each class of minerals should, if possible, be denoted by one single word, e.g. Salts, Earths, Metals and *Phlogista* (i.e. inflammable bodies). Acids were considered as salts, but Bergman pointed out that it was unneccessary to use the word 'salt' in the name. For the earths he suggested the terms *Calx, Magnesia, Argilla, Silex* and *Barytes*. The latter term was based on Guyton's suggestion of *barote*, but Bergman adopted it, not for Guyton's reasons but because he wanted one word to express the earth. Bergman then proposed that the (Latin) names of all metals should have a common ending in *-um* and he only had to alter the Spanish term *platina* to *platinum* to achieve complete uniformity.[51] This principle has been important in the naming of elements up to the present day.

He then considered the nomenclature of 'salts'—a term which included alkalis, acids and neutral salts. He suggested that it would be a great advantage if acids and alkalis could be denoted by one word. The acids could therefore be called *Vitriolicum, Nitrosum, Muriaticum, Regalinum,*[52] *Fluoratum, Arseni-*

49. The term *acidum aereum*, for example, was open to this objection.

50. e.g. in the case of 'triple salts'; thus he proposed to call sodium potassium tartrate *tartareum Seignetti*.

51. The alkaline earths excepted, since their metals were only isolated in the following century.

52. Guyton also thought that *aqua regia* could form its own salts and he introduced the term *régalte* to denote them.

cale, Boracinum, Saccharinum, Oxalinum. Tartareum, Benzoinum, Citrinum, Succineum, Galacticum, Formicale, Sebaceum, Phosphoreum and *Aereum.*[53] What was then called 'phlogisticated vitriolic acid' (i.e. sulphurous acid) could be called *Sulphureum* and 'phlogisticated nitrous acid' (i.e. nitrous acid) could be called *Nitreum.* Similarly the alkalis could be denoted by the single word *potassium, natrum* and *ammoniacum* respectively.[54] The advantage of this system would be that most neutral salts could then logically be expressed by two, or at the most, three words. In this aim he was influenced both by Guyton and also by Linnaeus. The influence of Linnaeus becomes even clearer when Bergman discussed the order in which to write the two parts of the name of a neutral salt.[55] Earlier in his paper Bergman had debated the question of whether compound salts were to be classed as acidic derivatives of metals, earths and alkalis or vice versa. In the cases of salts derived from metals and earths he had now reached the conclusion that 'whatever imparts the saline nature ought to determine the genus'. In the case of salts derived from alkalis, he considered that the base governed the genus, but to introduce uniformity, he denoted all compound salts by combining the name of the acid with an adjective derived from the base, e.g. *vitriolicum potassinatum, Muriaticum ammoniacum, Nitrosum baryticum, Nitrosum argentatum,* etc. Bergman rather spoiled the consistency of his scheme in the case of what he termed 'saline earths with such an excess of earthy matter as nearly to obliterate their saline character', where he preferred to write: *Barytes vitriolatus, Calcareum aeratum,* etc.[56]

Salts in which either constituent might be in excess could also be expressed by two words, e.g. tartar with an excess of acid could be called *tartareum potassini* as opposed to the neutral salt which was *tartareum potassinatum.* What in modern terms is sodium bisulphate Bergman called *vitriolicum natri* as distinct from

53. Note that since 1782 the number of acids considered had increased from 12 to 18.

54. i.e. he accepted Guyton's terms for the alkalis with the exception of *soude* (soda).

55. The next few lines may seem strange to the modern reader unless seen as an aspect of a wider eighteenth-century problem in natural history (cf. Linnaeus).

56. Guyton also made an exception in the case of his *méphites* (i.e. carbonates).

vitriolicum natratum which was the modern sodium sulphate. So convinced was Bergman of the superiority of a binomial nomenclature that he was prepared to subjugate his systematic principles to it.[57] He pointed out that, following the example of Linnaeus, not only botany but zoology and mineralogy had made good use of trivial names in their respective nomenclatures:

> But, although these names may be assumed from the inventor, some virtue, ancient appellation, property or accidental circumstance respecting the species, yet they should generally be limited to one word, and very seldom indeed extended to two. They may be considered as surnames (*cognomina*), distinguishing the individuals contained in the same genus.

He was prepared to use such 'trivial' names in chemistry to denote salts of three or more constituents, because he was determined to shun descriptive phrases in nomenclature.[58] Looking to the future, however, he did see the difficulty of inventing new simple names for complex compounds and of remembering such non-systematic names.

Bergman concluded his important paper (and, incidentally, his life's work on chemical nomenclature) with a plea for the use of Latin as a common language on which to base the international reform of chemical nomenclature:

> I would wish that, in the establishing of new names, a preference should be given to the Latin language. This is, or at least was formerly, the mother tongue of the learned; and as it is not now the living language of any nation, it is no longer liable to innovation or change. If, therefore, the reform we propose is made first in Latin it may easily be carried into execution afterwards upon the same model in the modern languages, as far as their peculiar genius and construction will admit. In this manner the language of chemistry (*lingua Chemica*) will become everywhere uniform and consistent, and considerable advantage will be derived, not only from the reading of foreign publications, but also the facility with which they can be translated.

Bergman said that he was glad to see the agreement between his own ideas on nomenclature and those of Guyton, and he hoped

---

57. Another example is his preference for the incomplete name *Muriaticum dulce* for '*Mercurius dulcis*' rather than the unambiguous phrase: *Muriaticum hydrargyratum dulce*.

58. '*Nomina certa plurium vocabulorum definitionibus sunt longe deteriora*' (op. cit., p. 123).

that the remaining differences could be removed for the greater benefit of science.

With Bergman's untimely death in July 1784 no more collaboration between the two great founders of systematic chemical nomenclature was possible. Instead, Guyton was destined to collaborate with Lavoisier, whose fame as the exponent of the antiphlogistic theory was growing. But first we must examine Guyton's early ideas on nomenclature.

The Chemical Nomenclature proposed by Guyton de Morveau

Guyton's Early Dissatisfaction with Nomenclature

When at the age of thirty-six the Dijon chemist Louis Bernard Guyton de Morveau[59] pointed out the impropriety of the term *oil of vitriol* in the course of an article he contributed to *Rozier's Journal*,[60] he was merely repeating a criticism which had been made for over a century and there was little reason to prophesy that he would become one of the leaders of the reform of chemical nomenclature. Four years later, in his *Élémens de Chymie* (prepared in collaboration with other members of the Dijon Academy), Guyton suggested that chemists should refrain from giving the names of 'semi-metals' to their ores; the name *antimony*, for example, should be used to describe the semi-metal itself and not its naturally occurring compound with sulphur.[61] Although he rightly pointed out that 'this would make language simpler and would prevent many equivocal expressions', he was again not expressing an original opinion. Another incursion by Guyton into the field of chemical terminology was made in an article in one of the supplementary volumes of Diderot's *Encyclopédie*. In the article *Hépar*[62] we see the emergence of two

59. He varied his name in successive stages of his career: in the following pages he is referred to simply as Guyton. An account of the introduction of the new nomenclature with particular reference to the work of Guyton de Morveau has been published by W. A. Smeaton, *Annals of Science*, *10* (1954), 87–106.

60. *Observations sur la Physique*, *1* (1773), 440.

61. *Élémens de Chymie*, vol. i, Dijon, 1777, pp. 122–3n. He was, however, still forced to speak of *regulus of manganese* to distinguish clearly the metal from the mineral (ibid., vol. ii, 1777, p. xi). In his translation of Bergman's works in 1780 Guyton did not neglect the opportunity of suggesting that the term *manganese* should be given to what was currently called the *regulus*, since chemistry was already 'too much burdened with useless words' (*Opuscules*, vol. i, Dijon, 1780, p. 41n.).

62. Diderot and D'Alembert, *Encyclopédie, Supplément*, Amsterdam, 1777, vol. iii, p. 347.

principles which Guyton was to make more explicit in his important *Mémoire sur les Dénominations Chimiques* of 1782, viz. that chemical terms should be expressions without any meaning in the ordinary language so that confusion might be prevented and also that classical languages were a convenient source for such unequivocal terms. He condemned the expressions *liver of sulphur* and *liver of antimony* as 'absolutely improper', and by substituting the Latin word *hepar* he hoped to avoid any accidental associations connected with 'liver'. He considered that he had not the authority to change chemical terms and therefore compromised by suggesting that,

we should at least prefer a name which is further removed from common use, because it is much better if the technical terms of a science express nothing which is known and recall no idea than indicate false resemblances which lead beginners astray and always astonish the most educated people.

The Influence of Bergman on Guyton

Having shown some interest in chemical terminology, Guyton came under the influence of the Swedish chemist Bergman, whose reputation was then spreading in scientific circles throughout Europe. Bergman had not only stated his ideas on the theory of chemical nomenclature, but had actually put such a system into use, including the important nomenclature of salts. By undertaking the French translation of Bergman's *Opuscula*, Guyton associated himself with the first exponent of a systematic nomenclature. It may be recalled that in 1779 Bergman had advocated a binomial system of naming salts in which the first word indicated the name of the 'base' (i.e. the alkali, earth or metal) and the second was an adjective derived from the name of the acid. Guyton remarked:

This system of nomenclature is obviously the best and we should not hesitate to adopt it as much as possible for new salts.[63]

Referring to *argilla vitriolata, alkali minerale vitriolatum,* etc. (which he translated as *vitriol d'argille* and *vitriol de soude*), he claimed that such names 'indicate equally clearly the solvent and the base [respectively]'. Guyton preferred the term *vitriol de magnésie* to *magnésie vitriolée,* which would have been a more

63. *Opuscules,* vol. i, Dijon, 1780, p. 404n.

literal rendering of Bergman's *magnesia vitriolata*. Guyton, however, despite his claim to faithful translation,[64] was not consistent in his translation of Bergman's nomenclature and we
find such terms as *nitre lunaire* and *sucre de saturne* given for
Bergman's *argentum nitratum* and *plumbum acetatum*, respectively.
To describe what we now call chlorides Guyton often resorted
to the expedient of using descriptive phrases, although two
years later he established himself as a stern critic of such a
practice.[65] Thus *terra ponderosa salita* of Bergman was translated
as *le sel marin à base de terre pesante* and *alkali vegetabile salitum*
became *alkali végétal uni à l'acide marin*.[66]

Guyton's criticisms of current chemical expressions and his
suggestions for new terms were not to remain unchallenged for
long. In 1781 he criticized the vague use of the phrase *terre
absorbante*[67] and this immediately brought a strong letter of
protest from the crystallographer Romé de l'Isle. The latter
insisted[68] that *terre absorbante* had been given a perfectly precise
meaning in the works of certain authors.[69] Having insinuated
that Guyton's ideas really came from Bergman, Romé de l'Isle
remarked,

Before trying to exclude terms which are accepted or trying to
introduce new expressions, it seems to me essential to see if his own
terms are not at all improper, equivocal, or even false, such as the
expressions *air fixe*, *alkali phlogistiqué*, *nitre fixe*, *fer sucré*, *chaux aérée*,
etc.[70]

Guyton replied in a long letter[71] that expressions like *chaux aérée*
had the advantage of being part of a general scheme of nomen-

64. '*Je ne crois pas avoir le droit de le* [i.e. Bergman] *faire parler en notre langue
autrement qu'il ne l'auroit fait lui-même*' (ibid., p. 4). See, however, the conservative terminology on e.g. pp. 112, 116.
65. *Obs. sur la Physique, 19* (1782), 373. Even in vol. ii of the *Opuscules*,
published in 1785, Guyton translated *alkali fixum aeratum* as *l'alkali fixe
saturé d'acide méphitique* (loc. cit., p. 163).
66. *Opuscules*, vol. i, pp. 110, 149, 189.
67. *Obs. sur la physique, 17* (1781), 216–31. We cannot, however, accept
this as an original criticism. Joseph Black in 1756 had complained that
several substances were commonly confounded under the one name of
'absorbent earth' (*Experiments on Magnesia Alba*, A.C.R. No. 1, p. 7).
68. *Obs. sur la Physique, 17* (1781), 353–8.
69. e.g. Sage and Demeste.
70. Used by Guyton in his translation (*Opuscules*, vol. i, Dijon, 1780,
pp. 41ff, 107, 288, 26).
71. *Obs. sur la Physique, 18* (1781), 69ff.

clature but, in any case, he adopted this expression only in his capacity as a translator. He went on to defend the term *terre calcaire* and complained

> No one, it seems to me, understands clearly what I intend to express by these terms. They have the advantage of expressing the abstract objects of my thought without demanding definitions and without changing a single term from the commonly accepted meaning.

Guyton's Memoir of 1782

In the next few months Guyton continued to think about a systematic chemical nomenclature and he may even have discussed the subject with Durande, his colleague at the Dijon Academy.[72] In May 1782 Guyton published a paper of fundamental importance in the *Observations sur la Physique*: '*Mémoire sur les dénominations chimiques, la necessité d'en perfectionner le système et les règles pour y parvenir.*' He said that by publishing his ideas on the reform of chemical terms and inviting the criticism of men of science, he hoped to achieve the two-fold object of forestalling criticism of his boldness and, secondly, of increasing the chances of success of a final scheme of reformed nomenclature. From the outset Guyton did not pretend to be able to change chemical terms by his own authority alone.

Having disarmed the critics by the expression of such modest sentiments, he carefully selected some of the worst examples of absurd and misleading chemical terms in order to show the necessity of a reform. He then set out at length the principles on which he intended to base his reformed chemical language and he made detailed suggestions for what amounts to an extension of Bergman's nomenclature to the French language together with a few necessary new expressions.

Guyton remarked that the state of perfection of the language of a science reflected the state of perfection of the science itself. To keep misleading terms in chemistry prevented the ready communication of the results of chemical research. Chemistry in particular needed a clear language because it had to deal

---

72. The opening words of Guyton's paper of 1782 (*Obs. sur la Physique, 19*, 370–82): '*Je sais qu'il n'y a que la convention qui puisse fixer la valeur des termes...*' might well have been a reply to an assertion by Durande the previous year: '*C'est par la convention seule que les mots prennent une signification...*' (*Notions Élémentaires de Botanique*, Dijon, 1781, p. 14).

with particular substances in a number of different states (i.e. as a simple substance and combined in numerous compounds). Guyton made use of the authority of Bergman's name when he observed that the most celebrated chemists had deplored the confusion and obscurity in chemical terms and he implied that Bergman had given way to those who asserted that only confusion could result from changing chemical names. The main reason why a systematic nomenclature had become necessary was the burden of remembering the individual names of the increasing number of substances known to chemists—very many more than had been known twenty years previously:

> No doubt it was still possible to remember the improper names of some thirty salts and to retain them in the memory by re-reading them and hearing them; but to-day chemistry is familiar with eighteen acids . . . it has newly discovered two earths and several semi-metals; if we are to examine with care the action of so many substances on each other . . . it becomes essential to adopt a system of nomenclature to indicate the result without confusion.

Guyton insisted that it was not enough to agree on names for newly discovered substances. If old names continued to be used at all, their use would cancel out the advantages of any rational system. In the absence of any accepted criteria of nomenclature, these old names had been based on accidental properties such as colour or consistency, and when substances were named according to their method of preparation, the same substance was often given several different names.

Having exhibited the worst features of the old terminology, Guyton laid down five principles on which a new chemical language might be based:

(1) A phrase cannot be regarded as a name; chemical entities and their products must have their own names, which refer to them all the time, without any necessity of having recourse to circumlocutions.

As an example, he cited 'the alkaline liquor saturated with the colouring matter of Prussian blue', which was a definition rather than a name. If such names as *sel marin à base de terre pesante*[73] had not been changed, it was because of the difficulty of abbreviating them to a satisfactory expression which would need no explana-

73. An expression he himself had used in translating Bergman (*Opuscules*, vol. i, p. 139).

tion. But in the kind of system he was proposing any term would be self explanatory.

(2) Denominations should be as much as possible in conformity with the nature of things.

This generalization was a quotation from Bergman[74] and Guyton presumably used it to give more authority to his suggestion. As an example of the application of this principle he took the term *acide vitriolique*; given this term, it was reasonable to use the word *vitriol* to describe the combination of this acid with other substances, e.g. with lead it would form *vitriol de plomb* or *plomb vitriolé*.

Guyton stated three corollaries to this principle:

(i) that a simple substance should preferably be given a simple name. He repeated what he had said previously about the meaning of the term 'antimony'.

(ii) that the denomination of a chemical compound is only clear and exact in so far as it recalls its constituent parts by names in conformity with their nature.

If a separate name were given to each compound, this would give rise to a host of useless and cumbersome words.

(iii) the names of discoverers of substances should be excluded from a general nomenclature. He had found that students very easily forgot what substance was denoted by a particular name if names like *Glauber's salt* and *Seignette's salt* were used.

(3) When certain knowledge is lacking of the character which should principally determine the denomination, a name which expresses nothing should be preferred to a name which could express a false idea.

Guyton again referred to the authority of Bergman who preferred the expression 'pure air'[75] to 'dephlogisticated air' 'until the facts, which seem to announce the presence of phlogiston, have been fully clarified'. Guyton showed his sincerity by preferring the term *alkali prussien* to *alkali phlogistiqué*, even though he still accepted the phlogiston theory in general.

(4) In the choice of denominations to be introduced, those which have their roots in the most generally known dead languages are

74. Ibid., p. xxviii.
75. 'aer bonus', 'aer purus' (*Opuscula*, vol. ii, Uppsala, 1780, p. 366).

to be preferred, so that the word can easily be found again from the sense and the sense from the word.

Although the earth of heavy spar was known as *terra pesante*, this name was not fully acceptable because it could not easily be modified to form an adjective to denote its derivatives.[76] Another objection was that it had not been proved that the earth extracted from 'heavy spar' was actually heavier than any other earth.[77] To overcome these difficulties, Guyton suggested the term *barote* (from Gr. βάρος =heavy), which would form the adjective *barotique* to denote its salts.[78]

(5) Names should be chosen with due regard to the genius of the language for which they were formed. . . . This rule is not the least important.

Thus to denote the substances extracted from suet, ants and sorrel he preferred to use a root based on a synonym or a classical word and speak of *sebacé, formicin, oxalin* respectively, instead of '*suifacé*', '*fourmieux*' and '*oseillique*', which not only offended the ear but were less capable of forming nouns. Guyton concluded:

Such are the principles which seemed to me to establish at the same time both the necessity of changing a great number of chemical denominations and the system to be followed in the choice of those which should replace them.

Having set out the principles of his proposed reform, Guyton ended his paper by considering the nomenclature of the earths, alkalis, acids and, perhaps the most important of all, the salts. He first listed the names of the five earths and the adjectives derived from them, coining new terms where necessary. The terms he suggested were *quartz*[79] (*quarteux*), *alumine* (*alumineux*), *calce* (*calcaire*), *magnésie*[80] (*magnésien*) and *barote* (*barotique*). Turn-

---

76. A similar objection was made by Fourcroy in 1779 to Bergman's *acidum aereum* (*Mémoires de Chimie*, Paris, 1784, p. 122).

77. In the early nineteenth century when the metal barium was isolated, its density was found to be only one third of that of lead.

78. Kirwan modified *barote* to *barytes* (*Elements of Mineralogy*, London. 1784, p. 5) and in this form it was accepted by Bergman (*Nova Acta, 4,* 121).

79. The term *quartz* was adopted into the English language by E. M. da Costa in Cronstedt's *System of Mineralogy*, London, 1770, p. 57n. Posterity, however, chose the term *silica* (from the Latin *silex*) in chemistry, as favoured by Bergman.

80. Thus establishing *magnesia* and *magnesium* with their present meanings as opposed to the meanings given to these terms by Bergman.

ing to the alkalis, he remarked that nothing was more un-
bearable than being obliged to repeat continually *alkali fixe
végétal, alkali fixe minéral,* etc. Having rejected the use of the
term 'tartar' as one alternative, he proposed the use of the
terms *potasse, soude* and *ammoniac* for the three common alkalis.
This was one of the suggestions to which his critics took most
exception, not so much because of any objection to the terms
themselves which were by no means new,[81] but because they
had previously been used to denote impure commercial alkalis.
Coming to the natural sulphur-containing minerals, Guyton
had no better suggestion to make than that they should keep
the name *pyrites* and any other mineralogical names they already had.

Turning to the acids and the salts derived from them, his
remark that there was little to be done to rectify the nomenclature of *vitriols* and *nitres* was really a compliment to Macquer
who had suggested the systematic use of these terms. The situation was very different, however, in the case of the salts of *acide
marin* (i.e. chlorides):

> We have no name to indicate the genus. Some chemists have kept
> false or equivocal names like corrosive sublimate, horn silver, butter
> of antimony, etc. We were obliged to define the others each time we
> wished to name them. To re-establish the analogy I take, according
> to the fourth principle, the noun *muriate* and the adjective *muriatique*
> from the word *muria* used by those chemists who have written in Latin.

He then detailed his suggestions for the names of the other acids
and their salts, which were as follows:

acide méphitique	*méphites*
régalin	*régalte*
arsenical	*arseniate*
boracin	*borax*
fluorique	*fluor*
acéteux	*acète*
tartareux	*tartre*
oxalin	*oxalte*
saccharin	*saccharte*
citronien	*citrate*
lignique	*lignite*

81. e.g. Baumé used the terms *potasse* and *alkali de la soude* (*Chymie Expérimentale,* Paris, 1773, vol. ii, p. 219; vol. i, p. 210).

acide phosphorique	*phosphate*
formicin	*formiate*
sébacée	*sébate*
galactique	*galacte*

Although Guyton made some attempt to use similar terminations for the names of salts (especially in the case of names suggested by himself), his very slight success in this respect may be judged from the above list. Bergman on the other hand, writing in Latin, had made use of the uniform ending *-atum* as early as 1775 to denote the acid part of salts. Guyton was at a disadvantage in so far as he was trying to incorporate new words into a living language and he had to respect the conventions and phonetic prejudices of the language. Thus his term *méphite*, derived from *acide méphitique* (mephitic acid)[82] was no innovation, but it was more likely to be accepted by other French chemists than a term such as '*méphate*', although the latter would have been more in conformity with many of the other terms. When naming salts, Guyton placed the acid radical first and the base second; in certain cases the name of the base might form an adjective, e.g. *vitriol de fer, phosphate de plomb*, and *nitre alumineux, muriate calcaire, fluor ammoniacal*. His idea of the relative unimportance of 'mephitic acid',[83] however, led to the inconsistency of the expression *cuivre méphitisé*, instead of *méphite de cuivre*.

Altogether Guyton had considered some 18 acids and 24 'bases' (i.e. earths, alkalis and metals) and, by combining their names systematically, he was able to produce a nomenclature for nearly 500 simple salts. He concluded his paper by drawing up a table giving examples of his nomenclature.[84]

The Reception of Guyton's 'Memoir' by his Contemporaries

One of the first persons to support Guyton's ideas of reform was Macquer. In 1782, when Guyton published his *Mémoire sur*

82. Guyton considered the expression *acide méphitique* (i.e. carbonic acid) was a better name than Bergman's *acidum aereum*. Bergman had called the salts of this acid *aerata*, but for Guyton the adjective 'aerial' (*aérée, aeratum*) was of too wide application.

83. 'A subtle fluid which sometimes is only present in a small quantity' (*Encyclopédie Méthodique, Chimie*, vol. i, Paris, 1786, p. 142).

84. This table of nomenclature has been reproduced in *Annals of Science, 8* (1952), 38 and *10* (1954), 95.

les dénominations chimiques, he was a middle-aged provincial chemist who had yet to make his mark in French chemistry; whereas Macquer (two years before his death) was an honoured member of the *Académie Royale des Sciences* in Paris, the author of a chemical dictionary of European repute and a stern critic of the worst abuses of the old chemical terminology. Macquer had nominated Guyton to be his correspondent for the *Académie* and Guyton naturally sent him a copy of his table of chemical nomenclature, considering that Macquer's opinion would have some authority. Macquer wrote encouragingly to Guyton in July of that year:

> Your new nomenclature is excellent, and, for myself, I am ready to adopt it; but I cannot answer for everyone, because you know how much men—even the enlightened—are creatures of habit. It will only be with time that they will become familiar with names, most of which will seem at first very strange and barbaric.[85]

In the following year the great Buffon paid Guyton the compliment of including his table of chemical nomenclature in his encyclopaedic *Natural History*.[86] Guyton and Buffon were both members of the Dijon Academy and their acquaintance had earlier led Buffon to ask for Guyton's advice on chemical matters.[87] Buffon had a rather strange conception of chemistry and he also condemned those who made up new technical words unnecessarily,[88] but this did not prevent him from introducing into his work the table which his friend had just published. Further support came from Jean-André Mongez who translated Bergman's *Sciagraphia* into French. In his translation Mongez took every opportunity of advertising Guyton's nomenclature by mentioning in parentheses the latter's name for particular substances after the usual name.[89]

85. Reported by Guyton, *Encyclopédie Méthodique, Chimie*, vol. i, p. vi.
86. Le Clerc, Count de Buffon, *Histoire Naturelle des Minéraux*, vol. ii, Paris, 1783, pp. 160–2.
87. *Correspondence Inédite de Buffon*, ed. H. N. de Buffon, vol. i, Paris, 1860, pp. 146, 419–20.
88. *Histoire Naturelle des Minéraux*, vol. ii, p. 113. Buffon supported the term 'fixed air' and said (possibly influenced by his opposition to the botanical nomenclature of Linnaeus), 'Nothing has retarded the progress of the science more than the making of new words'; see also ibid., vol. i, pp. 74–5. Such remarks later enabled the reactionary de la Métherie to cite Buffon as a critic of the new nomenclature (*Obs. sur la Physique, 31* (1787), 274).
89. *Manuel du Minéralogiste* . . . traduit et augmenté de notes par M. Mongez le jeune, Paris, 1784, e.g. pp. 59, 64.

Further Proposals by Guyton

Meanwhile Guyton himself did what he could to propagate his nomenclature by using it in his own published works, particularly in the *Observations sur la Physique*, which was the only regularly-appearing French scientific journal and of which the editor at that time was Mongez. In particular Guyton was responsible for the nomenclature used in the translation of Scheele's works, which appeared in extracts in the *Observations* in the years 1782–3. Although Guyton himself did not undertake the translations, he edited them and added a series of footnotes to the text when they were published in book form in 1785. In the *Observations sur la Physique* for the years 1782–5 there are numerous examples of the use of Guyton's nomenclature, including the naming of two new acids by Guyton— succinic acid and prussic acid.[90] Guyton had already given the name *barote* to one mineral and he now gave his approval to the use of the term *tungstène* (Swedish: *tung sten* = heavy stone) to another heavy mineral. He thought that the adoption of a modified form of the Swedish term would have the double advantage that it would be readily accepted by the Swedes who had discovered it, and it would prevent confusion with the other heavy earth, *barote*.[91] In Britain Kirwan, in whose opinion Guyton ranked highly, accepted both terms in his text book of mineralogy of 1784, making the English names *barytes* and *tungsten*.[92] In Germany Crell pointed out that the literal translation into German of the word *tungsten* had already led to confusion with heavy spar and, following the example of Guyton and Kirwan, he recommended the use of the word *Tungstein* in German.[93]

The Relationship between Guyton and Bergman

The year 1784 brings us to the death of Bergman and this may

90. *Obs. sur la Physique*, *20* (1782), 345; *22* (1783), 126, 127, 267; *26* (1785), 463; *27* (1785), 65; *Mémoires de Chimie de Scheele*, Dijon, 1785, Part 2, p. 196n.

91. *Obs. sur la Physique*, *22* (1783), 124n.

92. Op. cit., pp. 5, 37. Romé de l'Isle (*Cristallographie*, 2nd edn., Paris, 1783, vol. iii, p. 559) accused Guyton and his friends of confusing 'tungstein' with tin; he accepted *tungstène* as '*le nouveau nom*' but added sarcastically, '*Il est, sans doute, permis à MM. les Chimistes de Dijon d'enrichir la Chimie d'une multitude de mots de leur invention. . . .*'

93. *Crell's Annalen*, *1784*, *II*, 201n.

be a convenient point at which to summarize the influence which Guyton and Bergman had on each other. We have seen that by the end of 1775 Bergman was using a systematic nomenclature of his own and when in 1779, Guyton started translating Bergman's collected works, he translated faithfully for the most part the systematic expressions used by Bergman. Probably the three important factors which prompted Guyton to undertake the reform of chemical nomenclature were: (i) his own dissatisfaction with the current terminology, (ii) his contact with Bergman's systematic terms, and (iii) his contract with the publisher of the *Encyclopédie Méthodique* to write a series of articles covering the entire field of chemistry.

Although Bergman and Guyton were both interested in the reform of nomenclature, there was some difference of approach between the two chemists. Bergman, as a Swede, was primarily interested in mineralogy,[94] whereas Guyton's interest was purely that of a chemist. This led Bergman to the description of complex naturally-occurring minerals which made systematic naming difficult, except by the use of long phrases. Also he tended to approach the subject from the standpoint of natural history and was, therefore, (following the example of Linnaeus) willing to accept trivial names in the nomenclature of substances where systematic naming was difficult. Another difference between Guyton and Bergman was that the latter thought that a general reform of nomenclature should first be drawn up in Latin; only at a later stage could the nomenclature be carried over to the various vernaculars of modern Europe. Bergman's preference for Latin was understandable for several reasons. In the first place he, unlike Guyton, held a university post and Latin was the official language of the universities. Secondly, when Bergman began to use systematic terms, his only precedent was Linnaeus' botanical nomenclature which was expressed in Latin. Thirdly, as a Swede, Bergman realized that his native tongue was almost unknown outside Scandinavia and this may have prejudiced him against other vernaculars. Fourthly, it has been seen that Bergman was very much influenced by Linnaeus who had successfully carried out a reform of botanical nomenclature in Latin. Finally, Latin, being a dead language, was neutral

---

94. Even in his 1784 paper Bergman made it clear that he was primarily interested in mineralogy—'*praesertim in Oryctologia*' (*Nova Acta Reg. Soc. Scient. Upsaliensis, 4,* 118).

and unlikely to arouse hostility for nationalistic reasons and, in any case, Latin had formerly been the language of science. Guyton, on the other hand, was only interested in a reform in the French language. If foreign words or Latin roots were introduced into chemical nomenclature, they should conform to the genius of the French language which many Frenchmen at that time considered to be the universal language of science.[95]

In his *Mémoire sur les dénominations chimiques*, Guyton continually referred to the authority of Bergman either directly or indirectly. Guyton's second principle of nomenclature was based on a quotation from Bergman, and in his nomenclature of salts, he not only made use of the general scheme of a binomial nomenclature but also Bergman's names for the acids: *boracis*, *fluoris*, *arsenicale*, *saccharinum*, *formicale*, which he adopted into the French language. On the other hand, the influence was not one-sided. Guyton's suggestion for the use of shorter terms to replace the old cumbersome names for the three alkalis was accepted by Bergman in a modified form, as was Guyton's term *barote*. Also Bergman was prepared to abandon his cherished *acidum aereum* in favour of Guyton's *acidum mephiticum* in order to produce greater unanimity between them.

A final point of comparison which, though perhaps trivial in retrospect, was at one time the subject of considerable discussion, was the order in which the acid and the base of a salt should be stated. Originally Bergman, following the precedent of *tartarus vitriolatus*, always wrote the name of the metal followed by the name of the acid used adjectivally, e.g. *magnesia aerata*. Guyton, on the other hand, preferred *vitriol de fer* to *fer vitriolé* and *nitre d'argent* to *argent nitré*, probably because the latter expressions involved greater innovations in the French language. It is strange that Bergman decided in 1784 to change his method, so that what he had previously called *argentum nitratum* now became *nitrosum argentatum*. Although he gave as his reason for this change, considerations based on ideas of genus and species taken from natural history, one cannot help wondering if he did not also realize that this would bring his nomenclature even closer to that of Guyton.

---

95. e.g. in the *Journal des Sçavans*, *1789*, 569, is found the remark that French '*est, pour ainsi dire, la langue universelle des Savans*'. (The context is the founding of a journal of chemistry in French, the *Annales de Chimie*.)

Although Guyton mentioned Bergman's adoption of some of his terms[96] and Bergman referred to Guyton's use of his own expressions, there was never anything less than an admirable spirit of co-operation existing between the two men. Each respected the talents and views of the other and was prepared to make concessions to achieve unity on the fundamentals of nomenclature. Bergman was not so much of an idealist as to suppose that everyone would accept his scheme of nomenclature, but he hoped that a majority of chemists might agree on a system. Having said this, he continued:

> Every real friend of chemistry, therefore, should wish for a happy issue to the plan of Mons. Morveau, to be attempted in the new Encyclopaedia.[97]

The encyclopaedia referred to was the *Encyclopédie Méthodique*, for which Guyton had been commissioned to write the section on chemistry. The first part of the first volume of the chemical section of the *Encyclopédie Méthodique* was printed in 1786 and Guyton used the opportunity of once more explaining his nomenclature and reviewing its progress since 1782.

Guyton was particularly proud of the encouragement and support he had received from Macquer and Bergman.[98] Regarding the reception of the nomenclature abroad, he mentioned Kirwan in Britain and other chemists in Italy and Germany who, he said, had supported his nomenclature, although an investigation of their published works gives little evidence for such a claim. Turning to works published in France, he pointed to the use of his nomenclature in translations of various books and papers by foreign chemists. It is significant that, of the works he referred to, the great majority were translated by members of the Academy of Dijon or natives of that town who were under Guyton's influence.[99] Guyton also mentioned what was to prove a more important source of sup-

96. 'Il [i.e. Bergman] a adopté mes dénominations' (*Encyclopédie Méthodique, Chimie*, vol. i, *Paris, 1786*, p. vi).
97. *Nova Acta Reg. Soc. Scient. Upsaliensis, 4* (1784), 118. See also p. 128.
98. Both these chemists died in 1784.
99. The translators of the papers in the *Observations sur la Physique* were described as M. le P. de V. and M.L.D.B. of the *Académie de Dijon*, M. MGN. of Dijon, M.B.S.T. of Dijon and, most frequently, Mme. Picardet of Dijon. Most of the memoirs contained in the *Mémoires de Chimie de Scheele*, Dijon, 1785 were also by Mme. Picardet.

port, the intention of Fourcroy to adopt the new nomenclature in the new edition of his text-book.[100]

Before Guyton wrote the second half of the first volume of the *Encyclopédie Méthodique*, a fundamental change in his thinking took place and this led in 1787 to the publication jointly with three other leading French chemists of the *Méthode de nomenclature chimique*.

100. *Élémens d'histoire naturelle et de chimie*, 2nd edn., Paris, 1786.

CHAPTER FIVE

The Events leading up to the Publication of the 'Méthode de nomenclature chimique' (1787)

The important *Méthode de nomenclature chimique* was published under the names of Guyton de Morveau, Lavoisier, Berthollet and Fourcroy. We have already studied Guyton's ideas on nomenclature before 1787 and here it is proposed to examine briefly the interests of the other chemists on the subject of chemical language before going on to consider the contents of the book and its reception.

Lavoisier's Interest in Nomenclature

The young Lavoisier's first lessons in chemistry at the *Collège Mazarin* had revealed to him a lack of methodical treatment in the subject at that time and he contrasted this unfavourably with the systematic and logical exposition which he found in mathematics and physics.[101] He was met with obscurity and words not clearly defined or even capable of definition. When Lavoisier later adopted the study of chemistry as the main pursuit of his life, he always sought for a logical clarity of thought and exposition, such as was finally expressed in his *Traité élémentaire de Chimie* of 1789, in which he emphasized the importance of clear language to clear thinking.

Some of the most important pieces of research carried out by Lavoisier were connected with gases, the study of which was still in its infancy. In his earliest experiments involving gases, and particularly the gases which were later to be called oxygen and carbon dioxide, Lavoisier's descriptions were vague; he

---

101. According to Lavoisier's unpublished notes in the archives of the *Académie des Sciences* in Paris, quoted by M. Daumas, *Lavoisier*, Paris, 1955, p. 93.

usually called the gases *air* and confused the two gases mentioned.[102] As a result of further experiments, however, the different properties of the gases became more evident and he tried to find suitable expressions for them. The importance which Lavoisier, early in his career, attached to the names of substances can be seen in several papers which he read to the *Académie des Sciences* in April and May 1777.[103] He coined the terms *mofette atmosphérique* and *air éminemment respirable* to denote the main constituents of the atmosphere and he adopted Bucquet's term *acide crayeux* in preference to the misleading *air fixe*. Lavoisier thought it important to establish a clear method of expressing the difference between gases and their aqueous solutions.[104] These gases (now known as carbon dioxide, sulphur dioxide, ammonia and hydrogen chloride) were described as either *aériforme* or *en liqueur*, a distinction which he described as 'a new nomenclature', although these terms were already in use to a limited extent. These terms themselves can hardly be considered as of much importance, but they illustrate the care with which Lavoisier chose his expressions to avoid any possibility of misunderstanding. When Lavoisier coined the term *principe oxigine* to describe the substance which combines with metals in calcination, he chose the expression deliberately to avoid referring to one of the constituents of a solid calx as an 'air':

> The use of this term will prevent circumlocutions, make my manner of expression more rigorous and will avoid the equivocations to which we should continuously be exposed if I made use of the word *air*.[105]

Another testimony to the importance attached to language by Lavoisier, is provided by his attitude towards the term *phlogiston*. In his public utterances, Lavoisier was continually critical of Priestley's term *dephlogisticated air*. He usually went out of his way to emphasize that this name had been given to the gas by

---

102. *Opuscules Physiques et Chymiques*, Paris, 1774, p. 449.
103. *Mém. Acad.*, *1777*, 191, 195.
104. Lavoisier first made this distinction in 1774 in his laboratory note book, *Registre de Laboratoire*, vol. iii, f.53, quoted by Berthelot, *La Révolution Chimique*, Paris, 1890, p. 261. In a paper read to the *Académie* in 1777 Lavoisier carefully distinguished between *acide sulfureux aériforme* and *acide sulfureux en liqueur* (*Mém. Acad.*, *1777*, 324) and in 1780 he extended these expressions to other gases (*Mém. Acad.*, *1780*, 334).
105. *Mém. Acad.*, *1778*, 536.

Priestley and not himself, and he called it a very improper expression.[106] Later, in 1783, when using the expressions *dephlogisticated marine acid* and *dephlogisticated nitrous acid*, he emphasized that these were names which Bergman and Scheele had used.[107] Indeed in 1785 Lavoisier could boast that in the numerous memoirs which he had presented to the Academy for many years he had not once made use of the term *phlogiston*.[108] His main attack on the abuse of the term *phlogiston* was contained in a paper entitled *Réflexions sur le phlogistique*,[109] which he read to the *Académie* in the summer of 1785. Lavoisier had to show the faults not of one theory but of a series of theories which shared the common term *phlogiston*. He dealt successively with the theory of Stahl, in which phlogiston had weight, that of Baumé in which phlogiston was akin to fire, and that of Macquer, in which phlogiston was identical with light. Lavoisier's main arguments were based on a *reductio ad absurdum*. To explain some facts, the disciple of Stahl accepted phlogiston as a principle without weight; yet at other times they had to admit that it did have some weight. In fact chemists had used the term 'phlogiston' to denote a vague principle which was not properly defined and consequently could be adapted to all kinds of explanations. It could be used to explain why a body was transparent or opaque, white or coloured, caustic or non-caustic, etc. There can be little doubt that Lavoisier was thinking of phlogiston in particular when he later insisted that no student of chemistry should accept any word without attaching a definite idea to it.[110]

Condillac's Influence

The common habit of using words without having a clear idea of their meaning was condemned by the French philosopher, the Abbé Bonnot de Condillac (1714–80). Condillac's *Logique*[111] (1780) was highly esteemed by Lavoisier, who quoted extensively from it in the *Méthode de nomenclature chimique* of 1787 and the *Traité élémentaire de Chimie* of 1789. Condillac's statement

106. *Mém. Acad., 1777*, 195.
107. *Oeuvres*, Paris, 1862–93, vol. ii, pp. 549, 552.
108. *Mém. Acad., 1782*, 492ff.   109. *Mém. Acad., 1783*, 505–38.
110. *Méthode de nomenclature chimique*, Paris, 1787, p. 19.
111. *La Logique, Oeuvres Complètes*, Paris, 1798, vol. 22. The quotations are from pp. 109, 30, 168, 134.

that 'the cause of our mistakes is the habit of judging according to words, the sense of which we have not determined' expressed a sentiment which could hardly have failed to appeal to Lavoisier. In his philosophy, and particularly his ideas on language, Condillac was strongly influenced by John Locke.[112] Condillac shared with other French philosophers of the eighteenth century a general interest in science and he laid down several important principles which he considered essential for its progress. He referred to people who led others astray by the use of a 'scientific jargon' (*un jargon scientifique*), and he considered that 'the progress of the sciences depends entirely on the progress of their languages'. Condillac was an extreme advocate of the view that language is necessary for thought:

> We only reason well or reason badly in so far as our language is well or badly constructed . . . the whole art of reasoning can be reduced to the art of speaking well.

Although Condillac died in 1780, he might almost be considered as one of the joint authors of the *Méthode de nomenclature chimique* of 1787. Not only did a summary of Condillac's views form a substantial part of Lavoisier's contribution to the book, but his conviction, that the progress of a science depended on the sound construction of its language, was really the whole basis for publishing a work advocating a revolution in chemical nomenclature.

Fourcroy and the Question of Nomenclature

After considering the interest in the reform of nomenclature shown by Guyton and by Lavoisier, we turn next to Fourcroy. Although his contribution to the reform of nomenclature was slight in comparison with the other two chemists, who were his seniors, there is no doubt that he was numbered among the many intelligent chemists of the 1770's who were not satisfied with many of the current chemical terms. Fourcroy, moreover, gave some thought to the elements of a systematic nomenclature.

In 1777–8 Fourcroy was investigating the compound now called ferrous carbonate and he suggested it might be termed

---

112. Condillac admitted his indebtedness to Locke in *Histoire Moderne, Oeuvres Complètes*, vol. 20, p. 526. Locke's critical attitude to language has already been noted.

craie de fer ('chalk of iron'). In 1779 he returned to the subject of naming this compound and other similar compounds derived from 'fixed air'. Fourcroy rejected Bergman's suggestion that such compounds should be called 'aereated metals' (*aerata*), because the expression was inappropriate and 'would be much better applied to metallic calces which really contain air'.[113] Fourcroy's teacher, Bucquet had suggested the term *acide de la craie* or *acide crayeux* for Bergman's *acidum aereum* and Lavoisier had accepted Bucquet's suggestion[114] and Fourcroy followed their example. Bucquet had given the name *tartre crayeux* to the neutral salt obtained from *acide crayeux* and the fixed vegetable alkali and Fourcroy extended this to other salts of *acide crayeux*, including *craie de fer*:

> In the same way, this name can apply to all the combinations of *acide crayeux* with other metallic substances; thus we can say *craie de cuivre, craie de plomb*, etc. It will even be useful in distinguishing these kinds of neutral salts from metallic calces, with which, it seems, they have up to now been confused, although they are really different.[115]

Fourcroy wrote this in 1779 at the age of twenty-four and when he wrote his first text-book of chemistry in 1782, he made some use of this nomenclature. Other systematic terms favoured by Fourcroy included *tartre phosphorique and soude phosphorique* for the phosphates of potassium and sodium respectively.[116]

So far Fourcroy does not appear to have been influenced to any extent by Guyton, but he was familiar with Guyton's translation of Bergman's *Opuscula*, of which the first volume appeared in 1780. In 1784 Fourcroy remarked:

> Several chemists, and M. Bergman in particular, have proposed that Epsom salts should be called *vitriol de magnésie*, so as to indicate its nature by its name.

He approved of this method, which would avoid the contingency of giving a vague name like *Epsom salt* to more then one substance and he adopted the term *vitriol magnésien* himself. In 1784 Fourcroy saw nothing wrong with the expression 'ponderous earth' despite Guyton's criticism published two years earlier,

113. *Mémoires et Observations de Chimie*, Paris, 1784, pp. 89, 122.
114. *Mém. Acad., 1777*, 195.
115. *Mémoires et Observations de Chimie*, p. 123. See also pp. 382, 320, 13.
116. *Leçons élémentaires*, Paris, 1782: vol. i, pp. 266, 283, 386; vol. ii, pp. 784–5.

but soon afterwards Fourcroy realized the advantage of some of Guyton's terms, and in the second edition of his *Leçons élémentaires*, published in the summer of 1786,[117] he did use some of the new names. Fourcroy acknowledged that the nomenclature of the 'ponderous' salts was misleading because 'these salts are not heavier than most others, if we except the ponderous spar'. In the preface to this book Fourcroy indicated that, although he confined himself for the most part in the text to the names accepted by chemists, he referred the reader to a chapter where he set out the nomenclature of Guyton de Morveau which, he said, he personally preferred. This preference was shown in a list of salts where Fourcroy set out the composition of each salt, its usual name and the name given by Guyton, the latter usually being described as a better name. Thus *Vitriol de Potasse, Muriate de Soude, Nitre Barotique* are representative examples of names listed as 'better' than the generally accepted ones.

Fourcroy, nevertheless, continued for the most part to use the old familiar expressions in his text-book, with only an occasional criticism.

Berthollet

Turning to Berthollet's contribution to the reform of chemical nomenclature, we are faced with an almost total lack of evidence of his interest in this aspect of the science. Like many chemists of the 1780's, Berthollet often preferred using long descriptive phrases,[118] rather than the old misleading terms, but, on the whole, he was singularly uncritical of chemical terminology and there is no evidence in the papers he published in the *Mémoires de l'Académie Royale des Sciences* and in the *Observations sur la Physique* that he was influenced in any way by Guyton's suggestions of 1782 for a reform of chemical nomenclature. The explanation of the appearance of Berthollet's name on the title-page of the *Méthode de nomenclature chimique* depends on his position as a practical chemist of the first rank and also as the first important convert of Lavoisier to the oxygen theory, for which Berthollet proclaimed his support in April 1785.

117. *Élémens d'histoire naturelle et de chimie*, 2nd edn., Paris, 1786. See especially vol. i, p. vii; vol. ii, pp. 287, 321–5.

118. e.g. *la dissolution de terre pesante par l'acide marin* (*Obs. sur la Phyiques, 28* (1786), 402). Guyton's names for the constituent parts of this salt were *barote* and *acide muriatique*.

For Berthollet's interest in nomenclature see also p. 192, f.n. 156a.

The Collaboration of Guyton and Lavoisier

The four joint authors of the *Méthode* are mentioned on the title-page in order of seniority. In 1787, the year of publication of the book, Guyton was 50 years old, Lavoisier 44, Berthollet 39 and Fourcroy 32. These chemists were brought together in the first place, not to reform nomenclature, but to examine Lavoisier's experiments which gave support to the new oxygen theory. Guyton, who had once been a leading supporter of the phlogiston theory, was only won over to the oxygen theory after the conversion of Berthollet and Fourcroy.[119] Although Guyton was an important figure in Dijon, the fact that he lived in the provinces was a great disadvantage to any Frenchman and Guyton was the only one of the four chemists who had not been elected a member of the *Académie des Sciences*. These considerations among others[120] suggest that, in the collaboration of the four chemists, the chairman was Lavoisier rather than Guyton.

Guyton's collaboration with Lavoisier is an important event in the history of chemistry and it is unfortunate that complete documentary evidence of the details of their co-operation is not available. We do know, however, that in about 1786 Guyton's faith in the phlogiston theory was being severely undermined by the accumulating evidence provided by Lavoisier. Before he was finally convinced of the truth of Lavoisier's theory, however, Guyton travelled from Dijon to Paris to discuss the new theory with its originator. The exact date of Guyton's historic journey is not known. With the conflicting evidence available it would seem that Fourcroy's testimony is unreliable;[121] the remaining evidence points to a date early in 1787, probably in February. Lavoisier himself, speaking in April 1787, said that Guyton had travelled to Paris earlier in that year[122] and from the subject of the new theory they had gone on to discuss the

119. According to a not very clear statement by Lavoisier, *Oeuvres*, Paris, 1862–93, vol. ii, p. 105.

120. Guyton himself stated that the initiative for the collaboration came from Lavoisier and his colleagues (*Annales de Chimie*, 25 (1798), 207).

121. Fourcroy, who was one of the participants in the discussion on nomenclature, said that Guyton came to Paris in the latter part of 1786 (*Système des connaissances chimiques*, Paris, 1801, 4to. edn., vol. i, p. 40) and a further statement by Fourcroy also implies the date 1786 (*Elements of Natural History and Chemistry*, 3rd edn., London, 1790, p. xxix).

122. *Méthode de nomenclature chimique*, Paris, 1787, p. 4.

Antoine-Laurent Lavoisier (1743–1794)

Louis-Bernard Guyton de Morveau (1737–1816)

Antoine-François Fourcroy (1755–1809)

Claude-Louis Berthollet (1748–1822)

PLATE 4. The authors of the *Méthode de nomenclature chimique* (1787)

possibility of reforming the nomenclature of chemistry. Lavoisier later repeated that Guyton's visit had taken place in 1787 and had lasted eight months.[123] The date is fixed more precisely by the evidence contained in two letters. In the first, written by Lavoisier to Meusnier on 4 March 1787,[124] Lavoisier wrote:

M. de Morveau is at present in Paris and we are taking advantage of this fact to work with him on the construction of a chemical nomenclature. This is now perhaps the most pressing need for the advancement of the sciences.

In another letter, written on 14 March 1787 by the physicist Monge to Van Marum, Monge wrote that 'M. Morveau of Dijon has been here for several weeks'[125] and this confirms that Guyton's collaboration with Lavoisier dates from about February 1787.

Once Guyton was convinced of the superiority of the new 'antiphlogistic' theory, he could apply himself wholeheartedly to the construction of a nomenclature related to it. Although Guyton had excluded phlogistic terminology from his nomenclature even in 1782, his nomenclature would hardly be complete as long as it wavered between the two theories. As Lavoisier said of Guyton:

He himself felt that, in a science which in some ways is in a state of mobility . . . [and] . . . in which theories have arisen, it was extremely difficult to form a language which suited different systems and which satisfied all opinions without adopting any one exclusively.[126]

The change in Guyton's theoretical views in 1787 was reflected in the *Encyclopédie Méthodique*. In 1786 Guyton was still a supporter of the phlogiston theory and in the first part of Volume 1 he had made occasional use of the terminology of the phlogiston theory. When confronted with the problem of writing a long article on 'Air' (i.e. the gases), Guyton had felt the need to consult Lavoisier, the author of the 'pneumatic theory'.

123. *Rapport à l'Académie sur les travaux de Guyton de Morveau*, Lavoisier, *Oeuvres*, Paris, 1862–93, vol. vi, p. 58.

124. quoted by Daumas (*Lavoisier*, Paris, 1955, pp. 60–1) from Lavoisier's correspondence which is being edited for publication by R. Fric.

125. A photograph of this letter was very kindly shown to the author by M. René Taton.

126. *Méthode de nomenclature chimique*, Paris, 1787, p. 4.

Previously Guyton had hesitated between the theories of Stahl and Lavoisier; now he accepted Lavoisier's theory fully. Previously he had used a nomenclature of his own; now he was using a nomenclature which was modified and extended by collaboration with Lavoisier and his colleagues. In a second preface inserted before the article 'Air' Guyton explained his new position. He explained the common aims of the four authors of the *Méthode de nomenclature chimique*, and he took the opportunity of including the contents of this book in an abbreviated form.

CHAPTER SIX

The 'Méthode de nomenclature chimique' and the Introduction of the Reformed Nomenclature into France

The *Méthode de nomenclature chimique*, published in the summer of 1787, is an octavo book of some 300 pages. The book is naturally divided into two parts dealing with nomenclature and symbolism respectively. The first and by far the larger and more important part of the book deals with chemical nomenclature. It begins with the text of a memoir read by Lavoisier to the *Académie des Sciences*, introducing the reform of nomenclature. There follow more detailed memoirs by Guyton and Fourcroy, the latter referring to a large folding plate (approx. 18 in. by 27 in.) on which are set out examples of the proposed nomenclature. An important item was a dictionary, occupying about one third of the book. The first part of the dictionary enables one to find the new name for a substance from its old name; in the second part the new names were arranged in alphabetical order with their corresponding equivalents in the old terminology. In the last part of the *Méthode* are two short memoirs by Hassenfratz and Adet, in which they put forward a scheme of chemical symbols based on simple geometric patterns which are illustrated in six folding plates at the end of the book. Both sections of the book are concluded by a report drawn up by other members of the *Académie* on the merits of the proposed reforms.

Lavoisier's Memoir

Lavoisier introduced the reform to the *Académie des Sciences* at a public meeting on 18 April 1787 in a memoir entitled 'On the necessity of reforming and perfecting the nomenclature of chemistry'. He began by tracing the events which had led up to the suggested reform. Lavoisier gave due credit to Macquer and Baumé who had used the words *vitriol* and *nitre* as general terms to describe the salts formed by the respective acids of these names. Bucquet and Fourcroy extended these beginnings of systematic nomenclature, as did Bergman, but the greatest step towards reform had been taken by Guyton. Having been commissioned to write the chemical part of the *Encyclopédie Méthodique*, Guyton had wished to systematize the entire nomenclature, but he had been faced with the difficulty that chemistry was advancing rapidly and new theories were springing up. Guyton had sought the advice of several members of the *Académie* and he had offered to sacrifice his own ideas and all his previous work in the proposed collaboration. From this visit there resulted many conferences, which, said Lavoisier, were characterized by a complete lack of personal considerations and past achievements. They had been over the whole field of chemistry several times and they had also considered the 'metaphysics' of language.

Lavoisier did not intend to try the patience of his audience (since it was a public meeting) by giving details of the technical words they had adopted. Guyton de Morveau had undertaken this task for one of the private meetings of the *Académie*. Lavoisier, therefore, confined himself to dealing with general principles and considering the philosophy behind these principles.

It was commonly believed, said Lavoisier, that language had no other object than to express ideas by means of signs. But languages were more than this; they were true analytical methods, by the help of which men proceeded from the known to the unknown in the same way as mathematicians. Algebra he considered to be the most perfect analytical method and algebra was a true language. Thus a language and an analytical method were two expressions of the same things, as had been clearly shown by the abbé Condillac in his *Logique*.[127] Now, if languages were true instruments which men had formed to assist the process of thought, it was important that these instruments were the best possible. The perfection of language was most important to those beginning to study science, for once false

127. A large part of Lavoisier's memoir (pp. 6–14) consisted of a summary of Condillac's views. Lavoisier recommended unreservedly Condillac's *Logique* to young men studying the sciences.

ideas had become established, they became prejudices which were difficult to discard:

> A well-made language . . . will not allow those who profess chemistry to deviate from the march of nature; it will be necessary, either to reject the nomenclature, or to follow irresistably the path which it indicates.

If language were considered merely as a collection of representative symbols, it would follow that an imperfect language could also transmit false ideas, even if the original idea were not false. From this point of view, the perfecting of the language consisted in expressing in words the facts—no less and certainly no more.

Lavoisier pointed out that the current language of chemistry had obviously not been formed according to these principles. To emphasize this point he gave examples of metaphorical expressions used by the alchemists. It was true that a new nomenclature might be far from perfect, considering that chemistry was far from complete, but if a nomenclature were founded on sound principles, provided that it was conceived as a method of naming substances rather than a rigid nomenclature,[128] it would adapt itself to the work ahead; it would mark in advance the new substances which could be discovered and it would only require minor local reforms in the future.

In drawing up their scheme, the authors had considered as simple all substances which they were unable to decompose. When new names had been introduced for these simple substances, the authors had tried to make the new names express the most general property of the body concerned.[129] In the case of compounds of two substances, Lavoisier considered that 'natural logic' suggested that the general name was put first, followed by the specific name. To accomplish the desired effect for the new nomenclature it had been necessary to introduce some new words which, at first, might seem harsh and incongruous to the ear, but these new words were certainly no worse than *pompholix*,

128. '*Une méthode de nommer plutôt qu'une nomenclature*' (*Méthode de nomenclature chimique*, p. 17). The title of the book had obviously been chosen deliberately to suggest this idea.

129. Lavoisier had in mind particularly *oxigène* (from its supposed property as the principle of acids), *hidrogène* (one of the constituents of water) and *azote* (which did not support life).

colcothar[130] and many other terms which were accepted. Also in current use were many misleading terms based on false ideas, terms like *oil of vitriol, oil of tartar, flowers of zinc*, etc.

Shall we be pardoned for having changed the language which was spoken by our masters. . . . We hope so, all the more because it was Bergman and Macquer who suggested this reform. . . . M. Bergman wrote to M. de Morveau towards the end of his life: 'Have no mercy on any improper denomination. Those who already know chemistry will always understand; those who do not as yet know it, will understand the sooner'.

Guyton's Memoir

A fortnight after Lavoisier had introduced the general scheme of nomenclature, Guyton presented at a private meeting of the *Académie* a paper setting out the details of the proposed new nomenclature. Guyton explained that his collaborators and himself had given particular attention to the nomenclature of simple bodies (*corps simples*), since the names of these would be incorporated in the names of compound bodies containing these elements. These simple bodies (i.e. substances which had not yet been decomposed) could be divided into five classes, beginning with substances considered the simplest of all. These included *luminère* and *calorique*; the latter word had been coined by the nomenclators to express not so much 'heat' as 'matter of heat'. Lavoisier considered that all gases contained *calorique*. Third in the list came *oxigène*, a name previously[131] introduced by Lavoisier to indicate the base of vital air; when combined with *calorique* it formed *gaz oxigène*. The names *hidrogène* (or *hydrogène*) and *azote* (i.e. nitrogen) followed.[132]

The second section of the Table consisted of the 'acidifiable bases' or principles of acids and this class could be divided into the acids of which the 'acidifiable bases' were known (e.g. the acids related to sulphur, phosphorus and carbon) and those

130. i.e. zinc oxide and ferric oxide respectively.
131. Lavoisier had introduced the expression '*principe acidifiant ou principe oxygine*' in November 1779 (*Mém. Acad., 1778*, 536). According to Fourcroy, the committee of reform decided to change the ending to *-gène* as corresponding more closely to the Greek (*Elements of natural history and chemistry*, London, 1790, vol. i, p. 147n.).
132. The etymology of the names of these three gases was:
oxygène from ὀξύς (acid) +γείνομαι (to be engendered)
hydrogène from ὕδωρ (water) +γείνομαι.
azote from a- (without) + ζωή (life).

which had not yet been decomposed. Examples of the latter were the bases of *acide muriatique, acide boracique* and *acide acétique* which were considered to be composed of oxygen and a particular *base acidifiable* or *radical* which was still to be investigated. The same base might be capable of forming more than one acid and more than one compound with alkalis, earths and metals the method adopted to express these combinations was to use various terminations joined to the root of a common word. In the case of sulphur there would be:

(*A*) *Acide sulfurique*—where the sulphur is saturated with oxygen.

(*B*) *Acide sulfureux*—containing less oxygen than the former acid.

(*a*) *Sulfate*—the generic name of all salts formed from A.

(*b*) *Sulfite*—the generic name of all salts formed from B.

(*c*) *Sulfure*[133]—compounds of sulphur not related to an acid.

To denote the acid which Guyton had previously called *acide méphitique*, he now, following Lavoisier's example, used the term *acide carbonique*, to which were related *carbonate, carbure* and *carbone*. Guyton's preference for the term *acide muriatique* to *acide marin* was accepted and the product when treated with oxygen (i.e. chlorine, which forms an aqueous solution containing hypochlorous acid) was called *acide muriatique oxigéné*. The salts of the latter were to be called *muriates oxigénés* and those of the former, *muriates*. As examples of *muriates*, Guyton cited *muriate mercuriel corrosif* and *muriate mercuriel doux*, to denote corrosive sublimate and sweet sublimate respectively. *Acide nitrique* and *acide nitreux* formed series of salts called *nitrates* and *nitrites* respectively and the two acids of phosphorus then known were named in a similar way. Believing that two acids were related to vinegar, the terms *acétique* and *acéteux* were coined to denote their respective salts. Supposing, though mistakenly, that most acids could be obtained in two states according to the proportion of oxygen they contained, the nomenclators had to decide, in cases where only one acid of a particular base were known, whether to consider the acid as saturated with oxygen or not. Rather than make a uniform assumption about them all, the authors had preferred to consider the sound of the resulting terms and to

---

133. This replaces previous terms such as *foie, hépar, pyrite*, etc.

deviate as little as possible from current usage. Thus they spoke of *acide benzoique* (forming *benzoates*) but *acide tartareux* (forming *tartrites*).

A system was also adopted, by which salts containing different proportions of the same acid and base could be distinguished. The term *acidule* was used to describe salts with excess of acid, e.g. *le tartrite acidule de potasse*,[134] but if the base appeared to be in excess, this was indicated by the term *sursaturé* as in *borate sursaturé de soude*.[135] It will be seen that Guyton in some cases had had to abandon his principle that 'a phrase cannot be considered as a name'.

In the third section were the metals, the names of which belonged more to ordinary language than to the language of chemistry. No change, therefore was proposed in their names but, following Bergman's example, they were all to be considered of the same gender in order to introduce uniformity. The words *molybdène, tungstène, manganèse* and *platine* were therefore to be considered as masculine to bring them into line with the others. The use of the word *regulus* to describe certain metals was to be proscribed and in any case most chemists had already abandoned it. To denote the compounds of metals with *oxigène*, the term *oxide* was used in preference to *chaux*, which previous writers (including Guyton) had used, but which was originally based on a false analogy with quicklime. The examples given of the use of *oxide* sometimes included a reference to the consistency or method of preparation e.g.:

> *l'oxide d'antimoine sublimé cristallin (fleurs d'antimoine)*
> *l'oxide de mercure par le feu (précipité per se)*
> *l'oxide mercuriel par l'acide nitrique (précipité rouge)*

In the fourth and fifth sections the earths and alkalis were all to be of the feminine gender, thus: *la silice, l'alumine, la chaux, la baryte* and *la magnésie; la potasse, la soude* and *l'ammoniaque*.

After dealing with minor points of nomenclature, mainly concerned with organic chemistry, Guyton concluded his memoir by asking the Academicians to consider the great advantages to be gained by the adoption of the new nomenclature, advantages which were surely worth the sacrifice of a few words of the old terminology.

---

134. i.e. potassium hydrogen tartrate.
135. i.e. borax (which is alkaline in aqueous solution due to hydrolysis).

Other Important Contents of the Méthode

Fourcroy's contribution to the *Méthode de nomenclature chimique* was a memoir which explained the details of the large folding table of nomenclature. Lavoisier had told the *Académie* in April of the intention of the four chemists to compile tables showing how the new nomenclature was to be applied. These tables were to be on view in the *salle de l'Académie*. It would seem[136] that the large table which the authors compiled was presented to the *Académie* in June 1787.

As published in the *Méthode*, the table was a large folding plate, divided into six columns. Each column was subdivided into two so that each new name was accompanied by its old equivalent wherever possible. The first column contained the names of 'Substances not decomposed' in which *lumière* and *calorique* were followed by the bases of *oxigène*, *hydrogène* and *azote*, non-metals, 'radicals' of complex acids, metals, earths, and alkalis. In the second column, devoted to the same simple substances in a gaseous state ('combined with *calorique*') only the three gases mentioned appeared. In the third column were the simple substances combined with oxygen, which for Lavoisier in most cases meant the corresponding acids (e.g. *soufre—acide sulfurique, acid sulfureux*). In column 4 these were named in the gaseous state (e.g. *gaz acide sulfureux*) and in column 5 examples of the salts were given (e.g. *sulfate de potasse, de soude, de chaux*, etc., *sulfite de potasse*, etc.). The last column contained the names of such compounds as *sulfures* (sulphides) and *carbures* (carbides) and also alloys of various metals. At the foot of the table were mentioned a few substances which would now be classed as organic compounds.

Much of Fourcroy's memoir involved repetition of what Guyton had already said, the main difference being that Fourcroy's explanations were closely related to the table. Fourcroy laid great stress on the importance of having similar suffixes in the names of similar compounds:

> If one reflects on the rigorous etymological method which we have followed to denote neutral salts and on the slight resemblance which the names given to salts had in the old nomenclature, one will perhaps understand why this column more than any other shows the greatest number of changes. . . .[137]

136. Daumas, *Lavoisier*, Paris, 1955, p. 61.   137. *Méthode*, p. 97.

Guyton had explained at length why the terms *vitriol* and *acide vitriolique* had not been kept in the new nomenclature and Fourcroy was equally at pains to point out how few new words had been introduced into the nomenclature (except for newly discovered substances). He claimed that the main difference in the new scheme was not new terms, but new systematic endings. Fourcroy's confidence in the superiority of the new nomenclature was partly based on the use he had already made of it earlier in the year (1787) in lectures at the *Jardin du Roi* and the *Lycée* of the Rue de Valois. He had found that it made the study of chemistry easier because the terms were much clearer and, above all, they avoided the equivocations of the old nomenclature.

The two dictionaries of synonyms of the old and new nomenclatures were preceded by an *Avertissement* which pointed out the use of the first dictionary in translating the old nomenclature into the new. The fact that the second dictionary was more than twice as long as the first was worthy of comment. In the second dictionary it was the new names which were listed alphabetically and the greater number of terms was due to the recent investigation of many new substances:

This nomenclature might therefore be regarded as in some way an inventory of the contemporary state of chemical knowledge.[138]

The fact that a large proportion of the new names had no equivalent in the old terminology was an important factor in securing the acceptance of the 1787 reform.

With regard to the synonyms of old names, the authors remarked that they had omitted to include purely alchemical synonyms. Although they confined these synonyms to words used in the eighteenth century, *carbonate de soude* had no less than a dozen equivalent names in the old terminology, *sulfate de magnésie* had six and many other substances can be seen to have been known by a variety of names. A significant point about the second dictionary was the inclusion of Latin names corresponding to the new French terms. These Latin names were intended to serve as a basis for uniformity in international communications.

The Reception of the 'Méthode' by the Académie

The publication of any book under the auspices of the *Académie des Sciences* involved the appointment of a committee

138. Ibid., p. 104.

to review the work and give its approval. Before the *Méthode de nomenclature chimique* was published, therefore, it was studied critically by a committee consisting of Baumé, D'Arcet, Sage and Cadet de Vaux.[139] Of these men, only Cadet de Vaux, who was the youngest, subsequently associated himself publicly with the new theory and nomenclature.[140] Two members of the committee, Baumé and Sage, were not only opposed to Lavoisier's theory and nomenclature in 1787, but remained hostile after more than ten years,[141] when the rest of France had long been won over. Bearing these prejudices in mind, we could hardly expect an enthusiastic report from the committee.

Although the book under review was concerned primarily with nomenclature, the latter was closely connected with the new theory and the reviewers found it impossible to dissociate the one from the other, so that their criticisms passed insensibly from the subject of nomenclature to the 'antiphlogistic' theory. Whereas many experiments were put forward in support of the latter, was it not also true, they said, that the phlogiston theory was supported by a series of convincing experiments? The old phlogiston theory was no doubt incomplete, but were there not also some difficulties in the new theory? The experiment on the composition of water, for instance, was not convincing. The committee, nevertheless, 'no more pretend to attack the new theory than defend the old' but they were on their guard against 'the prestige of something new' because 'the accepted ideas of a science cannot be overthrown in a day'. On the subject of nomenclature they made the astonishingly complacent remark that chemistry had already for half a century expressed itself with wonderful clarity (*avec une merveilleuse clarté*)!

139. '*Rapport sur la nouvelle nomenclature*' (*extrait des Registres de l'Académie Royale des Sciences du 13 juin 1787, Méthode de nomenclature chimique*, pp. 238–252).

140. Cadet de Vaux associated himself with Fourcroy in a very favourable review of the theory and nomenclature described in Lavoisier's *Traité élémentaire de Chimie* (see op. cit., Paris, 1789, pp. 651–2).

D'Arcet, who was the oldest member of the committee, was interested almost exclusively in applied chemistry (porcelain, dyes, etc.). He was, however, one of the three who approved the 3rd edn. of Fourcroy's *Elements* for the *Societé Royale d'Agriculture*. The reviewers adopted a neutral attitude to the new nomenclature.

141. Baumé, *Opuscules Chimiques*, Paris, 1798, e.g. p. 196. Sage, *Exposé des Effets de la Contagion Nomenclative*, Paris, 1810.

It is not a matter of a day to reform and nearly obliterate a language which is already understood, already widespread and well known over the whole of Europe, and to put in its place a new language built on etymologies either foreign to its nature or often taken from an ancient language already unfamiliar to scientists. . . .

Having, therefore, shown its support both for the old theory and for the old terminology which Lavoisier and Guyton had attacked, the committee rather hypocritically declared itself to be neutral:[142]

We think it necessary to submit this new theory together with its nomenclature to the test of time, to the trial of experiments, to the weighing of ensuing opinions and finally to the judgement of the public as the only tribunal from which they can and must come. Then it will no longer be a theory but will have become a system of truths, or else a mistake. In the former case, it will provide one more solid foundation for human knowledge, but if the latter, it will fall into oblivion with other physical theories which have preceded it. And it is in this light that we believe that the table of the new chemical nomenclature and the memoirs relating to it can be printed and published under the privilege of the Academy, in such a way, however, that it will not be possible to infer either that it [i.e. the Academy] accepts or rejects the new theory.

Finally, the committee suggested that, when the general body of opinion had decided what it thought of the new nomenclature, it would be the concern of the Academy 'to legalize in this nomenclature what usage has decided and what the ear and the nature of the language favour'. In fact the Academy played very little part in deciding on the acceptance of the nomenclature. This was the concern of individual practical chemists and chemical authors both in France and abroad.

Lavoisier had an opportunity of defending his theory and the new nomenclature against the passive hostility of the committee of the Academy when later in June 1787 he reviewed, in collaboration with Berthollet and Fourcroy, the scheme of chemical symbols which had been proposed by Hassenfratz and Adet.[143]

---

142. *Méthode*, pp. 245, 250, 251.
143. 'Rapport sur les nouveaux charactères chimiques', extrait des Registres de *l'Académie Royale des Sciences du 27 juin 1787* (*Méthode*, pp. 288–312).

Criticisms of the Nomenclature in France

One of the sternest and most influential critics in France of the new nomenclature was Jean Claude de la Métherie (1743–1817), editor of the *Observations sur la Physique* from 1785 until his death. Although in September 1787, immediately after the publication of the *Méthode de nomenclature chimique*, he compiled a very fair summary of the book for readers of his journal, in the following month he wrote a long and hostile criticism of the work.[144] La Métherie was opposed both to the idea of a completely new nomenclature and to the particular scheme proposed in the *Méthode*. He considered that any change in nomenclature should be gradual and cautious and take into account the fact that chemistry shared much of its terminology with pharmacy and commerce. The reformers should have respected the old terms, but instead they had introduced new ones which were 'hard and barbarous' (*durs et barbares*) like *carbonate*, *nitrate*, *sulfate*. He criticized the term *oxigène* because not all its compounds were acids as its name implied and he criticized *azote* because it already had an alchemical meaning.[145] He did not believe that a new nomenclature should be based on a theory of chemistry—'otherwise each school having a different system will also have a different nomenclature.

In the next few years la Métherie published many letters attacking the new nomenclature. An anonymous letter published in the December number of the *Observations* criticized Lavoisier's terms *oxygène* and *hydrogène* as the former, for instance, appeared to mean 'engendered by acid' instead of 'acid generator'. Such terms as *pyroligneux* and *muriatique oxigéné* were hybrids from Greek and Latin.[146] In any case, the basic words of a science should be developed from popular idiom, rather than be derived from dead languages. The writer of this letter

144. *Obs. sur la Physique*, *31* (1787), 210–19. This summary is particularly important because the first published accounts in Germany and Italy of the new nomenclature were based on it. For the adverse criticism, see ibid., pp. 270–85.
145. Viz. 'Philosopher's Mercury' or 'Universal Medicine' (Ruland, *Lexicon Alchemiae*, Frankfurt, 1612, p. 96). This objection was ridiculed by Guyton (*Encyclopédie Méthodique, Chimie*, vol. i, p. 641n.
146. *Obs. sur la Physique*, *31* (1787), 418–24. Guyton replied by citing Cicero, Pliny and Virgil who all made use of Greek as well as Latin terms (*Encyclopédie Méthodioue, Chimie*, vol. i, p. 646n.).

did, however, concede that the four joint authors of the *Méthode* were more capable than anyone else of providing a model chemical nomenclature. Other criticisms of the new nomenclature which appeared in the *Observations sur la Physique* included three letters violently attacking the new theory and nomenclature written by Balthazar Sage, director of the École des Mines, who had been a member of the committee of the *Académie* appointed to examine the new nomenclature.[147]

In 1790 la Métherie published three long letters from de Luc who was then in England.[148] De Luc admitted some of the improprieties of the old terminology, but he submitted that in practice these names were not misleading since the true composition of the substances concerned was well known. A new nomenclature was merely a hindrance to chemistry unless the new nomenclature were permanent, and the doubtful theory on which the nomenclature was founded made this unlikely. He would have preferred that the substances previously known as *dephlogisticated air* and *phlogisticated air* had been given neutral names like 'air A' and 'air B'. De Luc quoted the example of a nomenclature suggested by Joseph Black, when he pointed to the danger of rival nomenclatures springing up without control. It is clear that de Luc had studied the *Méthode de nomenclature chimique*, since he quoted the approval expressed for the *old* nomenclature by the committee of the Paris Academy. He also pointed out the inconsistency of Lavoisier who, although he did not use the term *nitrogène*, called the radical derived from it *nitrique*.

In 1792 la Métherie brought out a second French edition of Bergman's *Sciagraphia* and he took this opportunity of casting doubts on the new theory and maligning its nomenclature. It appears, therefore, that a small group of people in France were still actively hostile to the new theory and nomenclature two or three years after its publication and that one of the leading figures in this opposition was la Métherie whose power lay in his position as editor of the *Observations*. La Métherie's bitterness

147. Ibid., *33* (1788), 478–9; *34* (1789), 66–7, 138–42. See also: ibid., *32* (1788), 61–3; *33* (1788), 262–86; *34* (1789), 76–8; *35* (1789), 75–6, the latter containing extracts from letters said by la Métherie to have been sent from Spain, Italy, England, Sweden and Germany.

148. *Obs. sur la Physique*, *36* (1790), 144–54; 193–207; 276–90. Jean André de Luc was of Swiss birth but he spent most of his life in Germany and Britain.

towards the authors of the *Méthode*, and particularly Lavoisier,[149] is reflected in his sarcastic review of Lavoisier's *Traité élémentaire de Chimie*, in which he once more attacked the nomenclature.[150]

The Spread of the Nomenclature in France

Owing to the conservative views of the editor of the *Observations*, Lavoisier and his colleagues sought to found another journal in which they could publish their work without interference. In 1789 they brought out (with the approval of the *Académie*) the first number of their *Annales de Chimie*. In most of the articles contributed to this journal the new theory and nomenclature were accepted, although the editors had bound themselves to respect everyone's opinions and 'to keep each contributor's language unchanged'.[151]

In Paris several of the younger chemists had associated themselves with Lavoisier (e.g. in the *Annales de Chimie*) and in the south of France an important convert was Chaptal, professor of chemistry at Montpellier, who publicly adopted the new theory and nomenclature in his *Élémens de Chimie*, published in 1790, when the author was thirty-four. Writing to Chaptal in the following year, Lavoisier remarked:

It is a real pleasure to see you adopt the principles which I was the first to announce. It is the fulfillment of my ambition to win over you, M. de Morveau, and a small number of chemists throughout Europe, and my success exceeds my expectations.... I see only elderly people, who no longer have the courage to start new studies again or who cannot adapt their imagination to a new order of things, who still cling to the phlogiston theory. All young people adopt the new theory and I conclude that the revolution in chemistry is complete.[152]

Chaptal devoted a dozen pages of the introduction to his textbook to a discussion of the reform of chemical nomenclature; he mentioned the importance to chemistry of its language and he set out the details of the nomenclature. Chaptal, like Fourcroy,

149. Lavoisier's work had destroyed many basic ideas to which la Métherie had committed himself, particularly his belief in the phlogiston theory and the elementary nature of water.

150. *Obs. sur la Physique*, *34* (1789), 304–18.

151. *Annales de Chimie*, *1* (1789), 4.

152. Letter quoted by Grimaux, *Lavoisier*, Paris, 1888, p. 126.

had used the new nomenclature in his lectures and the advantages gained had been apparent. With regard to the details of the nomenclature, Chaptal differed from Lavoisier only in one important term; he preferred to use the word *nitrogène* for the latter's *azote*. Chaptal claimed, quite rightly, that this alteration was consistent with one of the principles of the *Méthode* since the name *nitrogène* was analogous with the names of its compounds, *acide nitrique, nitrates*, etc.

Of even greater influence than Chaptal's *Élémens* was Lavoisier's own *Traité élémentaire de Chimie* (1789). Although in many ways Lavoisier's *Traité* can be compared with the great text-books which came before and after it, like Lemery's *Cours de Chymie* (late seventeenth century) or Thomson's *System of Chemistry* (early nineteenth century), it differed from these in the avowed intention of the author. Lavoisier stated that his aim in writing the book was not primarily to summarize chemical knowledge, nor even to expound his own oxygen theory, but to clarify his ideas on chemical language:

My only object when I undertook this work was to develop further the memoir, which I read at the public meeting of the *Académie des Sciences* in April 1787 on the necessity of reforming and perfecting the nomenclature of chemistry.[153]

But, as Condillac had said, there was an intimate connection between thought and language and

. . . whilst I thought that I was only dealing with nomenclature and whilst my only object was to perfect the language of chemistry, my work was transferred insensibly in my hand, without my being able to control it, into an elementary treatise of chemistry.

Much of the introduction to the *Traité* consisted of a repetition of Lavoisier's memoir on nomenclature read to the *Académie* in 1787 and he again quoted freely from Condillac. In the first part of the book the titles of two chapters referred specifically to nomenclature[154] and a special feature of the work was a series of forty-four tables, accompanied by notes, in which were listed thirty-three 'simple substances' and well over a thousand chemical compounds. These were listed according to the base

153. *Traité élémentaire de Chimie*, Paris, 1789, *Discours Préliminaire*, p. v.
154. Partie 1, chap. 4, *Nomenclature des différentes parties constitutives de l'air de l'atmosphère*; chap. 6, *De la nomenclature des acides en général* etc.

or acid from which the compound was derived and the corresponding names in the old terminology were given where appropriate.

In attempting to study the introduction into the civilized world of the new nomenclature—and the oxygen theory which was closely connected with it—the two main relevant works are the *Méthode* of 1787 and Lavoisier's *Traité* of 1789. Both these books were widely circulated in the late eighteenth and very early nineteenth centuries.[155] There were at least seven French issues of the *Méthode* as well as full translations into English, German, Italian and Spanish. The *Traité* was even more popular, the editions being no less than nine in French, five English, three German, two Dutch, three Italian, one Spanish, three American and one Mexican—all these editions being published up to 1805. It would, however, be quite unrealistic to attribute the spread of the new theory and language solely to these two books. Parts of the *Méthode*, particularly the table and dictionary were widely reproduced in scientific periodicals, text-books, dictionaries and encyclopaedias. Fourcroy, too, played a large part in the dissemination of the nomenclature by means of his *Élémens d'Histoire Naturelle et de Chimie*. The third edition (and subsequent editions) of this book contained the table of new terms and the dictionary taken from the *Méthode*. Fourcroy's *Élémens* was translated into English, German and Spanish, thus making the new terms even more widely known.

The authors of the *Méthode* did what they could to bring the new nomenclature into circulation by using it themselves on every possible occasion. An interesting early example of this occurs in a paper which Lavoisier presented to the *Académie* in November 1786, before the reform of nomenclature.[156] The usual delay in the publication of memoirs resulted in Lavoisier being obliged to wait more than a year to have his work published. He therefore took the opportunity of revising the terms used in the memoir so that it was in conformity with the nomenclature outlined in the *Méthode*.

The real watch-dog of chemical nomenclature, however, was

155. Duveen and Klickstein, *A bibliography of the works of Lavoisier*, London, 1954, pp. 126, 160.

156. '*Réflexions sur la décomposition de l'eau par les substances végétales et animales*' (*Mém. Acad., 1786*, 590–605).

Guyton,[156a] who scrutinized books and periodicals published in France and abroad to assure himself that the reform was being adopted on the lines suggested in the *Méthode*. As one of the editors of the *Annales de Chimie*, and a survivor (unlike Lavoisier) of the political revolution of 1789, Guyton was in a particularly favourable position to comment on the whole field of chemistry and especially that part of the subject which he had cultivated for so long. In 1797 he found occasion to chide some Spanish chemical authors for imperfect understanding of the principles of the 1787 reform and also to criticize the Irish chemist Richard Kirwan whose mineralogical nomenclature was at variance with the changes in chemical terms. Guyton again referred in the *Annales de Chimie* to the subject of nomenclature in the following year when he replied at some length to the criticisms of Dickson published in London. In 1803 Guyton was still on the alert to deplore the modifications in nomenclature proposed by Mitchill in America; Mitchill's ideas, he said, were mere speculations unrelated to experiment. Guyton considered that changes in the nomenclature were only permissible if they were dictated by new experimental observations.[157]

156a. For evidence of a real, if somewhat belated, interest by Berthollet in the subject of nomenclature, see: C.-L. Berthollet, *Essai de statique chimique*, Paris, 1803, vol. i, pp. 449–56; see also ibid., vol. i, p. 386; vol. ii, pp. 235–6, 431–2.

157. *Annales de Chimie*, *21* (1797), 223; *23* (1797), 103–4; *25* (1798), 205–15; *44* (1803), 305–13.

CHAPTER SEVEN

The Reception of the New Nomenclature
in Britain

Despite a complete English translation of the *Méthode* which
was published in London in 1788, the new nomenclature came
into use in this country much more slowly than in France.
Supporters of the phlogiston theory had little patience with the
nomenclature and many others only accepted it with reservations. The publication in 1794 (2nd edn. 1799) of a translation
of the table of nomenclature gave some impetus to the introduction of the new terms. Gradually English ears became accustomed to the sounds of the new French terms, or rather their
anglicised equivalents.

The Translation of the 'Méthode'

The men who were chiefly responsible for the translation of
the new nomenclature in Britain were James St John and
George Pearson in London and Robert Kerr writing in Edinburgh. The full translation made by St John of the *Méthode* was
one of the first translations into any language. St John had
studied in Paris, he had corresponded with Fourcroy on the
subject of his translation and he was convinced of the superiority
of the oxygen theory and the new nomenclature. He pointed
out that, since a fair proportion of the new terms such as
benzoats, formiats, citrats, etc. had no corresponding name in the
old chemistry, their establishment had the right of priority and
he considered it unlikely that any opposition to the new nomenclature would succeed. St John established three important
principles of orthography in the English rendering of the new
nomenclature. The first two suggestions are accepted to this
day:

It has of late been customary in France to change the ph into f in
several words of Greek derivation; and therefore they write sulfur,

sulfite, etc., but I have thought proper to write the words sulphur, etc. agreeable to the custom of English authors. It is also common in France to change the letter y into i, in words derived from the Greek; and therefore they write oxigen and hidrogen, and not oxygen and hydrogen; but as in English we generally retain the figure of the Greek upsilon (Y), though very seldom the sound, I have everywhere written the word oxygen and hydrogen, agreeable to their derivations and conformable to the custom of England.[158]

The third problem concerned compounds of the type now known as sulphides, phosphides, etc. St John proposed that the French term *sulfure* should be translated as 'sulphuret', a term which is even found occasionally to-day in the expression 'sulphuretted hydrogen'.

To-day St John's *Method of Chymical Nomenclature* is quite a rare book and it may be that in 1788 the demand for such a work in England was not as great as it deserved to be. Yet considerable use was made of St John's translation by other writers although they sometimes modified his terms. Part of St John's work was reproduced by Robert White as an appendix to his *Analysis of the New London Pharmacopoeia*,[159] and in 1800 the translator of Gren's text-book of chemistry claimed to have followed St John's terms, which he regarded as standard in the English language.[160]

English Translations of Fourcroy and Lavoisier

The next British publication involving the new nomenclature was a supplementary volume to the English translation of the second edition of Fourcroy's *Élémens*.[161] William Nicholson, who was responsible for this work, was not enthusiastic about the new nomenclature; he nevertheless included a translation of a dictionary of the old and new names in chemistry. In his translation Nicholson sometimes adhered to the French spelling, as in such words as *oxigene, carbone, sulphure*. etc.[162] The translation

158. *Method of Chymical Nomenclature*, trans. St John, London, 1788, pp. viii–ix.
159. *A Summary of the Pneumato-Chemical Theory with a Table of its Nomenclature*, op. cit., Newmarket, 1792.
160. Gren, *Principles of Modern Chemistry*, London, 1800, vol. i, p. vi.
161. *Supplement to the Elements of Natural History and Chemistry of M. de Fourcroy, Carefully extracted from the edition of 1789 and adapted to the English . . .*, London, 1789.
162. These examples resemble the French terms by retaining the final e. This spelling was accepted in the third edition of the *Encyclopaedia Britannica*

of the third edition of Fourcroy's text-book was carried out by a young writer, Robert Heron, who was hardly more optimistic than Nicholson about the chances of success of the new theory and nomenclature. Heron, too, used a spelling similar to the French for many of the new terms and even in 1812 Humphry Davy in his *Elements of Chemical Philosophy* continued to use a similar orthography.

When a further edition of Fourcroy's text-book appeared and Heron was asked to translate it, he abandoned the cloak of anonymity which he had previously assumed and, at the same time, took the opportunity to express his views on translation:

> It is piteous to see what a Babylonish jargon the translation of many books of chemistry, natural history and natural philosophy from foreign tongues has introduced into the English language. . . . Foreign words unnecessarily intermingled with English idioms . . . can never serve the interests of science, and ought never to be employed on the enunciation of it. . . . I have therefore laboured at once to make Fourcroy speak pure perspicuous, intelligible English; and to preserve strictly the propriety, the peculiar phraseology of the science and of the new theory.[163]

More famous than Heron as a translator was Robert Kerr who, in 1790, translated Lavoisier's *Traité Élémentaire* into English. Generally he accepted the orthography of St John including the terms *sulphuret, phosphuret*, etc. but he occasionally showed his independence of Lavoisier's terms. An unfortunate example of this was when he translated Lavoisier's *carbone* as 'charcoal',[164] but he admitted in the preface that this was an oversight and it might be excused considering the hurried conditions of publication of the work.[165]

A Translation of the Table of Nomenclature

Although only one complete English translation of the *Méthode* was published, George Pearson translated the table of

---

(vol. 3 [1791], table opp. p. 598) which was one of the first sources of the new nomenclature in America.

163. *Elements of Chemistry*, 4th edn., London, 1796, vol. i, p. viii.

164. Even nearly 20 years later Dalton often used the term 'charcoal' for carbon, e.g. 'Carbonic oxide is a binary compound, consisting of one atom of charcoal and one of oxygen' (*A New System of Chemical Philosophy*, Part 1, Manchester, 1808, p. 215).

165. Kerr states in the 'Advertisement' that 'the French copy did not

nomenclature which was published, together with a critical
commentary by Pearson, in 1794. Pearson was a fellow of the
Royal Society and a regular contributor on chemical subjects
to the *Philosophical Transactions*. In his *Translation of the Table of
Chemical Nomenclature* Pearson briefly traced the history of the
reform of nomenclature and then went on at some length to
explain the general principles of the new nomenclature. The
table given by Pearson is much larger than that from the
Méthode since the former contained additional synonyms taken
from the London, Edinburgh and Swedish pharmacopoeias.
Pearson published a second enlarged edition of the *Translation*
in 1799 and in this he expressed some concern for the haphazard way in which many of the French terms had been
translated into English. For example, oxygen appeared
variously in translation as *oxigen* or *oxigene*, oxide, as *oxid*, *oxyd*
or *oxyde* and sulphate as *sulphat* or *sulfate*. In his attempt to
standardize the spelling of the new terms, he apologized for his
own practice in the previous edition in writing *oxyd* and *gaz*
for oxide and gas respectively. The same standardization of
spelling was also demanded by Chenevix three years later.[166]

The Attitude to the New Nomenclature of Cavendish, Black and Priestley

The revolution in chemical thought by Lavoisier was largely
based on the work of Black, Cavendish and Priestley and for
this reason it is all the more interesting to consider how these
chemists received Lavoisier's new theory and the language he
used to propagate it. We have on record[167] the remarks made
by Cavendish on reading the *Méthode* soon after its publication.
Cavendish wrote scathingly about the fashion of making up
new names for substances and considered that the new nomenclature would harm chemistry by presupposing the antiphlogistic theory. Any systematic nomenclature was improper,
said Cavendish, because there would spring up as many nomenclatures as there were theories of chemistry. In any case, con-

reach his hands before the middle of September; and it was judged necessary by the publisher that the translation should be ready by the com-
mencement of the University Session at the end of October'.

166. *Remarks upon Chemical Nomenclature*, London, 1802, p. 183.

167. *The Scientific Papers of the Hon. Henry Cavendish*, vol. ii, ed. Sir E.
Thorpe, Cambridge, 1921, pp. 324–6. This is a rough draught of a letter
written by Cavendish in reply to a letter from Blagden (Sept. 1787), in
which the latter commended the *Méthode* to Cavendish's attention.

tinual alteration and improvement would be necessary in the light of subsequent experiments. The only point that Cavendish was willing to concede to the nomenclators was the desirability of having nomenclature based on the composition of neutral salts, since their number was so great, but even then, Cavendish was only referring to the less common salts without established names.

In Edinburgh Black soon became a convert to Lavoisier's theory. On the subject of nomenclature a contemporary of Black remarked,

Dr. Black highly approved of a systematic nomenclature and thought the French extremely ingenious. . . . He disapproved, however, exceedingly of the entire substitution of this for all other denominations of chemical substances.[168]

Black's approval of the reform was therefore a conservative one and he not only continued to use the old terms but even suggested a few names of his own, because of what he considered to be the imperfections of the French terms:

These names have evidently been contrived to suit the genius of the French language in the first place and then have been transferred into . . . Latin words. . . . These latinised French words appeared to me at first very harsh and disagreeable. This, it must be confessed, cannot be avoided in making an attempt of this kind and must therefore be overlooked.[169]

In the naming of acids, Black differed only slightly from the *Méthode* but for the three alkalis he proposed the names *Lixiva*, *Trona* and *Ammonia*. He rendered the French *sulfate de potasse* and *sulfite de potasse* as *lixiva sulphurica* and *lixiva sulphurea* respectively. Although these suggestions occur in his posthumously published lectures, there is evidence that they were made in, or before, 1790.[170]

Priestley, who had contributed so much both to the investigation and naming of many gases, continued to speak of them as

168. Black, *Lectures on the Elements of Chemistry*, ed. Robison, Edinburgh, 1803, vol. i, p. 555.
169. Ibid., pp. 492–3.
170. In a letter from de Luc to la Métherie written in February 1790, *Obs. sur la Physique*, *36* (1790), 290. Robert Kerr incorporated Black's terms into the second edition of his English translation of Lavoisier's *Traité élémentaire* (*Elements of Chemistry*, 2nd edn., Edinburgh, 1793, e.g. pp. 215n., 240n.).

'airs' and was not favourably disposed towards Lavoisier's terms.[171] Priestley remained an adherent of the phlogiston theory right up to his death in 1804 and, in a reference to Lavoisier's followers, maintained that 'their *charbon* or *hydrogène* was nothing but phlogiston'.[172] He recorded his opinions on the new nomenclature after his emigration to America in 1794 and he made it clear that his objection to it was based on his opposition to the antiphlogistic theory. Yet, because the new theory was accepted by most other chemists, the nomenclature based on it was in common use

so that whether [we] adopt the new system or not, we are under the necessity of learning the new language, if we would understand some of the most valuable of modern publications.[173]

Keir's Criticisms

One of the most powerful critics in England of the new chemical nomenclature was James Keir, the English translator of Macquer's *Dictionary of Chemistry* and the author of a dictionary of chemistry in his own right.[174] Keir said that he was provoked to write this dictionary, using the old nomenclature because he had heard that

Mr. Morveau, having enlisted himself under the banners of the antiphlogistic sect, had adopted their new nomenclature, which being adopted to their peculiar opinions, cannot be considered as the general language of chemistry.

Keir's greatest objection to the new nomenclature was its intimate connection with the antiphlogistic theory. He thought that the reformers had exaggerated the harm arising from the use of the old terms *oil of vitriol, butter of arsenic*, etc.[175] Even if it were

171. e.g. 'The *azote* of the new nomenclature is not expressive of anything peculiar to what I have called *phlogisticated air* and the term *vital* does not sufficiently distinguish *dephlogisticated* from *common* or *atmospherical air*' (*Experiments on different kinds of air*, Birmingham, 1790, vol. i, p. 10).

172. *The Scientific Correspondence of Joseph Priestley*, ed. H. C. Bolton, New York, 1892, p. 134.

173. *Considerations on the doctrine of phlogiston*, Philadelphia, 1796, pp. 11–12, 36–7.

174. *First Part of a Dictionary of Chemistry*, Birmingham, 1789, see pp. ii, xv.

175. Preface to the English translation of Macquer's *Dictionnaire* (London, 1790), quoted by Pearson, *A Translation of the Table of Chemical Nomenclature*, London, 1794, pp. 42–3.

generally agreed that a new nomenclature was desirable, he was sceptical about the idea of giving compounds names based on their constituent parts, since these were often imperfectly known; a nomenclature based on the properties of compounds would be more likely to achieve permanence. Keir finally disputed the authority of the French chemists to impose a nomenclature on others. George Pearson, one of the protagonists of the new nomenclature, realized how great Keir's influence was in Britain and remarked:

The eloquence of this author has been, probably, one of the principal causes of the very slow progress of the new chemistry in this country.[176]

Irish Views on the New Nomenclature

An interesting book on chemical nomenclature was published in 1796 by an Irish physician, Stephen Dickson, who was a professor at Trinity College Dublin. His *Essay on Chemical Nomenclature* was lent authority by the inclusion of observations by Richard Kirwan, almost to the extent that it might be called a joint work. Although Dickson agreed with Lavoisier on the importance to chemistry of its language, he did not accept the new terms and his position was fundamentally opposed to that of the reformers. Dickson did not even accept the principle of naming compounds according to their constituent parts, since he considered that the analysis of compounds was not infallible and a major error might necessitate the re-naming of large numbers of compounds. As he himself dramatically asserted:

A single unforeseen and great discovery might one day subvert the entire system of chemical nomenclature [and] bereave every substance in the material world of its name. . . .[177]

Yet, on the other hand, Dickson realized that if every compound had a particular name unrelated to any other, the task merely of learning these names would retard the advance of knowledge. Dickson and Kirwan shared the view that a reform was necessary only on a very limited scale to correct the outstanding misnomers of the old terminology. The language of chemistry

176. Pearson, op. cit., p. 40.
177. Op. cit., London, 1796, p. 12. See also pp. xvi, 44.

could not undergo a reform which completely ignored the common language. As Kirwan said,

> The language of science, not being a language apart, but a branch of that of the country . . . should strictly conform to the parent stock.

Although many of the criticisms of the new nomenclature contained in the *Essay* were of a constructive character, the whole tone of the book was conservative and any influence it had could only have tended to delay the general acceptance of the new chemical nomenclature in Britain.

Kirwan made use of Bergman's terminology in his own writings and in the second edition of his *Elements of Mineralogy* (1794, 1796) he continued to avoid using any form of the French nomenclature. Kirwan gave full expression to his views on the subject of nomenclature in a paper which he read in Dublin in the year 1800.[178] His position then was not so much that he rejected the new terms as that he still reserved the right to use some of the old terms of his own choosing. Although Kirwan had accepted Lavoisier's oxygen theory since 1790, he clearly valued his independence in the matter of chemical and mineralogical names and he objected to the imposition by the French chemists of a comprehensive systematic nomenclature.

The Influence of Bergman's Terminology in Britain

Another person to make use of a systematic nomenclature independent of the French reform and, indeed, previous to it, was Dr Charles Webster. Webster used such a nomenclature in his lectures on chemistry and materia medica in Edinburgh in or before 1786. An account of Webster's lectures was given by Andrew Duncan in a preface to the *Edinburgh New Dispensatory* of 1786. Webster gave examples of Bergman's 'Double Elective Attractions' (i.e. double decomposition) and used most of Bergman's systematic terms such as *aerated vegetable alkali, muriated mineral alkali, sulphurated mercury, barytes,* etc. Webster improved on Bergman's terms by the use of the prefixes *super-* and *sub-* to

---

178. 'Of Chymical and Mineralogical Nomenclature', *Transactions of the Royal Irish Academy,* 8 (1802), 53–76. Kirwan was prompted to write this paper by Guyton de Morveau, a man whom he greatly admired but who had singled him out for attack because of his unorthodox terminology (*Annales de Chimie, 23* (1797), 103–4).

indicate the proportions of the constituents of salts. Although faulty conceptions marred the application of this principle, we cannot but admire its use in certain cases, as when he referred to corrosive sublimate and sweet sublimate as *Super-muriated Mercury* and *Submuriated Mercury* respectively.

The use of Bergman's terminology in the works of Webster, Kirwan and other authors, as well as in the pharmacopoeias,[179] illustrates the fallacy of regarding the reception of the 1787 reform in the British Isles as being a simple issue between, on the one hand, the adherents to the old chemical language with all its abuses and, on the other hand, the supporters of the French reformed nomenclature. Bergman's terms were favoured by a number of chemists because they had all the advantages of being systematic with none of the disadvantages of being linked to the new oxygen theory of 'the French chemists'.

Connected with Bergman's terms, a second rival nomenclature in England in the last decade of the eighteenth century was that introduced in the 1788 edition of the *London Pharmacopoeia*. It was an unfortunate coincidence that the Royal College of Physicians of London decided on a further revision of their pharmacopoeia in the same year (1787) as the French chemists published their *Méthode de nomenclature chimique*. The new pharmaceutical terms, although based on chemical constitution, were thus quite independent of the French reform. Its unhappy timing led to further multiplication of the chemical synonyms current in England. The French nomenclature was only accepted into British pharmacy in the early nineteenth century, first in the *Edinburgh Pharmacopoeia* (1804–5) and finally in the *London Pharmacopoeia* in 1809.

The Names of the Alkalis

A great deal of the opposition to the details of the 1787 reform was directed against the names chosen to denote the alkalis. Lavoisier complained that the reformers were criticized on the one hand for having changed chemical language too much and on the other hand for not having abolished more of the old terms.[180] It was in an attempt to coin as few new words as pos-

---

179. John Rotheram, who edited the fourth edition of the *Edinburgh Pharmacopoeia* (1794), added a table which included Bergman's names for all the neutral salts mentioned in the pharmacopoeia (op. cit., p. 331).

180. *Traité élémentaire de Chimie*, Paris, 1789, pp. 79–80.

sible that the committee of reform of 1787 decided to adopt Guyton's earlier proposal for the use of *soude* and *potasse*. These two terms, together with *ammoniaque*, were attacked, particularly in England and Germany, on the grounds that their use was ambiguous:

> As these names Potash, Soda and Ammoniac have been so long familiar in commerce and different arts, that the united authority of all chemists in Europe, phlogistians and antiphlogistians, could not alter their popular meaning, a confusion seems unavoidable and frequent uncertainty whether the philosophical or popular language be meant.[181]

There was the very real danger that the caustic alkalis (i.e. the hydroxides) might be confused with the mild alkalis (i.e. the carbonates) since the same word could have either meaning according to the system of nomenclature adopted.[182]

Various alternative names for the alkalis in the English language were proposed. Thus in the schemes of Black, Dickson and Kirwan, potash was to be called *lixiva*, *planalkali* and *tartarin* respectively.[183]

Other Proposals for Chemical Nomenclature

One of the first alternative systems to that of the French chemists was published by Hopson in 1789 in his *General System of Chemistry*. The author claimed that his system had been thought of in 1778 before Guyton had published his important memoir on chemical nomenclature. Hopson based his names on

---

181. J. Keir, *First Part of a Dictionary of Chemistry*, Birmingham, 1789, p. xvi.

182. R. Kerr in his translation of Lavoisier's *Traité* had to point out that the word *potash* was used in the book to denote the alkali deprived of carbonic acid (*Elements of Chemistry*, Edinburgh, 1790, p. 93n.). The word *ammonia* was open to an even wider misunderstanding. Kirwan's objection to the term was that 'ammonia' on its own would be generally understood to stand for its most common compound, *sal ammoniac* (*Transactions of the Royal Irish Academy, 8* (1802), 69). The London and Edinburgh pharmacopoeias used 'ammonia' to denote the volatile alkali combined with carbonic acid, as was pointed out by Pearson (*Translation of the Table of Chemical Nomenclature*, London, 1794, p. 23).

183. Black, *Lectures on the Elements of Chemistry*, Edinburgh, 1803, vol. i, p. 493; Dickson, *Essay on Chemical Nomenclature*, London, 1796, p. 242n.; Kirwan, *Elements of Mineralogy*, 2nd edn., London, 1794, 96, vol. i, pp. 5–7.

Greek etymologies. The following are some of the terms he suggested together with their equivalents in the 1787 nomenclature:

spodium	potash
natrum	soda
ammonium	ammoniac
photocratia	phosphates
oxycratia	acetates
vitrioloxys	sulphuric acid
sulphuroxys	sulphurous acid

For many salts composed of more than two constituents, he suggested that trivial names might be used. His suggestion of *Tartarus spodiconatrosius* for Rochelle salt was based on a more accurate analysis than the name *Tartrite de soude* of the French nomenclature. Hopson divided the simpler salts into three classes: the neutral salts, 'the *hyperoxea* or *superacidated* in which the acid part predominates and *hypoxea* or *subacidated* in which the alkaline part abounds'.

The young Humphry Davy also had his own ideas about chemical terms. He proposed the name *phosoxygen* for oxygen, an amendment which he extended to its compounds, e.g. *Nitrous phosoxyd* and *Phosmuriate of Soda*.[184] In 1810–12 Davy again tried to contribute to chemical nomenclature by proposing a comprehensive system of suffixes to denote the proportions of constituents in a compound.[185] These suggestions of Davy like those of Hopson are mentioned, not because they ever became accepted, but because they illustrate what one writer called '*la contagion nomenclative*'.[186] Living in the shadow of men who had earned fame through the reform of nomenclature of 1787, it was hard for some chemists to refrain from trying to make their own contribution.

The Introduction of the New Terms as Synonyms

One of the chief arguments of the opponents of the new nomenclature was the impracticability of any general change

184. *An Essay on Heat, Light and the Combinations of Light* in Beddoes, *Contributions to Physical and Medical Knowledge*, Bristol, 1799, pp. 5–147. For Davy's lasting contributions to chemical nomenclature see p. 221.

185. *Collected Works*, London, 1839–40, vol. iv, pp. xi–xiii. See also vol. v, p. 346.

186. B. Sage, *Exposé des Effets de la Contagion Nomenclative*, Paris, 1810. See also *Encyclopaedia Britannica*, 3rd edn., Edinburgh, 1797, vol. 14, pp. 597–8.

of terms. It was not possible, as the committee of the *Académie des Sciences* appointed to review the *Méthode* had pointed out, to change overnight from one set of terms to another. It is probable that if the reformers had merely proposed a new system of terms, the critics might have been more successful in dissuading chemists from using the new nomenclature. Lavoisier and his colleagues, however, were sure enough of their position to adopt the strategy of using the new terms without apology in all their published works,[187] so that even a convinced phlogistian like Priestley complained that, although he did not accept the new nomenclature, he had been forced to learn it in order to follow the development of chemistry in the last decade of the eighteenth century.[188] The problem which concerns us here is how the new terms were explained to chemists and others who had been accustomed to the old terminology. Apart from the method of guessing a word from its context, chemists came to understand the meaning of the new terms from published lists of synonyms, of which the prototype was included in the *Méthode* of 1787. This list of synonyms and its various translations must have been widely used at the end of the eighteenth century.

The dictionary of synonyms had its precedent in the indices of old and new names appended to the eighteenth-century pharmacopoeias, notably the *Pharmacopoeia Londinensis* of 1746. It was particularly important in pharmacy, where a human life rather than a laboratory experiment might be involved, that there should be no confusion of terms. When the committee of the Royal College of Physicians therefore recommended that certain terms should be changed, they not only explained the alterations in an appendix, but added the old name to the new one:

> To avoid any unnecessary perplexity . . . where the name only of the medicine is altered, the old appellation, however absurd, is subjoined to the new one.[189]

Lavoisier appreciated that the easiest way of introducing a new term into chemistry was to use it as a synonym, and in a memoir read to the *Académie des Sciences* in March 1780, he first

187. Lavoisier and Fourcroy in particular had a reading public in the 1790's which extended across Europe and to America.

188. *Considerations of the Doctrine of Phlogiston*, Philadelphia, 1796, p. 37.

189. *A Draught for the reformation of the London Pharmacopoeia*, London, 1742, p. xxiii.

explained the term *oxygine* and then repeatedly used the phrase '*principe acidifiant ou oxygine*' in an attempt to give his term currency.[190]

The continual use of synonyms was related to the instability and uncertainties in chemical nomenclature in the 1790's in Britain and Germany. We cannot but sympathize with a writer in England, who in January 1798 was uncertain whether he should use the old or new terms in a book on gases. He therefore adopted a curious compromise in which he used such expressions as 'the dephlogisticated or oxygen air':

> By the mixt use of the old and the new chemical names in various parts of the work, the author imagines that his meaning may be rendered less equivocal and more generally intelligible; for at a time when the old names are not quite disused, and the new chemical nomenclature not universally understood, it is difficult to determine whether the greatest number of readers may remain satisfied with the exclusive use of either.[191]

Guyton was complaining in 1797 of his disgust with the copious lists of synonyms, which would be necessary if people were unwilling to accept the 1787 reform.[192] Lists of synonyms might have been necessary under the old regime (in which the same substance might have different names) and we have seen their use in the period of transition. The advantage of the new terms was that ideally they should be short and self-explanatory and in the early nineteenth century when they had become generally well known, the need for synonyms had passed and the nomenclature of inorganic chemistry enjoyed a short period of stability before it was again disturbed, this time by quantitative considerations.

The Acceptance of the New Nomenclature in Britain

In conclusion, we may review the progress of the new nomenclature in Britain in the last decade of the eighteenth century. A few months after the publication of the *Méthode de nomenclature chimique*, Cavendish was prophesying that the new nomenclature

190. *Mém. Acad.*, *1780*, 349ff.
191. T. Cavallo, *Essay on the Medicinal Properties of Factitious Airs*, London, 1798, pp. v–vi.
192. *Annales de Chimie*, *23* (1797), 104.

would never come into use.[193] Even in 1795, William Nicholson, who was then inclined to favour the new nomenclature, refrained from using it in his *Chemical Dictionary* since, as he put it, to do so would be to anticipate the public choice.[194] It seems that even in 1800 the old nomenclature was still the one most generally known, the reformed nomenclature being known only to students of chemistry. One writer revealed an important dichotomy when he related that he had

many times witnessed an article being asked for in the new style, and the shop-man not being able to comprehend what was meant; while on the other hand, the pupil of modern Chemistry, unacquainted with the old name of the substance, was unable to explain what he wanted.[195]

The new chemical nomenclature was accepted by students of chemistry long before those engaged in commerce or pharmacy became familiar with the terms. The chemist Thomas Thomson said that when he studied under Black in Edinburgh in 1796, the new chemical nomenclature was in common use among the students and, indeed, some students there had been using it since about 1791.[196] Yet, even as late as 1807, a chemical author remarked that the old terms were still retained in shops and laboratories.[197] It was, nevertheless, admitted that by that time the new terms had become 'the vernacular tongue of scientific chemistry'.

193. *The Scientific Papers of the Hon. Henry Cavendish*, vol. ii, ed. Sir E. Thorpe, Cambridge, 1921, p. 326.

194. Op. cit., London, 1795, vol. i, p. vii.

195. Gren, *Principles of Modern Chemistry*, trans., London, 1800, vol. i, p. xiii.

196. *History of Chemistry*, London, 1830, 31, vol. ii, p. 133. *Annales de Chimie*, *8* (1791), 228.

197. A. and C. R. Aikin, *Dictionary of Chemistry and Mineralogy*, London, 1807, vol. i, p. viii.

CHAPTER EIGHT

The Adoption of the New Nomenclature in Other Countries

Germany

Germany held quite an important place in late eighteenth-century chemistry, even though this was the period when it was outshone by its neighbours. One of the first German chemists to advocate the use of the new nomenclature was Hermbstaedt. In his text-book of 1791 [198] he outlined the new terms and regularly made use of them in footnotes. In the following year he published a translation of Lavoisier's *Traité*, in which he did his best to translate the original terms faithfully, although several of his terms were not happily chosen. [199]

Probably the first exposition of the French nomenclature to appear in German was by Göttling, editor of the *Taschen Buch für Scheidekünstler und Apotheker*, [200] who gave a short summary of the nomenclature in response to the request of his readers. Göttling had not been able to secure a copy of the *Méthode de nomenclature chimique* and his account was therefore based on la Métherie's summary of September 1787 in the *Observations sur la Physique*. Göttling tried to find equivalent German expressions for each French term so that he explained *la baryte* as *Schwerstoff*, *carbone* as *Kohlenbasis*, etc. He hardly faced at all the important problem of founding a German nomenclature and many of his terms were descriptions rather than names.

Of more consequence than Göttling's names were those coined by C. Girtanner and J. F. von Jacquin in the summer of 1790 and published in a booklet by Girtanner in the following year under the title *Neue Chemische Nomenklatur für die Deutsche*

---

198. *Systematisches Grundriss der allgemeinen Experimentalchemie*, Berlin, 1791, Part 1, pp. 248–9, etc.
199. *System der antiphlogistischen Chemie*, Berlin and Stettin, 1792.
200. Op. cit., *1790*, 147–55.

Sprache. The following are examples of Girtanner's rather cumbersome terms:

Rothe Quecksilber Halbsäure	(*oxide de mercure rouge*)
Kochsalzgesäuertes Gas	(*gas acide muriatique*)
Salpetergesäuerte Pottasche	(*nitrate de potasse*)

It was Girtanner's nomenclature in the main which was used by Meidinger in his translation of the *Méthode de nomenclature chimique* in 1793. Although Meidinger did not adhere strictly to all Girtanner's terms, he paid tribute to him as the man who had 'broken the ice' and had set an example of translation from which later writers could profit.[201] Meidinger had been prepared to accept Girtanner's *Halbsäure* for 'oxide' for want of a better expression, but few others were prepared to accept Girtanner's terms.[202] J. B. Trommsdorff, professor of chemistry in the University of Erfurt, remarked resentfully that it was Girtanner's ambition to be the chief reformer of chemistry in Germany. Trommsdorff was one of those who, whilst not complacent about the current German terms, condemned the French nomenclature outright as a monstrosity (*eine Missgeburt*).[203] This represented one extreme view; in contrast Gren applauded the 1787 reform as a masterpiece (*ein Meisterstück*).[204]

There were three main obstacles to the adoption of the new French nomenclature in Germany. In the first place the phlogiston theory had been propounded by Becher and Stahl and was regarded in a nationalistic light as a German theory as opposed to the 'French theory' of oxygen. Secondly we should remember that the country we call Germany did not exist in the eighteenth century. There were instead a number of independent states sharing a common language. The language itself presented a third difficulty. Many Germans were averse to taking over the French terms into the German language as had been done with many common words. As one writer later expressed it, the genius of the German language would not

201. *Methode der chemischen Nomenklatur für das antiphlogistische System*, Vienna, 1793, p. 9.
202. Girtanner's *Halbsäure* was criticized by J. A. Scherer, in his *Versuch einer neuen Nomenclatur für Deutsche Chymisten*, Vienna, 1792, p. 37.
203. *Journal der Pharmacie*, ed. Trommsdorff, *1* (1794), 186, 190.
204. *Neues Journal der Physik*, ed. Gren, *1795, II*, 176.

tolerate being clothed in so motley a garment as the Franco-Greek nomenclature.[205]

Certain expressions were particularly difficult to translate into German. The term 'oxygen' (rendered by several literal translations and finally translated as *Sauerstoff*) was not so much of a stumbling block as the word 'oxide' which was translated into German variously as *Kalk* (calx), *Oxyd*, *Halbsäure* (half-acid) and *Säuerling*. It was probably in the German language that most difficulty was experienced in translating the new French words denoting the proportion of oxygen in an acid or salt. In the early years of the new nomenclature there was a general reluctance to admit terms so closely linked to the oxygen theory, for example, as sulphur*ous* and sulphur*ic* acids. Even when the majority of the leading German chemists had accepted Lavoisier's theory,[206] they found difficulties in adapting into the German language the simple system of suffixes suggested by the French chemists. A final translation of the French terms into German was only achieved after many years of trial and discussion.

An example of the diversity of nomenclature prevalent in Germany in the 1790's, which was not without influence on the main stream of chemistry, is provided by J. B. Richter who, while admitting the advantages of adhering to a common system of nomenclature, insisted on using such curious terms as *Wasserschwefel* ('water-sulphur') for hydrogen, etc.[207] There is little doubt that the eccentricity of his terminology was one reason why Richter's contemporaries paid slight attention to his quantitative chemical work, especially the Law of Reciprocal Proportions.

If anything approaching a standard German chemical nomenclature came into being in the last few years of the eighteenth century, it was that of Gren, whose diplomacy in his attitude towards both the phlogiston and the oxygen theories[208] and his use of latininized terms earned him the support of many leading chemists. The editors of the scientific

205. L. W. Gilbert, *Annalen der Physik*, 59 (1818), 232n.
206. Kahlbaum and Hoffmann list some twenty leading German chemists who had accepted Lavoisier's theory by 1795 (*Die Einführung der Lavoisierschen Theorie im Besonderen in Deutschland*, Leipzig, 1897, p. 111).
207. *Ueber die neuern Gegenstände der Chymie*, Breslau, Part 7, 1796.
208. '*Entwurf einer neuen chemischen Nomenclatur, die auf keine Hypothesen gegrundet ist*', *Neues Journal der Physik*, 1795, II, 173–285, 376–93.

journals were in a position to exercise some authority in standardizing nomenclature. Unfortunately Crell, whose *Annalen* could have done much to standardize German chemical names, remained hostile to the new nomenclature.[209] Gren, however, as editor of the *Neues Journal der Physik* from 1795–7, was able to exert his influence to introduce some stability in chemical terms and in the early nineteenth century Gilbert, the editor of the *Annalen der Physik*, worked towards the unification of German chemical nomenclature.[210]

Sweden

It was only in 1795 that a serious attempt was made to translate the French terms into Swedish.[211] The difficulties encountered were similar to those in the German language. Thus oxides were referred to as *syrsatt kropp* and to denote a particular sulphide a circumlocution such as *svefelbundet järn* (i.e. iron joined with sulphur) was required.[212] Although these examples of nomenclature were accepted by Swedish chemists including the young Berzelius, the latter in 1811 was outspoken in his criticism of many of the chemical terms which were then passing into the Swedish language.[213] Berzelius wanted a standardized chemical nomenclature based on the Latin language and he referred to the successful international nomenclature of botany introduced by his fellow-countryman, Linnaeus.

Italy

The transmission of the new nomenclature to Italy was a little more rapid. A summary of the proposed nomenclature was published in Italian in 1789[214] and in the following year there appeared a translation of the *Méthode de nomenclature chimique* by Calloud. Dandolo, the translator of Lavoisier's works, also translated the new terms in the form of a dictionary,

209. *Chemische Annalen*, ed. Crell, *1800*, I, 523–36.

210. e.g. *Annalen der Physik*, *49* (1815), 2–3.

211. Ekeberg and P. Afzelius, *Försök till svensk nomenklatur für Chemien*. A. Sparrmann's Swedish translation of Fourcroy's *Philosophie Chimique* also appeared in 1795.

212. H. G. Söderbaum, *Berzelius' Werden und Wachsen*, Leipzig, 1899, pp. 198–9.

213. *Journal de Physique*, *73* (1811), 253–86.

214. 'Methodo di Nomenclatura Chimica . . . estratte de Sig. del a Metherie', *Opuscoli Scelti sulla Scienze*, *12* (1789), 11 -20.

which went through three editions in the years 1791–6. Even the briefest reference to the reception of the French nomenclature in Italy would be incomplete without mention of Luigi Brugnatelli, professor of chemistry at Pavia. Brugnatelli advocated several important deviations from the French terms[215] and his influence as the author of text-books of chemistry and a pharmacopoeia as well as editor of several scientific journals was sufficient for several other Italian chemists to use the terms he proposed. Most of Brugnatelli's terms were suggested as little more than a gesture of independence and their effect was merely to delay the general acceptance of a standard chemical nomenclature in Italy.

Spain and Portugal

In Spain, Pedro Gutierrez Bueno, professor of chemistry at the *Real Laboratio* in Madrid published a translation of the chief contents of the *Méthode de nomenclature chimique* in October 1788[216] and further impetus was given to the new nomenclature in Spain, as in other countries, by the translations of the later editions of Fourcroy's *Élémens*. The first national pharmacopoeia to make some use of the reformed nomenclature was the *Pharmacopoeia Hispanica* of 1794.[217] In Portugal the chief protagonist of the new nomenclature was Vicente Coelho de Seabra Silva Telles (1764–1804), who used the new terms in the second part of his *Elementos de Chimica* (1790) and later published a book on the subject of nomenclature.

Russia

In Russia there was some delay in the adoption of the new nomenclature.[218] Whereas in the rest of Europe the new nomen-

215. e.g. *Opuscoli Scelti*, *18* (1795), 217–31 and *Annali di Chimica*, *18* (1800?), 195ff.

216. J. R Mourelo: '*Quelques antécédents de la chimie scientifique en Espagne*', *Beiträge aus der Geschichte der Chemie*, ed. P. Diergart, Leipzig and Vienna, 1909, pp. 406–12.

217. The new terms were used in an index to the pharmacopoeia and not in the main part of the book. Credit must be given to the Prussian pharmacopoeia for being the first to make full use of the reformed chemical nomenclature. At the same time it should be appreciated that there was little language difficulty involved, since the *Pharmacopoeia Borussica* of 1799 used Latin terms.

218. H. M. Leicester, 'The Spread of the Theory of Lavoisier in Russia', *Chymia*, *5* (1959), 138–44. See also *J. Chem. Ed.*, *28* (1951), 581–3.

clature had been adapted to the various languages and was widely used by chemists by the year 1800, in Russia educated people, who used French as a second language, were content at first to use the French chemical terms. It was only in the first decade of the nineteenth century that the leading chemists, men such as A. N. Scherer, V. M. Severgin and Y. D. Zakharov, recognized the need to establish the new chemical nomenclature in the Russian language. Although they began to use the new terms in their published work, Russian chemical nomenclature did not assume its essentially modern form until the publication of G. H. Hess's *Fundamentals of Pure Chemistry* (1831–1833). The Russian words for some of the elements (e.g. hydrogen, oxygen) show the influence of the German practice of literal translation, although the French *azote* was incorporated into the Russian language and the names of many other elements were simply transliterations of the terms used in Western Europe.

America[219]

Although no complete translation of the *Méthode de nomenclature chimique* was published in the United States, three major works concerned with the new nomenclature were published in America between the years 1794–9, apart from articles in encyclopaedias, etc. and works published in Britain and brought across the Atlantic.

One of the first recorded references to the new nomenclature by an American was made by the statesman Thomas Jefferson, who was in France from 1784–9. Jefferson, who kept up to date with the scientific developments of his day, referred to the French nomenclature in a letter written from Paris in July 1788. He considered that Lavoisier's theory was not sufficiently established by experiment. It was therefore too soon to undertake a reform of nomenclature:

One single experiment may destroy the whole filiation of his terms and his string of sulfates, sulfites and sulfures may have served no other end than to have retarded the progress of the science by a jargon, from the confusion of which time will be required to extricate us.

Later in the same year Jefferson wrote that much of what had been published in the new nomenclature would have to be

219. The contents of this section are based principally on two papers by Duveen and Klickstein, *Isis*, *45* (1954), 278–92, 368–82.

translated into the ordinary chemical language before it would be useful.

The first American printed version of the new nomenclature was published in Philadelphia in 1791 in a pirated edition of the *Encyclopaedia Britannica*, published by Thomas Dobson. To illustrate the new nomenclature Dobson reproduced a table taken from the Edinburgh *Encyclopaedia Britannica*, which was itself based on Heron's English translation of the third edition of Fourcroy's *Élémens d'histoire naturelle et de chimie*.

The first American exponent of the new nomenclature was Samuel Mitchill, who published his *Nomenclature of the new chemistry* in 1794. Although Mitchill had originally supported the phlogiston theory, by 1792, when he was appointed to a chair at Columbia College New York, he had been won over to Lavoisier's theory[220] and made full use of the new nomenclature in his lectures. In 1794 Mitchill considered that it was essential for people to understand the new terms, since they were adopted in England, Holland and Italy and were then being introduced into Germany. Mitchill's book was in fact based on Girtanner's *Neue chemische Nomenklatur für die deutsche Sprache* (Berlin, 1791) since Mitchill considered that Girtanner's discussion of the subject was preferable to a translation based on the *Méthode* of 1787. The English terms used by Mitchill were taken from St John's translation of 1788. Mitchill remarked that

the table of the new nomenclature [is] a beautiful specimen of the analytic method, and an arrangement happily calculated to systematise and simplify the study of chemistry.[221]

In fact the entire course of Mitchill's lectures on chemistry at Columbia was based on the table of nomenclature.

A second important work on nomenclature was published at Hanover (N. H.) by Lyman Spalding in 1799.[222] Spalding had graduated in 1797 and was almost immediately appointed as lecturer in chemistry at the newly founded Dartmouth Medical School. It was to his students at Dartmouth that Spalding ad-

220. Mitchill, nevertheless, assumed the role of arbitrator between the supporters of the new theory and the phlogistians led by Priestley, who had left England for America in 1794 (see e.g. *Medical Repository*, 1 (1798), 514ff.).

221. *Medical Repository*, 1 (1798), 225.

222. *A New Nomenclature of Chemistry proposed by Messrs. de Morveau, Lavoisier, Berthollet and Fourcroy with additions and improvements*.

dressed his work on nomenclature, which was apparently written independently of Mitchill's work. The third American to contribute to the introduction of the new chemical nomenclature was John Vaughan, a physician from Pennsylvania. His *Chemical Syllabus* (Wilmington, Delaware, November 1799) was an explanation of the new terms intended primarily for the layman. It was a more faithful translation of part of the *Méthode* than the books of Mitchill and Spalding. This book concludes the eighteenth-century contributions to the introduction of the new nomenclature in America, but we should not forget Lavoisier's own *Traité*, the English translations of which were known in the American colleges and American editions of which appeared from 1799 onwards. It is safe to conclude that by the end of the eighteenth century the new chemical nomenclature was generally accepted in America.

CHAPTER NINE

Early Nineteenth-Century Amendments and Improvements to the 1787 Reform in the Field of Inorganic Chemistry

Lavoisier and his colleagues chose the title of their book deliberately. It demonstrated a *method* of naming substances and made no claim to be complete. As chemistry expanded, the authors hoped that the new names coined by chemists would be in conformity with the principles set out in their book.[223] One of the greatest limitations of the 1787 reform was that in establishing a qualitative nomenclature it largely ignored the quantitative aspect. Yet it could hardly have been expected to achieve a quantitative nomenclature until a greater number of compounds had been subjected to accurate quantitative analysis. Another weakness recognized by Lavoisier was the use of radicals of an unknown base, particularly the *radical muriatique*. He made it clear that further experiment might necessitate an alteration of this name, as indeed it did.

Once the 1787 reform had become accepted and the *Méthode de nomenclature chimique* had become a historical document, voices of some extremists were heard demanding a second complete reform of nomenclature in chemistry. Thus, only fifteen years after the publication of the *Méthode* and a much shorter time after its general acceptance in Britain, the English chemist Chenevix claimed that

> Chemistry is now in a state that demands a full revision of the nomenclature ... for this purpose a select number of chemists should be deputed. . . .[224]

At the other extreme were those who preferred to keep the old names rather than accept a continual change in chemical terms:

223. *Méthode de nomenclature chimique*, Paris, 1787, pp. 17, 106.
224. *Remarks upon chemical nomenclature*, London, 1802, pp. 191-2.

A stable nomenclature not exactly correct is better than one varying with the discovery of new analogies.[225]

Some changes, however, were necessary—those occasioned by the progress of chemical theory and by new discoveries. Additions were accordingly made here and there to the nomenclature until its structure was more of a patchwork than a system. It was the Swedish chemist Berzelius, who had been engaged in 1811 in compiling a new Swedish pharmacopoeia, who came forward with constructive proposals for a unified nomenclature based on Latin terms. Berzelius' terms expressed the constitution of compounds *quantitatively* and his international authority in chemical circles was sufficient to bring about their eventual adoption.

The early nineteenth century saw the completion of the general system of nomenclature of inorganic chemistry by the use of methods of indicating the proportions of elements in compounds. The beginnings of this quantitative aspect of nomenclature can be seen already in the work of Bergman. The essence of this nomenclature lies in the use of a system of prefixes and suffixes which owe not only their Latin or Greek etymologies but also their application to the classical tradition in late eighteenth-century Europe. Bergman had made use of suffixes to bring together analagous substances, and in 1784 he turned this method to good account in distinguishing different compounds of the same elements:

> In the *Sciagraphia Regni Mineralis* lately published I have overlooked the mutual proportions; but on further reflection, I find the consideration of them absolutely necessary.[226]

In those cases where an acid formed more than one series of salts, Bergman denoted the difference between the acid salt and the corresponding neutral salt by an appropriate suffix, e.g. *tartareum potassini* (potassium bisulphate), *tartareum potassinatum* (potassium sulphate), The French reformers did not find it so easy, however, to express concisely the salts in which there was a preponderance of either acid or base, and in denoting compounds of two elements which could combine in different proportions, they made little progress. Corrosive sublimate and calomel were merely called *muriate de mercure corrosif* and *muriate*

225. Dickson, *Essay on Chemical Nomenclature*, London, 1796, p. 149.
226. *Nova Acta Reg. Soc. Scient. Upsaliensis, 4* (1784), 99.

de mercure doux, and the two common oxides of iron were referred to as *oxide de fer rouge* and *oxide de fer noir*.

An improvement on this method was very much needed especially when, in the early nineteenth century, the proportions in which elements combine had been accurately estimated and various laws of chemical combination were established. In Britain Thomas Thomson adopted the prefixes *super-* and *sub-* to denote the various proportions of the constituents of compounds. He credited Pearson (1799) with originating this use, but as early as 1786 (or even earlier) Dr Charles Webster was using the expressions *Super-muriated Mercury* (corrosive sublimate, $HgCl_2$) and *Submuriated Mercury* (calomel, Hg_2Cl_2) in his lectures in Edinburgh.[227] Pearson later suggested the use of these prefixes in the second edition of his commentary on the French nomenclature (1799). He distinguished between *Tartrite of Vegalkali* (potassium tartrate) and *Super-tartrite of Vegalkali* (potassium hydrogen tartrate). His *Sub-borate of soda* was common borax and his *Sub-carbonate of Vegalkali* was normal potassium carbonate. Pearson would have liked to have distinguished the different oxides of a particular metal according to the proportion of oxygen it contained, but, as he admitted in 1794, 'the proportions are not yet investigated'. He therefore continued to use the method tolerated by Lavoisier and his colleagues of using epithets usually related to colour, to distinguish the oxides. It was Thomson who pointed out that such a method could be misleading:

One of the oxides of iron, for instance, was called *black oxide*, another was termed *red oxide*; but it is now known that the same oxide is capable of assuming different colours according to circumstances. The mode of naming them from their colour, therefore, wants precision, and is apt to mislead; especially as there occur different examples of two distinct oxides of the same metal having the same colour.[228]

Thomson suggested a better method of distinguishing the oxides:

I shall, till some better method be proposed, distinguish them from each other by prefixing to the word *oxide* the first syllable of the Greek ordinal numerals. Thus the *protoxide* of a metal will denote the metal

227. *The Edinburgh New Dispensatory*, ed. A. Duncan, Edinburgh, 1786. p. xxx. Webster also used the prefixes *super-* and *sub-* in several other cases, often inappropriately in the light of subsequent analysis.
228. *System of Chemistry*, 3rd edn., Edinburgh, 1807, vol. i, p. 140.

combined with a minimum of oxygen or the *first oxide* which the metal is capable of forming; *deutoxide* will denote the second oxide as the metal. . . . When a metal has combined with as much oxygen as possible, I shall denote the compound formed by the term *peroxide*, indicating by it that the metal is thoroughly oxidised.

In Thomson's scheme then, the lowest oxide was the *protoxide*, the highest the *peroxide* and the intermediate oxides were called *deutoxide, tritoxide, tetoxide* [*sic*], *pentoxide*, etc. as required.

Berzelius pointed out that, although Thomson's method seemed very good, in practice it would lead to great confusion. The method depended on a complete knowledge of the oxides of any metal but, since in the early nineteenth century the oxides of many metals had not been fully investigated, the discovery of another oxide (particularly one containing a smaller proportion of oxygen) would upset the nomenclature of the whole series:

Up to now the yellow oxide of lead has been called the *protoxide*. M. Dulong has found that lead can form a lower oxide, which must necessarily assume the name of protoxide; this will necessitate changing the names of the three others and the *protoxide* of 1818 will be the *deutoxide* of 1820.[229]

There were other examples of these quantitative chemical names leading to confusion. It had at one time been thought that there were three oxides each of sodium and potassium, but by 1825 it had been shown that only two had been discovered. This led to the following change of names:[230]

Old name	New name
Protoxide	(not a chemical compound)
Deutoxide	Protoxide
Tritoxide	Deutoxide

The introduction of quantitative names was a necessary corollary to the Atomic Theory. At first, these names merely indicated proportions, but when the atomic theory was accepted, the names came to denote definite numbers of atoms. Dalton himself realized that his ideas on the constitution of matter entailed a new approach to nomenclature:

229. *Essai sur la théorie des proportions chimiques*, Paris, 1819, pp. 160–1.
230. Caventou, *Nouvelle nomenclature chimique*, 2nd edn., Paris, 1825, p. ix.

If the system I proceed upon be adopted, a general reformation of nomenclature will be the consequence, having reference to the number of atoms as well as the kind of elements constituting the different compound bodies.[231]

The extent to which quantitative names came to dominate chemistry in the nineteenth century is implied in Thomson's drastic statement in the preface to one of his text-books:

When the simple name of a compound occurs, it is to be understood that it is a compound of one atom of each constituent.[232]

An original method of nomenclature for acid and normal salts was introduced by Thomson about 1815 and, although it is misleading, it is still widely used to-day. By the use of the prefix *bi-*, Thomson dispensed with *super-* and *sub-* to distinguish salts of the same acid and base.[233] The results of analysis indicated that the salts then called *sulphate of potash* and *subcarbonate of potash* contained one part of potash and one part of the respective acid radical, whereas the so-called *supersulphate* and *carbonate* contained twice as much of the acid radical for the same quantity of potash. For the latter he therefore proposed the names *bisulphate* and *bicarbonate* respectively.

When Humphry Davy succeeded in decomposing soda, potash, baryta, etc. and isolated the respective metals, he performed an important service to chemistry. There is one aspect of his achievement, however, which had unfortunate consequences in chemical nomenclature. This was the clumsy method used to bring the nomenclature of the salts of the heavy metals into conformity with the salts of the alkalis and alkaline earths. The names *sulfate de soude*, *carbonate de baryte*, etc. had been given by the reformers of 1787 on the assumption that the bases of these salts were simple bodies. When this was found not to be so, instead of changing the names of these salts, the names of the salts of the heavy metals were altered and the name of every salt was related to the appropriate *oxide* of the metal. This method was favoured particularly by the leading French chemists in the first half of the nineteenth century.

---

231. *A New System of Chemical Philosophy*, Part 2, Manchester, 1810, preface.

232. *An attempt to establish the first principles of chemistry by experiment*, London, 1825, vol. i, p. xix.

233. *Annals of Philosophy*, 6 (1815), 233.

When Thenard[234] implied that the term *sulfate de protoxide de plomb* was equivalent to *sulfite de bioxide de plomb*, he was ignoring the different radicals involved despite the fact that the total degree of oxidation in both cases might be said to be equal. The method was, however, able to deal effectively (if somewhat clumsily) with salts of the same metal, so that what we now call ferrous and ferric sulphates were *sulfate de protoxide de fer* and *sulfate de peroxide de fer*. In England the shorter expressions *protosulphate of iron* and *persulphate of iron* were used, although such terms were logically inferior to the exact statement of the French and were criticized for this reason by Vauquelin.[235] Dumas, for his part, would consent to no abbreviation of expressions like *bi-sulfate de deutoxide de cuivre*, etc.[236] An alternative system of referring to the oxides of the metals, used mainly in France and Germany, was to make use of the diminutive term *oxidule* as well as oxide. The two sulphates of iron would then be *sulfas ferri oxidulati* and *sulfas ferri oxidati*.

It was Berzelius who saved chemistry from all these circumlocutions and he did this mainly by extending the 1787 proposals for the naming of the acids. The authors of the *Méthode* had suggested that the difference of oxygen in acids should be indicated by the use of suitable suffixes, e.g. *acidum sulfurosum, acidum sulfuricum*. On similar principles Berzelius proposed the names *oxidum ferrosum* and *oxidum ferricum* as well as *sulfas ferrosus* and *sulfas ferricus*.[237] Where a metal had more than two oxides, Berzelius used suitable prefixes to distinguish them and spoke of suboxides, oxides and peroxides. Berzelius adopted the idea of Wollaston[238] of indicating in the name of a salt the numerical proportion of the constituents.[239] The three oxalates of potash then acquired their present names: *potassium oxalate, potassium binoxalate, potassium quadroxalate*. Berzelius' use of other prefixes is shown in such names as *nitras biplumbicus, triplumbicus, sesquiplumbicus*. Each of these names reflected the analytical results of Berzelius as well as his insistence on clear terminology. He had

234. *Traité de Chimie*, 6th edn., Paris, 1834, vol. v, p. 496.

235. '*Rapport Verbal*' in Caventou, *Nouvelle nomenclature chimique*, Paris, 1825, p. xviii.

236. *Traité de Chimie*, Paris, 1828, vol. i, p. xv.

237. *Journal de Physique*, *73* (1811), 262, 266.

238. 'On the Super-Acid and Sub-Acid Salts', *Phil. Trans.*, *98* (1808), 96–102.

239. *Essai sur la théorie des proportions chimiques*, Paris, 1819, p. 169.

nothing but criticism for the *sub protosulphates* and even *sub- bi- per-sulphates*, of Thomson.[240]

Many of Berzelius' ideas on nomenclature were accepted only after some delay, particularly in France where, perhaps, a reform by Frenchmen would have been more welcome. Writing in 1828 to Jourdan, the translator of his *Traité*, Berzelius remarked that nomenclature was rather a delicate subject and he was quite aware of the sensitivity of Frenchmen about nomenclature.[241] He deliberately refrained from proposing more alterations than he considered absolutely necessary, and he thus arrived at a system of terms not very unlike those then current in France.[242]

It fell to the chemists of the early nineteenth century to extend the principles of the 1787 reform to new substances. When Davy applied the voltaic pile to the analysis of the alkalis soda and potash, he was able to isolate their bases for the first time. To the new metals Davy gave the names *sodium* and *potassium* by combining the name of the respective compound with the suffix *-um*, used by Bergman to denote metals. By the same electrical method Davy was able to isolate metals from the alkaline earths and he gave these the names *barium, strontium, calcium* and *magnium* (magnesium).[243]

More appropriate names also had to be given to substances the nature of which had become better known. Such a substance was the muriatic radical, which, on oxidation, was found by Davy to yield an element for which he proposed the name *chlorine* instead of the current term *oxymuriatic acid*:

> To call a body which is not known to contain oxygen, and which cannot contain muriatic acid, *oxymuriatic acid*, is contrary to the principles of that nomenclature in which it is adopted; and an alteration of it seems necessary to assist the progress of the discussion and to diffuse just ideas on that subject. . . .

> After consulting some of the most eminent chemical philosophers of this country, it has been judged most proper to suggest a name founded upon one of its obvious and characteristic properties—its colour, and to call it *Chlorine*[244] or *chloric gas*.[245]

240. *Annals of Philosophy, 10* (1817), 98–103.
241. *J. Berzelius' Bref*, ed. Söderbaum, Uppsala, 1912–35, Part 7, p. 177.
242. *Traité de Chimie*, Brussels, 1833, p. 12.
243. *Phil. Trans.*, *98* (1808), 31–2, 346.   244. from χλωρός = pale green.
245. 'Some Reflections on the Nomenclature of the Oxymuriatic Compounds', (1810), *Works*, London, 1839–40, vol. v, p. 345.

Four years later Davy suggested that the new element, which the French called *ione* after its violet vapour, should be termed *iodine* by analogy with the names *chlorine* and *fluorine*.[246] This proposal was accepted and later the similar name *bromine* was given to the fourth halogen to be discovered.

Related to the use of the name *chlorine* for *oxymuriatic acid* was the suggestion that the name *hydrochloric acid* should replace *muriatic acid*. The nomenclature of the hydracids was due to Gay Lussac.[247] The use of such names as *hydrochloric acid, hydriodic acid, hydrocyanic acid* emphasized an important analogy between these acids and, incidentally, was a reminder of one of the failings of Lavoisier's theory—that oxygen had no part in several important acids.

The principle of analogous names for similar substances was particularly important in the case of compounds. In Lavoisier's system of chemistry an important place had been given to oxygen and the term *oxide*, coined to denote its compounds, was unique. In the early nineteenth century it was appreciated that compounds in which metals combined with various elements— oxygen, chlorine, sulphur, etc.—were all analogous and deserved similar names. In 1812 Davy had mentioned that the name *chloride* (or *muride*) might well be used to denote the compounds of chlorine,[248] but it was Thomas Thomson, the editor of the *Annals of Philosophy*, who brought the word *chloride* into use:

I think that in the present state of our knowledge, we have no other alternative than to adopt the opinion that chlorine is a simple supporter of combustion analagous to oxygen and iodine, and capable, like them, of combining with different combustible bases and of forming a class of bodies analagous to the oxides and acids constituted by the union of oxygen to the same bases. . . . There is a very obvious method of naming these compounds, suggested by the term *oxide*. We have only to apply to them all the appellation *chloride*. . . . Thus . . . *chloride of silver* will be . . . *muriate of silver* and so on.[249]

Berzelius, who had been slow to accept the elementary nature of chlorine, eventually accepted the term chloride and spoke of

246. *Phil. Trans., 104* (1814), 91.
247. *Annales de Chimie, 91* (1814), 9; see also ibid., *96* (1815), 102, 162–3.
248. *Elements of Chemical Philosophy* (1812), *Works*, vol. iv, pp. xii–xiii.
249. *Annals of Philosophy, 4* (1814), 12.

subchlorides, chlorides and *perchlorides* just as he distinguished the various oxides. The prefix *hypo-* was introduced by Dulong in 1816 to denote the acid of phosphorus containing the least oxygen.[250] Thus *hypophosphorous acid* contained less oxygen than *phosphorous acid.*[251] The idea of the so-called polybasic acids made necessary the introduction of further new terms. The casual application of the prefixes *para-, meta-* and *ortho-* for this purpose[252] illustrate only too well how chemists have persisted in the use of terms which could only be justified as temporary labels.

The mid-nineteenth-century nomenclature of inorganic compounds is usually sufficiently close to the terms accepted to-day to be understood by the modern reader. Some care should be exercised, however, since terms were not always used in the same sense as to-day. One instance of this is the term 'hydrate', which was the usual designation for hydroxides. Another is the term 'acid', used to describe the oxides of non-metals. Thus *carbonic acid* was the name given to what we now call *carbon dioxide.* The latter name dates from the 1860's. About the same time the names *sulphur dioxide* and *sulphur trioxide* were introduced in place of sulphurous and sulphuric oxides.[253]

Of the many elements discovered in the nineteenth century, a considerable number were named after places, whether continents (e.g. *Europium*), countries (e.g. *Germanium, Polonium*) or towns (e.g. *Holmium, Lutecium*).[254] Characteristic spectral lines gave rise to names based on colour, like *Caesium, Rubidium, Thallium* and *Indium.* Elements have also been named after people (e.g. *Gadolinium*), characters from mythology (e.g. *Thorium*) or a characteristic property (e.g. *Argon*, the lazy one). In most cases, once the separate existence and characteristic properties of newly-discovered elements had been established. their names were accepted without dispute. In a few cases alternative names each found support (e.g. *Glucinum* and

250. *Ann. chim. phys.*, [2], *2* (1816), 141.
251. The application of such prefixes as *hypo-, hyper-*, etc. in senses contrary to their literal meanings was criticized in a *Report of the British Association, 1885*, 262.
252. See pp. 328–9.
253. G. Fownes, *Manual of Chemistry*, 10th edn., London, 1868.
254. M. E. Weeks, *Discovery of the elements*, 5th edn., Easton, Pa., 1948. In the twentieth century the names *Americium, Californium* and *Berklinium* follow a similar pattern.

Beryllium) and even to-day the term *Niobium* is retained in British usage in preference to *Columbium*. The term *Azote* was only abandoned reluctantly by the French, although it has gained acceptance in organic chemistry in such expressions as 'diazo compounds'.

Part 4

CHEMICAL SYMBOLISM

'Symbolic formulae . . . would deserve to rank among the chemist's most powerful instruments of research.'
A. W. HOFMANN, *Introduction to Modern Chemistry*, London, 1865, p. 87

CHAPTER ONE

Alchemical Symbols

The Origin of Alchemical Symbols

The main subject of this chapter is the symbols which were used in chemistry in the seventeenth and eighteenth centuries. In nearly all cases their precise origin is obscure, but it is possible to say that the pictograms implied in many chemical symbols bear some resemblance to ancient Egyptian hieroglyphics and the abbreviations on which many other symbols were based had a precedent in the system of abbreviations used in the earliest Greek alchemical manuscripts.

Sherwood Taylor, an authority on Greek and Latin alchemy, considered that the connection between the Greek and the Western alchemical symbols was slight, apart from what followed from the use of planetary symbols and initial letters. He estimated that about half a dozen of the Greek symbols found their way into Western alchemical practice.[1] This is confirmed by inspection of Fig. 1a[2]. The great majority of symbols used by Western alchemists, however, are not found in the Greek MSS. That some connection existed between the Greek and Latin traditions of alchemical symbolism is hardly remarkable. What is more surprising is the fact that some half dozen symbols used as late as the eighteenth century can be traced back much further and related to Egyptian hieroglyphics.[3] These include the symbol ≈≈ for water and the symbol ₒ°ₒ , originally denoting powder, which as an alchemical symbol was used to denote oil

1. F. Sherwood Taylor, 'Symbols in Greek Alchemical Writings', *Ambix*, *1* (1937–8), 64–7.
2. The relevant symbols are Nos. 5 (water), 7 (water), 8 (days), 9 (nights), 10 (day and night), 11 (leaves), 16 (arsenic as 𝒜), 27 (salt). All these symbols occur in Sommerhoff, *Lexicon Pharmaceutico-Chymicum*, Nuremberg, 1701, Part 2, pp. 110–14.
3. See Budge, *Egyptian Hieroglyphic Dictionary*, London, 1920, vol. i, pp. cviii–cxlv, and Bunsen, *Egypt's place in universal history*, 2nd edn., London, 1867, vol. i, p. 555.

and also (as .∴.) sand. The hieroglyphics ⊙ (sun) and ⌒
(moon) also reappeared as alchemical symbols for gold and
silver respectively.

Both the use of pictograms and abbreviations hardly suggest
that the function of symbolism was primarily to conceal primitive chemical operations and materials. The Egyptian hieroglyphics were a primitive method of expression and their persistence in the symbolism used in the Greek manuscripts and
in chemistry up to the eighteenth century depends on their
ready interpretations as simple pictograms. The reason why
pictograms were not even more common in alchemical symbolism was that it is only the minority of chemical substances
which lend themselves to pictorial representation. It is, nevertheless, possible to suggest certain chemical operations, vessels
and times by means of pictograms. The sign of a spiral found in
the Greek manuscripts is quite appropriate to its meaning of
'pound' or 'triturate'.[4] In Western alchemy a retort or a re-
ceiving vessel could be easily represented by a simple figure
and basically the same sign could denote the process of distillation.[5] The symbol ⊘ for *ignis rotae* is explained as a crucible
surrounded by a fire.[6] Further symbols for a cucurbit and an
alembic were used as late as 1775 by Bergman.[7] A fairly common representation of an hour was the outline of an hour glass
and the symbols ♂ and ♀ for day and night respectively
suggest the rising and setting sun. The symbol for glass ⟜
may be interpreted as a ray of light which could pass through a
transparent substance, and the reason why a skull was adopted
as the symbol for *caput mortuum* (the residue in distillation) is
too obvious to insist upon.

More than 1300 symbols taken from a selection of Greek
manuscripts were assembled by Zuretti. These provide overwhelming evidence of the habit of abbreviation. In Fig. 1*a*,

4. C. O. Zuretti, *Alchemistica Signa, Union Académique Internationale, Catalogue des Manuscrits Alchimiques Grecs*, vol. 8, Brussels, 1932, nos. 141, 1027,
etc.

5. All three symbols are found in J. Barnerus, *Chymia Philosophica*, Nuremberg, 1689, p. 59.

6. An illustration of the *ignis rotae* reproduced by Carbonelli (*Sulle Fonti
Storiche della Chimica e dell' Alchimia in Italia*, Rome, 1925, p. 153, Fig. 185)
shows very clearly the origin of this pictogram.

7. H. T. Scheffer, *Chemiske föreläsningar*, ed. T. O. Bergman, Uppsala,
1775. A facsimile of the plates of symbols is reproduced by Nördenskiöld
(ed.), *Scheele, Nachgelassene Briefe*, Stockholm, 1892.

taken from the St Mark's manuscript and reproduced by Berthelot,[8] the majority of symbols are fairly obvious abbreviations:

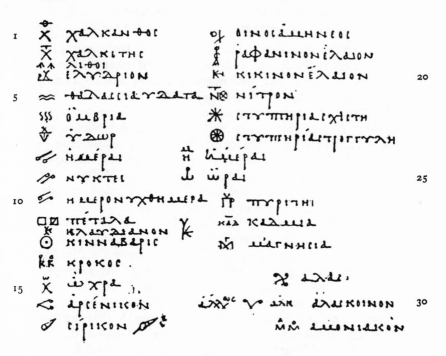

Fig. 1*a*. *Marcianus*, f. 6v. and f. 7.

No.	1	χάλκανθος	copperas
	2	χαλκίτης	copper ore
	3	λίθοι (i.e. Λι Λι)	stones
	7	ὕδωρ	water
	12	κλαυδιανόν	alloy
	14	κρόκος	saffron
	15	ὤχρα	ochre
	18	οἶνος ἀμηνέος	sweet wine
	19	ἠαφάνιον ἔλαιον	horse-radish oil
	20	κίκινον ἔλαιον	castor oil
	21	νίτρον	'nitre'
	24	ἡμέραι	days

8. Berth., *M.A.*, i, p. 108.

25	ὧραι	hours
26	πυρίτης	pyrites
27	καδμία	'cadmia'
28	μαγνησία	'magnesia'
31	ἀμμωνιακόν	'sal ammoniac'

It seems probable that the alchemical symbols of some of the metals (copper, lead, iron and mercury) and other substances (e.g. arsenic, alum) had their origin in abbreviations.[9] Taking the example of copper (Φωσφόρος) it is not unlikely that the abbreviation Φ was transformed in the course of repeated copying into ♀ . A table suggesting how various alchemical symbols developed from abbreviations was drawn up by Huet.[10] Perhaps the least convincing case is that of mercury, said to be derived from the abbreviation Στ (or Cτ) for Στίλβων, the Babylonian Greek term for mercury. It is possible that copyists, unfamiliar with the origin of the abbreviation, tried to give it a greater resemblance to the caduceus of Hermes or Mercury.

Another probable instance where what was originally an abbreviation developed into a more formal symbol is afforded by the case of alum. One term used for alum was στυπτηρία σχιστή; the latter word may be abbreviated as CXI and Singer[11] quotes the case of a fourth-century papyrus where the abbreviation C✳ is found. It seems very probable that the two symbols included in the St Mark's manuscript[12] depend on this abbreviation, although an attempt to convey crystalline form or efflorescence cannot be completely ruled out.

There were occasional examples of the use of the same symbol persisting but with a different meaning as alchemy passed from its Greek and Arabic traditions to the Latin West. One important example of this semantic change is the meaning 'sal ammoniac' for ✳ [13] instead of alum as in the Greek manuscripts.

9. The reverse process also took place occasionally and Lippmann has pointed out that in some cases the symbol ☉ degenerated into the Greek letter Θ and finally θ. Similarly ♂ gradually became transformed into the Greek letter delta Δ (*Entstehung und Ausbreitung der Alchemie*, vol. i, Berlin, 1919, p. 349).

10. *M. Manlii Astronomicon, Accesserunt P. D. Hueti animadversiones*, Paris, 1679.

11. C. Singer, *The Earliest Chemical Industry*, London, 1948, pp. 11–12.

12. See Fig. 1a, nos. 22, 23.

13. The present writer is not competent to examine Arabic manuscripts, but has verified that this symbol occurs with the meaning 'sal ammoniac' in a fourteenth-century MS, B. M. Sloane, 1754, f. 134v.

Another example is the meaning 'marcasite' for ⌗ [14] instead of 'gold', or rather, 'gold solder'.[15]

Alchemy was not, of course, the only science to make use of abbreviations and pictograms. In Greek manuscripts dealing with astrology abbreviations were not uncommon and the monogram ⌗ for example, denoted the time ($\chi\rho\acute{o}\nu o\varsigma$) Pictograms were also used and are exemplified by ⊕ for a sphere and ♈ and ♋ for rising and setting respectively.[16]

The Classification of Alchemical Symbols

It is possible to classify alchemical symbols in various ways depending on one's opinions and the purpose of the classification. Luedy[17] has devised a system of classification based on geometrical and logical similarities. Such a system provides an effective method of tracing any one of the more common symbols within a few moments, but it ignores the historical origins of the symbols. Previously Gessmann[18] had divided symbols into five groups:

(1) symbols based on letters
(2) symbols based on the signs of the seven heavenly bodies
(3) symbols connected with the signs of the zodiac
(4) symbols related to the symbols of the occult sciences
(5) symbols based on simple geometrical figures

Again, this classification is hardly suited to a historical approach, and in any case (3) and (4) do not concern us here[19] and (5) would often include symbols already assigned to other groups. The best scheme of classification known to the present writer is one drawn up by Bolton:[20]

(1) abbreviations   e.g. *āāā amalgama*
(2) pictorial signs e.g. ▽ crucible

14. e.g. Croll, *De Signaturis, Basilica Chymica*, Frankfurt, 1609, p. 79.
15. See Fig. 1*b*, no. 6.
16. These examples are quoted by Salmasius, *Plinianae Exercitationes*, Trajecti ad Rhenum, 1689, pp. 873–4.
17. F. Luedy, *Alchemistische und chemische Zeichen*, Berlin, 1929.
18. G. W. Gessmann, *Die Geheimsymbole der Chemie und Medicin des Mittelalters*, Graz, 1899.
19. It was not unusual for seventeenth and eighteenth-century chemistry books to include the 12 signs of the zodiac among alchemical symbols.
20. H. C. Bolton, 'History of Chemical Notation', *Transactions of the New York Academy of Sciences*, 2 (1882–3), 102–6.

(3) symbolical signs   e.g. ⚛ crucible (*crux*)
(4) arbitary signs   e.g. ∺ vinegar
(5) complex signs formed by uniting two or more of the pre-
    ceding groups, e.g. ▽R *aqua regia*.

Some explanation may be required of the difference between (2)
and (3). Bolton considered the symbols ≈≈ (water) and ♄
(retort) to be pictorial, whereas ♄ (hour) and ⚏ (regulus)
are symbolical. If this distinction is accepted, it is sometimes
difficult to decide to which group a given symbol belongs. Thus
Bolton considered ₒ°ₒ (oil) as symbolical, although it might
with more reason be called pictorial (3 drops). Again, Bolton's
decision to call several symbols 'arbitrary' could be criticized
in several cases where there were possibly definite reasons for
particular symbols. It is possible, for example, that the symbol
♓ [21] for salt is an abbreviation: ᵃλ ˢ (ἄλας). The symbol ▽
for water, considered by many—including Bolton—to be arbitrary, represents one of the four Aristotelian elements, the direction of the apex indicating whether it was considered to be
'specifically light' or 'specifically heavy'. This may have been
merely a late mediaeval rationalization of the scheme, but it is
possible that the symbol for water was really derived from the
Greek abbreviation for ὕδωρ.[22] Another letter which could be
represented like the upsilon was gamma and Zuretti gives
numerous examples[23] where the word γῆ (earth) was denoted
by ⌣ . This scheme may then have been rationalized by the
Latin alchemists into the familiar symbols ▽ =water,
▽̵ =earth, △ =fire, and △̵ =air. The closeness of the
latter symbol to the capital alpha or A has passed unremarked.
Yet no such symbol is listed by Zuretti and we should be
cautious in any attempt to read a hidden meaning into alchemical symbols.

The Interpretation of Alchemical Symbols

We have taken the view in this chapter that alchemical symbols were derived from pictograms or abbreviations or occasionally that they were merely arbitrary signs. Such a view

21. See Fig. 1*a*, no. 29.   22. See Fig. 1*a*, no. 7.
23. Op. cit., nos. 135, 261, 349, 471, 947, 1087, 1290.

was not shared by many chemists in the seventeenth and eighteenth centuries, who preferred to analyse symbols in search of a rational justification for every line, cross or circle. This attitude no doubt had its origin in the mediaeval doctrine of 'signatures', according to which every plant or mineral carried some indication of its purpose or use. So in the seventeenth century the author of the tract *Taaut*[24] attempted to analyse the symbols for the three 'principles': sulphur, mercury and salt. He started by supposing that a straight line denoted earth, a triangle fire, a semi-circle air, and a circle water. He then tried to show how these four basic symbols were incorporated in the symbols of sulphur, mercury and salt. We might well pass over this and similar[25] attempts to force hidden meanings on to the alchemical symbols if it were not for the fact that a great eighteenth-century figure like Boerhaave indulged in similar practices.[26] He repeated assertions such as that a cross denoted anything sharp and corrosive, whereas perfection was indicated by a circle. It was therefore appropriate that a half circle should stand for silver (since it was 'half Gold') and the symbol for copper ♀ was interpreted as showing that the metal was partly gold, but that it contained some crude, sharp and corrosive matter joined with it. The danger of basing serious chemical and medical judgements on such interpretations is well illustrated by what Boerhaave reports about iron:

♂ —that this too is intimately Gold; but that it has with it a great deal of the sharp and corrosive; though with but half the degree of Acrimony as the former, as you see that it has but half the sign that expresses that quality. And what the Alchemists assert, the Physicians observe to be true; Indeed it is almost the universal opinion of the adepts that the *Aurum vivum* or *Philosophorum* does lye concealed in Iron; and that here therefore we must seek for metalline Medicines, and not in Gold itself.

Even in the last quarter of the eighteenth century the French chemists Hassenfratz and Adet still believed that the alchemical

---

24. W. Kriegsmann, *Taaut, oder Ausslegung der Chemischen Zeichen*, Frankfurt, 1665, pp. 25–30.
25. e.g. Brouault, *Abrégé de l'Astronomie Inférieure*, Paris, 1664, pp. 16–43, where he attempts to analyse the symbols of the 7 metals. See also: Libavius, *Rerum Chymicarum Epistolica*, Frankfurt, 1595, Bk. I, p. 174.
26. *Elements of Chemistry*, trans. Dallowe, London, 1735, vol. i, p. 20.

symbols for the metals had been constructed to show their degree of perfection or imperfection:

> This order, which the old chemists introduced into their symbols, and which we notice with pleasure, was soon forgotten despite the fact that it was derived from purely chemical ideas.[27]

Hassenfratz and Adet then went on (this time with some justification) to analyse the symbols of Bergman, pointing out that he used a triangle to denote earths, a circle to denote salts and a cross to denote acids. It was not difficult, however, to find inconsistencies in Bergman's symbols according to this analysis. When Hassenfratz and Adet outlined their own system of synthetic symbols, they no doubt considered this as the third attempt to formulate such a system.

The importance to the historian of chemistry of a good understanding of alchemical symbols is demonstrated by the way in which these symbols were interspersed in the text of many chemical works. The writings of Becher and Stahl afford many examples of this practice. What in modern chemical language would be described as the preparation of silver chloride by dissolving silver in nitric acid and then adding hydrochloric acid, is described by Becher as follows:

> Recipe ☽, in Ω ☉ solve, cum Ω ⊖ praecipitata, filtra[28]

Stahl explains the composition of *mercurius sublimatus* in the following terms:

> ☿ itaque ♎ atus comm. nihil aliud est quam ☽ um vivum et concentratissimus ab omni phegmate liber Ω Salis . . . .[29]

On one occasion Stahl remarks that gold dissolves in '▽R ex Ω u ☉i et Salis' and in another place he refers to a reagent as 'Ω ⊡ ae aut ⊖ ✳ ci' (i.e. *spiritus urinae aut sal ammoniaci*).

Although the use of symbols no doubt had the desired effect of discouraging the uninitiated, it is doubtful whether in the eighteenth century this was the main motive for incorporating symbols into sentences. In the first place, every other manual of chemistry included a table of explanation of 'chemical Characters'. Also the use of Latin case endings in the above examples

27. *Méthode de nomenclature chimique*, Paris, 1787, p. 259.
28. Becher, *Tripus Hermeticus Fatidicus*, Frankfurt, 1689, p. 185.
29. Stahl, *Fundamenta Chymiae*, Nuremberg, 1723, p. 127. See also pp. 175, 50.

makes the motive of secrecy seem less likely than that of abbreviation. It had been a common practice in mediaeval manuscripts to abbreviate a word to one or two letters with the appropriate suffix.[30]

Compound Symbols

In one respect alchemical symbols represented the name of a substance rather than the substance itself. This is shown by the way the symbols were each given a literal meaning[31] and could be combined together to represent a substance with a compound name. Thus, in some Greek manuscripts the symbol for litharge (λιθάργυρος) was ↑(made up of the symbols for stone (λίθος) and silver (ἄργυρος). Quicksilver (ὑδράργυρος) was occasionally represented by the compound sign ⚥ which can be easily analysed into the abbreviation for water (ὕδωρ) and the symbol for silver.[32] Based more on physical than linguistic reasons was the symbol for an alloy of gold and silver in which the two constituents were represented.[33]

A very useful way of combining symbols is found in the St Mark's manuscript. The physical state of a particular substance was indicated by a small sign attached to the appropriate symbol. Thus gold, silver, copper, iron, lead and tin in the state of filings were denoted by two or three transverse lines incorporated in the symbol of the respective metal. How this method applied to gold in various forms is shown in Fig. 1*b*.

The same principle can be seen in later examples of alchemical symbols used in Western Europe. It is typical of alchemical symbolism in the seventeenth century that the same substance was often denoted by a variety of different symbols. This may be inferred from the first two of the following examples, although there were cases where the number of different symbols for the same thing was very much greater.

30. A. Cappelli (*Dizionario di Abbreviature Latine ed Italiana*, 5th edn., Milan, 1954, p. xix) gives examples of how abbreviations were declined, e.g. ēl =*elemen* . . . , ēla =*elementa*, ēltis =*elementis*, ēlm =*elementum*, ḳtc.

31. Thus the symbol of the moon was used to denote selenite (σελήνη = moon), Zuretti, op. cit., nos. 58, 196.

32. Zuretti, op. cit., nos. 53, 191, 981, 996.

33. See Fig. 1*b*, no. 5. This may be compared with the symbol ☾⊙ used by Bergman to denote platinum, which was then considered to be a kind of gold.

♂ ηλιος χρυσος	Sun, gold.
☾ σεληνη αργυρος	Moon, silver.
♄ κρονος φαινων μολιβος	Saturn (φαίνων), lead.
♃ ζευς φαεθων ηλεκτρος	Jupiter (φαεθών), electrum.
♂ αρης πυροεις σιδηρος	Mars (πυρόεις), iron.
♀ αφροδιτη φωσφορ χαλκος	Venus (φωσφόρος), copper.
☿ ερμης στιλβων κασσιτηρος	Mercury (στίλβην), tin.

χρυσος	Gold.
χρυσου ρινημα	Gold filings.
χρυσου πεταλα	Gold leaf.
χρυσος κεκαυμεν	Calcined gold.
χρυση ηλεκτρον	Electrum.
χρυσοκολλα	Chrysocolla. Solder of Gold.
μαλαγμα χρυσου	*Malagma* of Gold (Mixture of Gold).

Fig. 1*b. Marcianus*, f. 6.

Thus Sommerhoff gives 32 symbols for tartar and in another lexicon[34] 39 symbols for mercury are given. Examples of compound symbols[35] are:

Crocus martis   c♂ ♂ ♂ ∿♂   (Iron = Mars = ♂)
Crocus veneris   ♀c ♀ ♀ ∿♀   (Copper = Venus = ♀)
Limaturi argenti   ☽   (Silver = Luna = ☽))
Terra foliata tartari ▽̶   (= ▽ earth + ♇ tartar + F)
Mercurius sublimatus ☿̄   (= ☿ mercury + ≏ sublime)
Mercurius praecipitatus ☿̱   (= ☿ mercury + ⇌ precipi-
                                                    tate)
Flores antimonii   ♁̄   (= ♁ antimony + F)
Oleum vitrioli   °φ°   (= ∴ oil + ⊕ vitriol)

34. *Medicinisch-Chemisch und Alchemistisches Oraculum*, Ulm, 1772.
   35. The first four examples are taken from Sommerhoff, *Lexicon Pharmaceutico-Chymicum*, Nuremberg, 1701, Part 2, pp. 110–14. The next four examples are found in Planis Campy, *Bouquet composé des plus belles fleurs chimiques*, Paris, 1623, pp. 981–2.

'Water' in various forms was a common alchemical reagent, and the symbol for water ▽ followed by any of the letters D, P, F or R denoted distilled water, rain water (*aqua pluvialis*), *aqua fortis* and *aqua regia* respectively.

Bergman, who did much to revive and extend the use of alchemical symbols in the later eighteenth century, made extensive use of the synthetic aspect of symbolism. Deciding that the cross was a suitable representation for acids, Bergman denoted all acids by a cross followed by a suitable distinguishing character. His final list of some 25 acids is shown in Fig. 3. Bergman made extensive use of the symbol ♃ (lime, *calx*) to denote any metallic calx. Thus calx of lead was ♃♄, etc. The compound nature of these signs led some chemists to believe that Bergman thought of metallic calces as compounds of a metal with another substance.[36] There seems little foundation for this belief, however, and it seems clear that Bergman's literal use of the symbol for 'calx' was in conformity with the general practice. The following symbols illustrate the way in which symbols often depended on the literal interpretation of chemical names:

regulus of antimony ♛

plume alum ⚜

Bergman's term for carbon dioxide was *acidum aereum* and, if we did not know this, it would be difficult to understand Bergman's symbol for the gas △, a symbol which ignored the comparatively high density of the gas and stressed its acidic nature.

Probably the most important use of compound symbols was to denote physical combination as in the case of salts. The reform of chemical nomenclature in the eighteenth century by Guyton consisted largely of the general application of systematic names to salts, the constitution of many of which had already been represented systematically by symbols. Rouelle in 1744 and Bergman in 1775 both listed systematic symbols for salts, which clearly suggested their composition, even though these compounds often had no generally accepted systematic name. Examples of salts denoted symbolically by Rouelle[37] are:

36. Hassenfratz and Adet, *Méthode de nomenclature chimique*, Paris, 1787, p. 197.

37. *Mém. Acad.*, *1744*, 364, Pl. XVI.

Glauber's salt ⋈⊕ + ⊖ du ⊖   (i.e. vitriolic acid combined with mineral
alkali)

[potassium sulphite] ⋈⊕ sulph. vol. + ⊖ (i.e. volatile sulphurous
acid combined with
fixed alkali)

[copper chloride] ⋈⊖ + ♀   (i.e. spirit of salt combined with copper)

sugar of lead   ⚛ + ♄   (i.e. acid of vinegar
combined with lead)

Bergman used similar symbols (without the plus sign) some thirty years later. It is possible that Bergman's use of systematic symbolism led him to give parallel systematic names to the salts. Of the dozen symbols for compounds based on their constitution and used by Bergman in 1775,[38] we may cite the examples:

  ⍦ *Hepar calcis*   (⍦ =calx + ⚵ =sulphur-
                                 inverted)

  ⍤ *Mercurius sulphuratus* (☿ =mercury + ditto)
    (*cinnabaris*)

⊕ Ô *vitriolum zinci*   (⊕ =vitriol + Ô =zinc)

☽ ☉ *Luna nitrata*   (☽ =silver + ☉ =nitre)

His symbol for what he called *cuprum acetatum*, however, was not that which might be expected from the above scheme. He denoted it simply as ⊕ , which was the traditional symbol for this compound under the name *viride aeris*.

The Use of Alchemical Symbols in the Eighteenth Century

When Becher in 1689[39] set out in a table the materials which he considered should be included in a portable laboratory, he denoted the majority of materials by the customary symbols. In several cases, however, he was forced to use words and it would seem that there were no recognized symbols in the seventeenth century for bismuth, zinc, *zaffra* (ore of cobalt) and magnesia. In eighteenth-century books,[40] however, we find bismuth (known

38. H. T. Scheffer, *Chemiske Föreläsningar*, ed. T. O. Bergman, Uppsala, 1775 (see Nordenskiöld (ed.), Scheele, *Nachgelassene Briefe*, Stockholm, 1892).
39. *Schema Materialum pro Laboratorio Portabili, Tripus Hermeticus Fatidicus*, Frankfurt, 1689.
40. See Linnaeus, *Systema Naturae*, 1st edn., Leyden, 1735; Gellert, *Anfangsgründe zur metallurgischen Chymie*, 2nd edn., Leipzig, 1776, pp. 227–9; also Geoffroy and Bergman, Figs. 2 and 3.

in Germany and Sweden as *vismutum* or *Wismuth*) was denoted by U , ☿ or W , zinc by Ơ , Z or X ; cobalt was represented by ♀ or K and magnesia by ⚵ . The latter symbol is merely a variation on the cross and circle used to denote antimony and copper. Similarly Bergman's sign ♀ for nickel and ∞ for amber can be considered as little more than geometrical patterns.

Although Bergman introduced several new symbols and his ideas had considerable influence, it would be wrong to give the impression that he was the only eighteenth-century chemist to suggest new symbols. An important symbol used by Geoffroy to denote acids was ～. By referring to Fig. 2 it will be seen that Geoffroy actually said that this symbol was to represent *Esprits acides* and we can accordingly explain this symbol as compounded of Ω = spirit (even in the Greek MSS.) and the arrows or points to indicate the acid, since Geoffroy lived at a time when Lemery's theory that the corrosive action of acids was due to the spikes of their atoms was still widely accepted.

The decision of Lavoisier[41] to make use of symbols to explain the course of chemical reactions is particularly interesting. Lavoisier used some of Geoffroy's symbols and also three of his own:

acide nitreux ⊖╀ [42]

air nitreux △╀

principe oxygine ⋅⬦⋅

The first symbol is merely a compound of the symbol of nitre with Bergman's symbol for an acid. The second compound symbol can be easily understood in its context, although literally it might mean 'the aerial acid' as in Bergman's scheme.

Lavoisier believed that the symbol for any compound should give some idea of its composition and, instead of using the first symbol for *acide nitreux*, he showed that it contained water, the oxygen principle and nitrous air by writing its formula as:

$$(\nabla \quad \cdot\!\bigoplus\!\cdot \quad \triangle\!\!\!+)$$

He then went on to discuss the solution of iron in this acid and wrote something approaching a chemical equation in which algebraic symbols were used to denote quantities. Nevertheless,

---

41. *Mém. Acad., 1782*, 499.
42. Despite the fact that the usual meaning of ⊖ was 'common salt'.

he warned the reader that chemical symbols were not to be considered in the same way as algebraic symbols. Yet it was his hope that by the use of chemical symbols he could assist the working of the mind (*soulager les opérations de l'esprit*).

The eighteenth century witnessed a revival in the use of alchemical symbols and an important source of this revival was a table published by Étienne-François Geoffroy in 1718 entitled *Table des différents rapports observés entre différentes substances*. Geoffroy may be considered to have started a line of chemical enquiry which dominated the theory of chemical reactions in the eighteenth century. Chemists came to think of all chemical reactions in terms of affinities and many of them, following Geoffroy's example, drew up 'tables of affinities' which depicted the degree of affinity of one chemical substance for another. An important aspect of Geoffroy's and subsequent tables was the use of symbols to denote substances. Geoffroy claimed that the advantage of using symbols was that, once their meanings were understood, the relationship between various substances could be seen 'at a glance'. A copy of Geoffroy's table is seen as Fig. 2.

TABLE DES DIFFERENTS RAPPORTS
observés entre différentes substances.

Legend:

- ⌒ *Esprits acides .*
- ⊖ *Acide du sel marin .*
- ⊕ *Acide nitreux .*
- ⊕ *Acide vitriolique .*
- ⊖ᵥ *Sel alcali fixe .*
- ⊖ᴬ *Sel alcali volatil .*
- ▽ *Terre absorbante .*
- SM *Substances metalliques .*
- ☿ *Mercure .*
- *Regule d'Antimoine .*
- ☉ *Or .*
- ☽ *Argent .*
- ♀ *Cuivre .*
- ♂ *Fer .*
- ♄ *Plomb .*
- *Etain .*
- *Zinc .*
- PC *Pierre Calaminaire .*
- △ *Soufre mineral .*
- *Principe huileux ou Soufre Principe*
- ✚ *Esprit de vinaigre .*
- ▽ *Eau .*
- ⊖ *Sel .*
- *Esprit de vin et Esprits ardents*

Fig. 2. *Geoffroy's Table of Affinities* (*Mém. Acad.*, *1718, 212*).

On the top line were denoted a variety of chemical reagents. Underneath the symbol for each was depicted other substances in order of their affinity, so that the nearest was the one with the greatest affinity and that which none of the substances represented lower down in the column would be able to displace. Thus, according to the first column, a fixed alkali might be able to displace a metal from its combination with an acid, but the reverse could not happen.

Geoffroy realized that his table was far from complete and later chemists added to it, so that Bergman's important table of 1775 contained as many as 59 vertical columns compared with the 16 of Geoffroy. Each of these additional substances was denoted by a symbol which was often related to the symbol for similar materials. The 24 acids listed by Bergman included the common symbol of a cross and he also depicted 16 metallic calces by combining the sign ♆ with that of the appropriate metal. Bergman was not wholly consistent in his use of symbols, however, and Hassenfratz and Adet were able to criticize his scheme on the grounds of inconsistency, e.g. he had tolerated a cross as part of the symbol for several substances which were not acids. Also, of the five earths, he had only denoted two by a symbol based on an inverted triangle, the three other earths (lime, magnesia, barytes) being given symbols similar to that of 'calx'.

A further important use of chemical symbols was to represent the course of a chemical reaction and Bergman's extensive use of

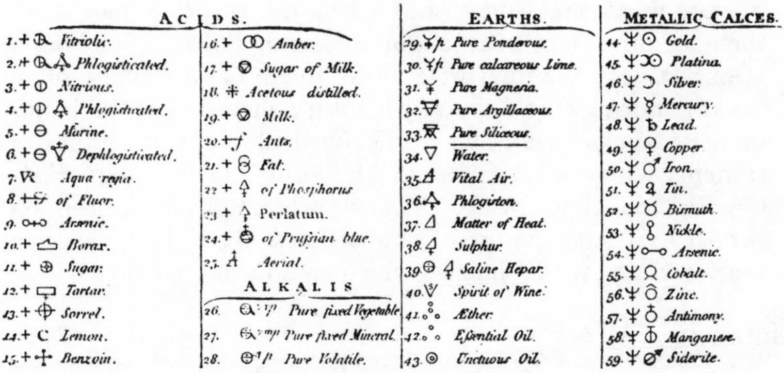
ACIDS.
1. Vitriolic.
2. Phlogisticated.
3. Nitrious.
4. Phlogisticated.
5. Marine.
6. Dephlogisticated.
7. Aqua regia.
8. of Fluor.
9. Arsenic.
10. Borax.
11. Sugar.
12. Tartar.
13. Sorrel.
14. Lemon.
15. Benzoin.
16. Amber.
17. Sugar of Milk.
18. Acetous distilled.
19. Milk.
20. Ants.
21. Fat.
22. of Phosphorus
23. Perlatum.
24. of Prussian blue.
25. Aerial.
ALKALIS
26. Pure fixed Vegetable
27. Pure fixed Mineral.
28. Pure Volatile.
EARTHS.
29. Pure Ponderous.
30. Pure calcareous Lime.
31. Pure Magnesia.
32. Pure Argillaceous.
33. Pure Siliceous.
34. Water.
35. Vital Air.
36. Phlogiston.
37. Matter of Heat.
38. Sulphur.
39. Saline Hepar.
40. Spirit of Wine.
41. Æther.
42. Essential Oil.
43. Unctuous Oil.
METALLIC CALCES.
44. Gold.
45. Platina.
46. Silver.
47. Mercury.
48. Lead.
49. Copper.
50. Iron.
51. Tin.
52. Bismuth.
53. Nickle.
54. Arsenic.
55. Cobalt.
56. Zinc.
57. Antimony.
58. Manganese.
59. Siderite.

Fig. 3. Chemical Symbols used by Bergman (from Nicholson's *Dictionary of Chemistry*, London, 1795).

symbols for this purpose can be regarded as early examples of chemical equations.[43]

A third use of symbols was in comparative tables to show the composition of certain compounds according to various schools of thought. One of these tables was drawn up by Guyton de Morveau,[44] who compared the composition of such substances as 'vital air', water and metallic calces according to seven schools of thought viz. (i) the disciples of Stahl, (ii) Kirwan, (iii) Scheele, (iv) Lavoisier, (v) Volta and Crell, (vi) Lamétherie and (vii) '*la Nouvelle Encyclopédie*', i.e. Guyton's own opinions in 1786 before his conversion to Lavoisier's system. Guyton was able to compare all these opinions on the composition of some eleven substances in a compact table measuring less than 9 in. × 6 in. In this table he used several of Bergman's symbols and in addition used the abbreviation G. for 'gas' and R. for 'radical'.

Finally, chemical symbols were most generally useful as abbreviations on all occasions. This use was particularly common in German printed books.

In the second half of the eighteenth century there was a reaction in certain quarters against the use of symbols, a reaction partly based on their former use to hide the mysteries of alchemy. Many chemists advocated their abolition and considered that the errors that arose through misunderstanding them outweighed any possible advantage they might possess as abbreviations[45] Yet, while criticizing their use, the very same chemists continued to publish lists of symbols with explanations so that (they said) when the reader came across them in other works he might understand them. Spielmann remarked that the interpretation of these 'hieroglyphics' often became a source of dispute. Chemistry should wash its hands of these ancient stains and stop burdening the memories of students with these symbols.[46] The author of the *Medicinisch-Chymisch und Alchemistisches Oraculum*, who might have been expected to defend the use of symbols, described in a preface to the work (1755) the dangers which could arise, particularly in

43. *Disquisitio de attractionibus electivis* (1775), trans. *Dissertation on Elective Attractions*, London, 1785, Table I where 64 such 'equations' are represented.
44. *Observations sur la Physique*, *30* (1787), Tab. opp. p. 81.
45. e.g. Erxleben, *Anfangsgründe der Chemie*, Göttingen, 1775, p. 22.
46. J. R. Spielmann, *Instituts de Chymie*, Paris, 1770, vol. i, p. 12.

medicine, from a confusion of these symbols. He therefore recommended the use of words rather than symbols.

It was certainly quite easy to misread the alchemical symbols. The difference between the symbol for alum and that for gold was only that the latter contained a dot in the centre.[47] The distinction between ♅ (*calx viva*) and ♃ (mercury)[48] is very slight and each of these symbols, if carelessly written, could be confused with ♆ (potash). The same symbol ⚥ was used occasionally for burnt copper, more often for arsenic[49] and was adopted by Bergman to denote nickel.

Yet there were some eighteenth-century chemists who were prepared to support the continued use of alchemical symbols. The English translator of Bergman's *Dissertation on Elective Attractions* (probably J. Beddoes) included a 'translation' of part of Bergman's tables into words instead of symbols but, nevertheless, he kept most of the symbols since he considered that they were 'so convenient that every student of chemistry ought to make himself familiar with them'.[50] William Nicholson, who was not a fervent supporter of any particular system of nomenclature, was enthusiastic in his support of symbols, which, in his opinion, had been unjustly overlooked. He thought very highly of chemical symbols as abbreviations:

> The tables at the end of Bergman's Essay on the Affinities exhibit in the most speedy and intelligible manner the greater part of many volumes of chemical results; and I know, from my own experience, that it is easy by a simple combination of chemical and algebraic characters, to write the whole contents of any chemical work in the small margin usually left by the printer; and that in a manner so full, clear and perspicuous, that whole pages may be read and understood in a few seconds.[51]

This claim does not sound so much of an exaggeration when one realizes that Nicholson was implicitly comparing the circumlocutions of the old terminology with the most systematic use of chemical symbols as exemplified in the works of Bergman.

47. In the table of chemical characters reproduced in Baron's revision of Lemery's *Cours de Chymie*, Paris, 1756, this dot is missing so that the two symbols are identical.
48. W. J. Wilson, 'Catalogue of Latin and Vernacular Alchemical Manuscripts in the United States and Canada', *Osiris, 6* (1939), 671.
49. Both these meanings are given in Lemery's table of symbols, loc. cit.
50. Op. cit., London, 1785, p. v.
51. *Dictionary of Chemistry*, London, 1795, vol. i, pp. 251–2.

The alchemical symbols, which had been used so widely in the eighteenth century,[52] continued to be used in the early nineteenth century and in 1818, after Berzelius had introduced the modern system of chemical symbols, he still included in his *Lärbok i kemien* a folding plate showing six columns of the old symbols.[53]

52. An interesting use of alchemical symbols is found in Guettard's geological maps of France—Guettard and Monnet, *Atlas et description minéralogique de la France*, Paris, 1780.

53. Op. cit., vol. iii, Stockholm, 1818, Tab. VI.

CHAPTER TWO

The Symbols of Hassenfratz
and Adet

When Lavoisier, Guyton, Fourcroy and Berthollet met in Paris in 1787 to discuss the reform of chemical nomenclature the question of a reform of symbols was raised. They invited Jean Henri Hassenfratz, *Sous-Inspecteur des mines,* and Pierre August Adet, *Docteur-Régent* of the Paris Faculty of Medicine—both young men with a common interest in chemistry—to join their discussions on the subject of a reform of chemical symbols. To these two chemists was delegated the task of constructing a system of symbols on similar principles to those adopted for the reform of the nomenclature. Before publication of their scheme, however, Hassenfratz and Adet again consulted their senior colleagues to obtain their approval.

Hassenfratz and Adet deplored the diversity of the chemical symbols then in use and they mentioned the confusion for which these symbols were often responsible. If one were to analyse the symbols used by even the great Bergman, inconsistencies in their construction would be found. They considered that the time had come to build up a new system of symbols in which simple substances were represented by simple symbols and compound substances were denoted by a combination of the symbols of the appropriate simple substances.

Lavoisier and his associates had classified simple substances into six categories[54] and Hassenfratz and Adet followed this in the main by assigning a characteristic symbol to each of their six classes of substances not yet decomposed:

(1) simple substances which are commonly found combined as part of a compound   —a straight line

54. *Méthode de nomanclature chimique,* Paris, 1787, pp. 28–9. The scheme of Hassenfratz and Adet is on pp. 253–87, but the pages are not numbered consecutively in this part of the book.

(2) alkalis and earths	—a triangle
(3) inflammable substances[55]	—a semi-circle
(4) metals	—a circle
(5) acid radicals (suspected of being compound)	—a square
(6) compound substances, the constituents of which were not yet known	—a square drawn obliquely.

Having distinguished each of these groups the authors calculated the total number of possible ways it could be used. In all cases the number of possible permutations exceeded the actual number of substances known in any particular class, thus leaving symbols available for substances discovered in the future.

The next step was to distinguish the various earths, alkalis, metals, etc. Hassenfratz and Adet, adhering to the traditional symbols for the Aristotelian elements, denoted earths by a triangle thus ▽ , whilst the alkalis, potash and soda, were represented by the triangle △ , bearing the letters P and S respectively. One of the faults of this system was the omission of the alkali ammoniac since the authors preferred to emphasize that it was a compound of *hydrogène* and *azote*. The metals were represented by a circle containing the initial letter of the Latin name of the metal, but the authors again bowed to tradition by continuing to denote gold as ☉ . Hassenfratz and Adet chose the Latin names because these would be recognized internationally. In the case of two substances with names beginning with the same letter a second distinctive letter was added. Thus silver was Ⓐ and arsenic Ⓐⓢ . Sometimes these letters were printed in the form of monograms and the reader had to accept, for example, that the symbol Ⓟ represented platinum. A further means of distinguishing substances beginning with the same letter depended on the classification into geometrical shapes so that no-one who understood Hassenfratz and Adet aright should confuse Ⓜ̄ (*magnésie*) with Ⓜ (*manganèse*).

It is sometimes considered[56] that Hassenfratz and Adet, by the use of initial letters in this way, paved the way for Berzelius

55. The other four chemists did not consider inflammable substances as a separate class.

56. P. Walden, '*Zur Entwicklungsgeschichte der chemischen Zeichen*' *Studien zur Geschichte der Chemie, Festgabe E. O. v. Lippmann*, ed. J. Ruska, Berlin, 1927, p. 90n.

and the modern system of notation. It is as well to point out that the two French chemists only used these letters with great reluctance. They had originally tried to distinguish the symbols for the earths and alkalis by triangles combined with lines and

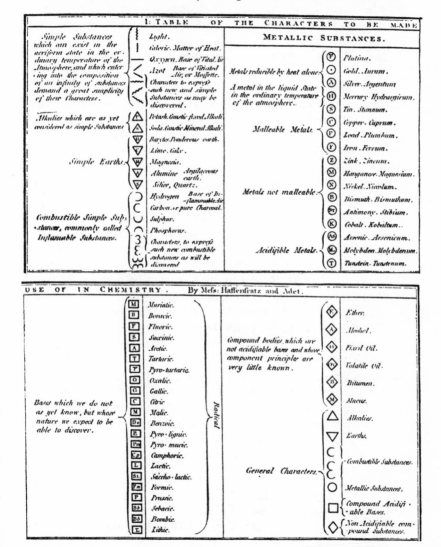

Fig. 4. Hassenfratz and Adet's Chemical Symbols for 'Simple Substances' (from Nicholson's *Dictionary of Chemistry*, London 1795—in common with Figs. 5 and 6).

dots, but they abandoned this attempt when they realized that their symbols looked as if they represented compound substances. Also the small size of the dots could easily lead to confusion between one symbol and another. The triangles could only be drawn in two distinctive positions and hence to differentiate between the two alkalis and the five earths they were forced to use initial letters. Apart from the latter concession their whole scheme was geometrical in conception and the two chemists may well have reproached themselves at first for this small inconsistency.

Having presented an outline of their proposed reform to the *Académie des Sciences*, Hassenfratz and Adet later presented a second memoir in which they explained how the six types of symbols for 'simple substances' might be combined together to denote compounds. A compound consisting of, for example, three simple bodies was to be denoted by three appropriate symbols *joined together*. The authors considered that if merely placed near each other there might be some confusion if the symbols of other substances were drawn close to them. The next consideration was a quantitative one. Where two or more simple substances could combine together to varying extents, the authors tried to show this by the relative position of the symbols. If two substances were combined together so that each was saturated with the other, the compound formed was denoted by the respective symbols side by side, but if one constituent were in excess, that symbol was written beneath the other. Hassenfratz and Adet supposed that potash and sulphur could combine together (*a*) with each saturated, (*b*) with sulphur in excess (*c*) with potash in excess. These combinations would be denoted by: (*a*) 🜍⌣ , (*b*) 🜍 , (*c*) 🜍 . The authors now had to deal with the problem of a series of compounds formed from two elements such as *oxygène* and *azote*, represented by the lines — and / respectively. The compounds were:

   ⌐   the base of nitrous gas
   ⊢   the base of nitrous acid
   ∟   the base of nitric acid
   ∟   the base of oxygenated nitric acid

It will be seen from this example that the more oxygen there was in a compound, the lower was the horizontal stroke. The authors also considered the more difficult case of organic acids.

These contained carbon, hydrogen and oxygen and it was possible that one organic acid should differ from another by a small proportion only of one of the constituent elements, so that the above method of representing excess of an element could not be applied. In such cases Hassenfratz and Adet again incorporated initial letters into their scheme, e.g.

$$)_\tau \quad \text{tartaric} \qquad)_o \quad \text{oxalic}$$
$$\text{C} \quad \text{acid} \qquad \quad \text{C} \quad \text{acid}$$

In the example quoted of the compounds of oxygen and nitrogen it will be noticed that the symbols given represented only the base of a particular compound and not the compound itself. To represent any particular substance the amount of caloric it contained had to be taken into account. We must now consider therefore the elaboration of the scheme of symbols to include caloric, a concept which two ardent disciples of Lavoisier could hardly be expected to ignore. According to the theory of caloric all bodies contained some 'fire matter' and the change of state from solid to liquid and liquid to gas was brought about by adding successive quantities of caloric. Hassenfratz and Adet, who used a vertical line to denote caloric, adopted the convention that the sign for caloric should be omitted for solids and should be incorporated into the appropriate symbols for liquids by writing the stroke above and for gases by writing it below.[57]

This increased the number of symbols threefold (see Fig. 5) and the authors calculated that, taking the simple substances two at a time, it was possible to denote over 4,000 compounds or over 300,000 compounds if the elements were combined in groups of three. By undertaking this calculation the authors hoped to convince the Academy of Sciences that their scheme had been planned to include all possible further discoveries and, indeed it could have done so, if chemists had found it a convenient system.

---

57. The idea of indicating the state of matter of a substance in its symbol fell out of use with the abandonment of the symbols of Hassenfratz and Adet. In 1848 however, J. E. Bowman re-introduced the idea in his *Introduction to Practical Chemistry*, London, p. xxiii. He indicated the difference between solids, liquids and gases by different thicknesses of type and by italics. In more recent times it has been found convenient to distinguish the three states of matter in problems on thermochemistry.

II.ᵉ TABLE. COMBINATIONS OF CALORIC.
with different Simple Substances, producing the Solid, Liquid, and Aeriform States.

	Solid	Liquid	Aeriform		Solid	Liquid	Aeriform		Solid	Liquid	Aeriform
Azot......				Copper.				Pyro-tartareous Radical			
Potash....				Lead.				Oxalic Radical.			
Soda.......				Iron.				Gallic Radical....			
Barytes......				Zink				Citric Radical...			
Lime....				Manganese.				Malic Radical. ..			
Magnesia. ...				Nickel.				Benzoic Radical.			
Alumine.. ...				Bismuth.				Pyro-lignic Radical			
Silex........				Antimony				Camphoric Radical.			
Hydrogen.....				Arsenic				Lactic Radical.			
Carbon......				Molybden.				Saccho-lactic Radical			
Sulphur.				Tungstein.				Formic Radical.			
Phosphorus...				Muriatic Radical.				Prussic Radical.			
Gold....				Boracic Radical.				Sebacic Radical.			
Platina.. ...				Fluoric Radical.				Bombic Radical.			
Silver.... ...				Succinic Radical.				Lithic Radical.			
Mercury:. ..				Acetous Radical.				Ether.			
Tin..... .				Tartareous Radical.				Alkohol.			

Fig. 5. Hassenfratz and Adet's Symbols for 'Simple Substances'
combined with 'Caloric'.

Lavoisier, Berthollet and Fourcroy in their report to the Academy on this system of symbols gave a favourable account of it, remarking that it was 'very ingenious'. The three commissioners commented that they did not intend to examine to what extent symbols were useful in chemistry, but in any case those proposed by Hassenfratz and Adet were preferable to the old symbols.[58] This remark might be interpreted as implying a certain reserve about their practical value and historians of chemistry have generally taken the view that their invention was no more than an academic exercise by Hassenfratz and Adet.

Fourcroy in 1801 emphasized that the symbols were completely in harmony with the new chemical nomenclature:

These simple signs are very distinct and as easy to recognize as to write and they form a methodical and systematic series of chemical characters based on the same foundations as the nomenclature ....[59]

When, however, we look through Fourcroy's text-books for these symbols we find little evidence of Fourcroy's use of them. The fact is that even Hassenfratz and Adet had been unable to

58. *Méthode*, pp. 288, 311–12.
59. *Système des connaissances chimiques*, Paris, 1801, vol. i, p. 108.

persuade the printer to introduce their complex geometrical symbols on an ordinary page of printing and in the *Méthode* they were confined to six folding plates bound at the end of the book.

The reason why these symbols are not found more commonly[60] in printed books at the end of the eighteenth century and the beginning of the nineteenth century are largely typographical. Guyton remarked that in order to make people familiar with the new symbols it was not sufficient to publish tables of them with explanations. They would have to be used in printed books, for example to explain chemical reactions. First, however, it would be necessary to construct special type which could be incorporated into an ordinary printed page just as the Germans made use of the old chemical symbols in the text of chemical books. It is indicative of the important part played by printing in the history of chemical symbolism that Berzelius, to whose influence we owe the use of the modern chemical symbols, gave as one of his reasons for choosing ordinary letters the typographical consideration that they could be printed 'without disfiguring the text'.[61]

Of the four authors of the reform of chemical nomenclature we have already noted Fourcroy's advocacy of the use of the new symbols. Lavoisier's personal approval of the symbols is suggested by the occasional use he made of them in his later laboratory note-books.[62] The symbols were, however, of the greatest use in lectures and both Berthollet[63] and Guyton[64] found them of great service in this way. Guyton used them over a period of many years, first in his lectures in Dijon and then at the *École Polytechnique*. He advocated their use partly on the grounds of simplicity, since he considered that the whole scheme could be reduced to thirteen symbols which could be learned

60. e.g. Adet's *Leçons Élémentaires de Chimie*, Paris, 1804, does not contain any examples of the new symbols and although both Hassenfratz and Adet became editors of the *Annales de Chimie*, this journal does not appear ever to have used them, even after a plea for their re-introduction by Guyton in 1798 (*Ann. chim.*, 25 (1798), 220–1).

61. *Essai sur la théorie des proportions chimiques*, Paris, 1819, p. 111.

62. Berthelot, *La Révolution Chimique*, Paris, 1890, p. 218. Berthelot, however, mentions only 2 symbols used by Lavoisier—those for potash and carbonate of soda.

63. According to Guyton, *Journal de l'École Polytechnique*, *1*, cahier 1 (1795); 141.

64. Ibid. and *Ann. chim.*, 25 (1798), 219–21.

in a short time. Guyton and Berthollet both recommended the use of the symbols as an effective means of explaining to students the composition of compound bodies. The symbols were most useful, however, in tracing the course of chemical reactions. It is clear from Guyton's account that he must have

TABLE IV. COMBINATIONS OF TWO SUBSTANCES.
Caloric forms a third in some of these Compositions.

Ammoniacal Gas	Sulphuret of Alumine	Sulphuret of Antimony	Amalgam of Silver
Concrete Ammoniac	Sulphuret of Gold	Sulphuret of Cobalt	of Copper
Carbonated Azotic Gas	Sulphuret of Silver	Sulphuret of Arsenic	of Tin
Sulphurated Azotic Gas	Sulphuret of Mercury	Sulphuret of Molybdena	Alloy of Tin & Copper
Carbonated Hydrogen Gas	Sulphuret of Tin	Phosphuret of Lead	of Tin & Lead
Sulphurated Hydrogen Gas	Sulphuret of Copper	Phosphuret of Iron	of Iron & Manganese
Phosphorated Hydrogen Gas	Sulphuret of Lead	Alloy of Platina & Gold	of Iron & Nickel
Sulphuret of Potash	Sulphuret of Iron	of Platina & Silver	
Sulphuret of Soda	Sulphuret of Zink	of Gold & Silver	
Sulphuret of Barytes	Sulphuret of Nickel	of Gold & Copper	Carburet of Iron
Sulphuret of Lime	Sulphuret of Bismuth	Amalgam of Gold	

TABLE V NEUTRAL SALTS COMPOSED OF THREE SUBSTANCES.
Caloric is not expressed, because they are all supposed to be in the solid state. The Ammoniacal State are composed of four Substances.

Calcareous Acetat	Calcareous Camphorat	Acidulous Oxalat of Potash	Sulphat of Lime
Acetat of Alumine	Citrat of Soda	Phosphat of Potash	Acidulous Sulphat of Alumine
Acetat of Magnesia	Ammoniacal Citrat	Phosphat of Soda	Sulphat of Alumine
Acetat of Potash	Calcareous Citrat	Ammoniacal Phosphat	Sulphat of Alumine with excess of base
Acetat of Soda	Fluat of Potash	Phosphat of Lime	Sulphat of Magnesia
Acetat of Copper	Fluat of Ammoniac	Phosphat of Iron	Sulphat of Silver
Acetat of Iron	Fluat of Lime	Phosphite of Soda	Sulphat of Mercury
Ammoniacal Acetite	Formiat of Soda	Prussiat of Iron	Sulphat of Tin
Acetite of Potash	Ammoniacal Formiat	Pyro turtrite of Potash	Sulphat of Copper
Calcareous Acetite	Calcareous Formiat	Pyro mucite of Soda	Sulphat of Lead
Bombiat of Potash	Lactat of Soda	Pyro lignite of Ammoniac	Sulphat of Iron
Ammoniacal Bombiat	Ammoniacal Lactat	Saccho-lat of Potash	Sulphat of Zink
Calcareous Bombiat	Lactat of Lime	Sebat of Soda	Sulphat of Manganese
Carbonat of Potash	Gallat of Potash	Sulphite of Potash	Sulphat of Nickel
Carbonat of Soda	Malat of Potash	Sulphat of Potash	Sulphat of Bismuth
Ammoniacal Carbonat	Muriat of Potash	Acidulous Sulphat of Potash	Sulphat of Antimony
Calcareous Carbonat	Muriat of Soda	Sulphat of Potash with excess of base	Sulphat of Cobalt
Barytic Carbonat	Ammoniacal Muriat		Sulphat of Arsenic
Magnesian Carbonat	Barytic Muriat	Sulphat of Soda	Sulphat of Molybden
Carbonat of Iron	Muriat of Iron	Acidulous Sulphat of Soda	Sulphat of Tungstein
Benzoat of Potash	Oxygenated Muriat of Soda		Succinat of Potash
Ammoniacal Benzoat	Nitrat of Potash, or Nitre	Sulphat of Soda with excess of base	Arseniat of Potash
Calcareous Benzoat	Nitrat of Soda		Acidulous Arseniat of Potash
Borat of Soda	Ammoniacal Nitrat	Sulphat of Ammoniac	Arseniat of Potash with excess of base
Ammoniacal Borat	Barytic Nitrat	Acidulous Sulphat of Ammoniac	Molybdat of Soda
Calcareous Borat	Nitrat of Silver	Sulphat of Ammoniac with excess of base	Ammoniacal Tungstat
Camphorat of Potash	Nitrite of Potash		Calcareous Tungstat
Ammoniacal Camphorat	Oxalat of Potash	Barytic Sulphat	Lithiat of Potash

Fig. 6. Tables showing Hassenfratz and Adet's Symbols for various Compound Bodies.

used them to construct what we should now call chemical equations, in which each elements which took part in the reaction was traced. Bouillon la Grange, the author of a widely read French text-book of chemistry, gave an example of the use of the symbols of Hassenfratz and Adet in a chemical equation of the type used by Bergman.[65] Another French chemist who helped to propagate the new symbols was Fourcroy's pupil Cadet.[66]

The symbols had some success in Germany where they were introduced by Meidinger, both as part of a complete translation of the *Méthode de nomenclature chimique*[67] and as a separate publication for the benefit of those who wished to study the new symbols apart from the nomenclature.[68] A book was also published by A. N. Scherer which contained a plate showing the new symbols which he considered 'very useful for lectures'.[69] Not all the translators into the various European languages of the *Méthode* considered that the system of symbols merited reproduction and, accordingly, the two memoirs by Hassenfratz and Adet, the report on them to the Academy and the six plates were omitted in the Spanish and Italian translations of the *Méthode*.[70] In Sweden the use of the new chemical symbols had become quite common in the first years of the nineteenth century and a study of Berzelius' letters to other Swedish chemists over the period 1804-15 shows that he used the symbols of Hassenfratz and Adet quite frequently as convenient abbreviations.[71]

65. *Décomposition de Muriate de Baryte par le Carbonate de Potasse, Manuel d'un Cours de Chymie*, Paris, 1799, vol. i, Bouillon la Grange continued to expound the system of symbols in later editions of this work. In the 5th edition (Paris, 1812, vol. i, p. 62) some improvements on the formulae of Hassenfratz and Adet may be seen. He gave the formula for sulphuric acid as $\bigcirc\!\!\!-$ instead of the compound symbols including only two elements (really the formula for the anhydride of the acid) as given by Hassenfratz and Adet.

66. *Dictionnaire de Chimie*, Paris, 1803, vol. ii, pp. 54-5. For a further use (in a modified form) of the symbols of Hassenfratz and Adet, see L.-J. Sevrin, *Dictionaire des nomenclature chimique at minéralogiques*, etc., Paris, 1807.

67. *Methode der chemischen Nomenklatur*, Vienna, 1793.

68. *System der chemischen Zeichen für die antiphlogistische Chemie und ihre Nomenklatur von Herrn Hassenfratz und Adet*, ed. Meidinger, Vienna, 1793.

69. *Nachträge zu den Grundzügen der neuen chemischen Theorie*, Jena, 1796, Vorerinnerung.

70. Duveen and Klickstein, *Bibliography of the Works of A. L. Lavoisier*, London, 1954, pp. 150, 153.

71. *J. Berzelius' Bref*, ed. Söderbaum, Uppsala, 1912-35, Parts 8 and 9.

The new symbols were first introduced into Great Britain by the translation of the *Méthode* by St John in 1788, but little notice was taken of them at this time. In 1795 Nicholson included two large folding plates showing the new symbols in his Dictionary of Chemistry and he wrote an article on 'Characters Chymical' in which he suggested that the use of symbols had fallen unjustly into neglect. His support of the new symbols was implicit, however, rather than explicit. When Pearson published his *Translation of the Table of Chemical Nomenclature* (1794), he did not concern himself with the symbols. In the second edition (1799) of this work, however, he included a plate illustrating the symbols of Hassenfratz and Adet and he also wrote several pages of explanation. Pearson considered that he was justified in using one of the spare symbols of Hassenfratz and Adet in order to denote diamond. A more important departure from the French system however was the use of the initials of the English names[72] for substances. This lack of agreement on the principle governing the choice of the initial letter was made even more apparent in works by Kerr[73] and Sylvester,[74] in which each put forward his own ideas on the adaptation of the symbols of Hassenfratz and Adet. The situation was made worse by a difference of terminology, so that for Kerr potash was △ (*lixiva*) and for Sylvester lime was ▽ instead of ▽

Kerr's translation of Lavoisier's *Traité* had first appeared in 1790, but it was not until the so-called fifth edition appeared in 1802 that Kerr showed any interest in symbols. Although he acknowledged the soundness of the general principles of Hassenfratz and Adet, Kerr allowed himself the liberty of making one or two alterations. He considered the division of simple bodies into six classes to be a very artificial classification. Since azote,

72. Pearson was criticized for this by Bouillon la Grange, *Manuel d'un Cours de Chymie*, Paris, 1799, vol. i, p. 229.

73. Lavoisier, *Elements of Chemistry*, trans. R. Kerr, 5th edn., Edinburgh, 1802, vol. 2, pp. 226–42: 'New System of Chemical Characters, adapted to the new nomenclature by Messrs Hassenfratz and Adet; with some alterations by the translator.'

74. Charles Sylvester, *An elementary treatise on chemistry*, Liverpool, 1809, pp. 14–21. James Parkinson used the abbreviation ⒶⓇ for arsenic in the first two editions of his *Chemical Pocket Book* (2nd edn., London, 1801, Frontispiece). After criticism by Chenevix (*Remarks upon chemical nomenclature*, London, 1802, p. 230), however, Parkinson reverted to the Ⓐⓢ of Hassenfratz and Adet in the third (1803) edition of his book; he also made several similar changes.

hydrogen, carbon, sulphur and phosphorus shared with the metals the property of being 'oxydated', he considered that they should all be grouped together. Thus he wrote:

   Ⓐ   Azote
   ©   Carbon
   Ⓒₐ   Metal of Lime (calcium)
   Ⓐᵣ   Silver

Kerr considered that the triangle symbol for the alkalis and earths would fall into disuse as these were shown to be compounds—there was already evidence that three of the five earths were metal oxides. Similarly the figures $\square$ and $\langle\rangle$ for little known compound acidifiable bases and non-acidifiable bases respectively would become redundant as the nature and composition of these bodies were more fully understood. It was a short step along the road suggested by Kerr to denote all substances with a circle. The logical conclusion of this—the abolition of the geometrical figure and the mere use of initial letters takes us very close to Berzelius' system.

The most interesting change made by Sylvestre to the symbols of Hassenfratz and Adet was the use of numbers to indicate proportions instead of relying on indications given by the relative positions of the symbols. Thus:

     Ⅿ⊦   muriatic acid
  2 Ⅿ⊦   oxymuriatic acid
3 Ⅿ—Ⓐ   hyperoxymuriat of potash
             (potassium chlorate)

Sylvestre expressed the view that the new symbols could play a vital part in chemistry:

This mode of using symbols will be found to facilitate an acquaintance with the different substances employed in Chemistry, in a greater degree than the mere name of the substance, or even the most minute description; for, when the symbolic characters of the elementary bodies are once strongly impressed in the mind, they will afford to the student, a means of resolving at one view, the most complicated Chemical compound, into its ultimate constituents.

CHAPTER THREE

Dalton's Atomic Symbols

John Dalton is well known as the early nineteenth-century English chemist who advocated an atomic theory of chemistry. Closely connected with the atomic theory was a system of symbols in which Dalton denoted the atoms of different elements by circles containing a distinguishing pattern or letter. The important difference between Dalton's symbols and those used earlier was that the former represented a definite quantity of an element, whilst the latter signified any amount of the substance in question. Thus Dalton's symbol $\oplus$ stood for *one atom* of sulphur to which he assigned a definite weight compared with that of hydrogen, whereas the symbol had previously denoted sulphur in general. This quantitative aspect of Dalton's symbols was inherited by the symbols of Berzelius and they still have this quantitative meaning to-day.

Dalton's formulation of the atomic theory was closely connected with his meteorological interests and in particular the study of the atmosphere and his interests in the properties of gases in general. In a paper read to the Manchester Literary and Philosophical Society in October 1803 Dalton observed:

A particle of gas pressing on the surface of water is analogous to a single shot, pressing upon the summit of a square pile of them.[75]

To illustrate this idea he drew a black sphere, which represented a particle of air, resting on white spheres which he chose to represent particles of water. Five years later in his *New System of Chemical Philosophy*, Dalton was still prepared to assign a spherical shape to the particles or atoms, at least when they were joined with the hypothetical caloric:

Whatever, therefore, may be the shape or figure of the solid atom abstractedly, when surrounded by such an atmosphere [i.e. of heat] it must be globular; but as all globules in any small given volume are

75. *Memoirs of the Literary and Philosophical Society of Manchester*, Second Series, *1* (1805), 284.

subject to the same pressure, they must be equal in bulk, and will therefore be arranged in horizontal strata, like a pile of shot.[76]

It seems clear from the above that Dalton's reason for representing atoms by circles was not arbitrary, but rather it was a deliberate attempt to picture the atoms as he imagined they really were. This applies also to the compound atoms which he usually drew symmetrically in accordance with his ideas on the repulsive influence of the atmosphere of caloric surrounding each atom. Thus, in Dalton's view, the formula ○●○ represented the actual arrangement of the atoms in carbonic acid, since the two oxygen atoms repelled each other while being attracted by the carbon atom. Dalton actually made 3-dimensional models of compound atoms, in which each elementary atoms was represented by a ball with suitable holes to carry pins to join it to the other atoms.[77] This was in conformity with Dalton's pedagogical opinion that

no conception was clearly grasped by the intellect, if it could not be visibly depicted or embodied to the external sense.[78]

The first record we possess of Dalton's use of symbols dates from September 1803 (see below) and it will be noticed that all the elements represented were either gaseous or the constituents of common gases. To each of the atoms represented symbolically Dalton attributed a definite weight. (These 'atomic weights' have been omitted from the Table, since our purpose in this chapter is to examine the symbols rather than the experimental results, which led to a progressive revision of these relative weights.) The character for carbon, a circle shaded black, was no doubt deliberately symbolic. The symbol for azote is identical with that previously used to denote nitre and it is just possible that the cross incorporated in the symbol for sulphur may be related to the lower half of the alchemical symbol for sulphur ⚵ . Five weeks later Dalton again wrote down some symbols in his note-books, this time giving an alternative symbol based on the use of initial letters.[79] It was probably

76. Op. cit., vol. i, Part 1, Manchester, 1808, p. 145.
77. Dalton, *On a new and easy method of analysing sugar*, Manchester, 1840, pp. 3–4.
78. According to Dalton's friend William Henry (*Memoirs of . . . John Dalton*, London, 1854, p. 130).
79. Dalton also made use of the symbol Ⓛ for lime in August 1804 (H. E. Roscoe and A. Harden, *A New View of the Origin of Dalton's Atomic Theory*, London, 1896, p. 64).

because Dalton was considering the use of initial letters that he reversed the symbols for oxygen and hydrogen, so that O now represented oxygen. Dalton next had occasion to draw up a list of symbols at the end of 1806 or early in 1807, for the purpose of illustrating the lectures he was to give in Scotland in April 1807. It will be noticed that the symbol for gold was unusually elaborate—it may have originally been intended to represent the sun, the letter G being afterwards added for clarity. In 1808 Dalton further extended his symbols for the elements and his symbol for mercury may well have been intended to suggest small globules of the metal. To avoid confusion with the symbol for gold, the latter was now denoted by the initial letter only. When in 1810 Dalton added zirconia to his list, he chose the wavy line (suggestive of the letter Z?) which he had formerly associated with magnesia, and he accordingly found another pattern to denote the latter.

Of the 36 'elements' represented in the 1810 list, exactly one half were denoted by a pattern rather than a letter and one has the impression that Dalton resorted to the use of letters only when the simple patterns were exhausted. This is confirmed by his original use of patterns rather than letters (September 1803, Spring 1807) and also by his preference for the use of a mixed system of patterns and letters rather than a consistent use of initial letters.

Dalton did not publish his symbols until 1808, but in the previous year Thomas Thomson gave a short account of the Atomic theory and the symbols in the third edition of his *System of Chemistry*. According to Thomson, Dalton showed him his table of symbols with the weight of atoms of 6 or 8 bodies in 1804,[80] but Thomson warned his readers that he could not vouch for the accuracy of the details of Dalton's scheme. Thomson frequently referred to Dalton's symbols,[81] although his representation of the atoms of carbon, sulphur and phosphorus differ from those of Dalton (see Table above). He also made the innovation of using the alchemical symbol for common salt to denote muriatic acid.[82] Thomson did not substantially alter his

80. *Annals of Philosophy*, 2 (1813), 445n.

81. *System of Chemistry*, 3rd edn., Edinburgh, 1807, vol. 3, pp. 429-540. See especially p. 425n.

82. Dalton held the curious view that muriatic acid was a compound of one atom of hydrogen and three atoms of oxygen (see Fig. 7).

Table showing the symbols used by Dalton up to the time of their standardization in 1808

DALTON 6 Sept. 1803 (A)	DALTON 12 Oct. 1803 (B) or thus:	DALTON Spring 1807 (C)	DALTON 1808 (D)	(F) THOMSON 1807 (E)
○ Hydrogen	Ⓗ Hydrogen ⊙	⊙Hydrogen	⊙Hydrogen	⊙Hydrogen
⊙ Oxygen	○Oxygen ○	○Oxygen	○Oxygen	○Oxygen
⦶Azote	Ⓐ Azote ⦶	⦶Azote	⦶ Azote	⦶Azote
● Carbon	● Carbon ●	●Carbon	● Carbon	⊕Carbon
⊕ Sulphur	Ⓢ Sulphur ⊕	⊕Sulphur	⊕Sulphur	⊜ Sulphur
	Phosphorus Ⓨ	☮ Phosphorus	☮ Phosphorus	⦶ Phosphorus
		ⓢMagnesia	⊛ Magnesia	
			[ⓢ Zircone] (g)	
		Ⓦ Lime	◎ Lime	
		✪ Gold	Ⓖ Gold	
			etc.	⊖ Muriatic Acid

(A) Roscoe and Harden, *New View of Dalton's Atomic Theory*, London, 1896, p. 26 and Plate 3.

(B) Ibid., p. 45.

(C) Coward and Harden, *Memoirs of the Literary and Philosophical Society of Manchester*, *59* (1915), No. 12, 43 and Plate III.

(D) Dalton, *New System of Chemical Philosophy*, Part 1, 1808, Plate 4, opp. p. 219.

(E) Thomson, *System of Chemistry*, 3rd edn., Edinburgh, 1807, vol. iii, pp. 429ff.

(F) Thomson was one of several chemists who used symbols which, although not identical with those of Dalton, were based on the same principle. Another influential British author to do this was Fownes who illustrated the composition of the oxides and acids of nitrogen, taking ⊕ for nitrogen (*Manual*, 1st edn., London, 1844, p. 183).

(g) This symbol appears only in op. cit., Part 2, 1810 (see also Fig. 7).

account in the fourth edition of his *System of Chemistry* (1810) but in the fifth edition (1817) he gave only the very briefest account of Dalton's atomic symbols, although he now used Dalton's own symbol for carbon. In the sixth and seventh editions of his famous text-book (1820, 1831) Thomson made no use at all of Dalton's symbols. This was not, however, because he thought them valueless, since he expressed the contrary opinion in his *History of Chemistry*, where he gave due place to Dalton's theory and symbols:

A bare inspection of the symbols and weights will make Mr Dalton's notions respecting the constitution of every body in the table evident to every reader . . . . It was this happy idea of representing the atoms and constitution of bodies by symbols that gave Mr Dalton's opinions so much clearness.[83]

Dalton's symbols were used more generally than may be thought, but they suffered from the same practical difficulty as the symbols of Hassenfratz and Adet, that they could only be incorporated into a printed text with some difficulty. The typographical obstacle was not so serious as in the case of the symbols of Hassenfratz and Adet, and the fact that it was overcome can be seen in books by Thomson[84], Turner[85] and Hume,[86] quite apart from reproductions of plates of symbols in the *Annals of Philosophy*[87] and also by William Higgins.[88] Dalton himself used his symbols in printed works covering a span of over thirty years. His first publication of them was in his *New System of Chemical Philosophy* (1808, 1810), each part of which contained plates of symbols at the end. When a second edition of the *New System* appeared in 1842, two years before Dalton's death, the symbols were again reproduced. In Dalton's paper *On the Phosphates and Arseniates*, which he published himself in 1840 after the Royal Society had refused to print it, there is another plate showing the compound symbols for three different phosphates and arsenates.

83. *History of Chemistry*, London, 1830, 31, vol. ii, p. 291.
84. Op. cit., also *An attempt to establish the first principles of chemistry by experiment*, London, 1825, vol. i, pp. 10–11.
85. E. Turner, *An introduction to the study of the laws of chemical combinations and the atomic theory*, Edinburgh, 1825, p. 35; *Elements of Chemistry*, 1st edn., Edinburgh, 1827, p. 132.
86. G. L. Hume, *Chemical Attraction*, Cambridge, 1835, p. 118.
87. *Annals of Philosophy*, ed. T. Thomson, 2 (1813), plate opp. p. 52.
88. *Experiments and Observations on the Atomic Theory*, Dublin, 1814, p. 171.

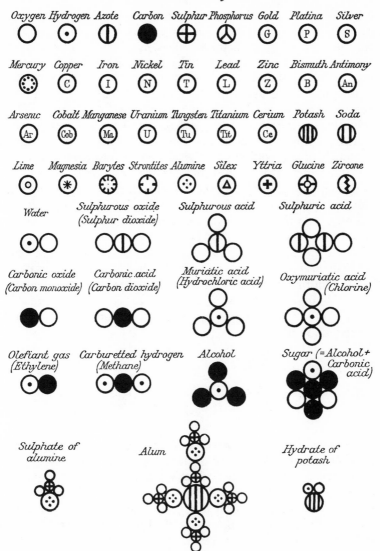

Fig. 7. Dalton's Symbols (from *New System of Chemical Philosophy*, 1810).

It has been shown,[89] however, that Dalton made greater use of his symbols in lectures on the atomic theory than in his pub-

89. W. Gee, H. F. Coward and A. Harden, 'John Dalton's Lectures and Lecture Illustration's, *Memoirs of the Manchester Literary and Philosophical Society, 59* (1915) No. 12, 1–66.

lished works or even in his laboratory note-books. Quite apart from two tables of atomic weights and symbols, an important source for a study of Dalton's ideas has deen a collection of over thirty sheets representing the composition of 'compound atoms' of the most diverse inorganic and organic compounds. A famous lecture given by Dalton was in October 1835, when he lectured at the Manchester Mechanics Institution. The subject was the atomic theory and the audience was issued with a lithographed sheet of atomic symbols.[90] This sheet contains examples of compounds containing from two to ten atoms and an interesting feature is the representation of chlorine by ⊝

Dalton was familiar with the Berzelian system of denoting the elements by letters, but he never used this system and indeed opposed it on the grounds that Berzelius neglected what Dalton called the 'allocation', i.e. the arrangement of the atoms.[91] This was one advantage possessed by Dalton's symbols—anyone using them thoughtfully could not help but consider the relative position of the atoms. Dalton was able to use this advantage to the full in organic chemistry and he expressed clearly by means of his symbols the concept of isomerism. In one of his lecture sheets[92] we find:

Albumen

Gelatin

These two compounds were considered to contain the same number of 'ultimate atoms' of the same kind, but differing in arrangement. It will be noticed that the group ⚭ is common to both these substances and this 'vegetable atom'[93] is found in Dalton's formulae for such different substances as citric acid, sugar and wood. It has been remarked that this concept of the radical marks an intermediate stage between Lavoisier's idea and later theories of compound radicals.

90. A facsimile is bound at the end of Henry's *Memoirs of . . . John Dalton,* London, 1854.

91. Ibid., p. 124. See also *Report of the British Association for the Advancement of Science, 1835,* p. 207.

92. Sheet 23 (reverse) (Gee, Coward and Harden, loc. cit. Plate VII).

93. Dalton's own expression (*Note Books,* iv, 56, cited by Coward and Harden, p. 57; see also p. 42).

Other chemists too made good use of the advantages of Dalton's symbols. Thomson used them to explain how it was possible for acetic and succinic acids to have apparently the same number of the same atoms and yet be different substances, because the atoms were differently arranged.[94] Even Gerhardt in 1844 found it useful to use symbols similar to those of Dalton to explain the relationship between oxalic acid and its salts.[95] He represented oxalic acid, the acid salt and the neutral salt of potassium respectively as follows:

It has been suggested by a younger contemporary of Dalton,[96] that by the use of his symbols Dalton familiarized men of science with the way in which chemical combination took place and thus paved a surer way for the reception of the Atomic Theory. Other chemists besides Dalton used these symbols to explain chemical reactions. The French chemist, A. M. Gaudin, explained the combination of hydrogen with oxygen, with chlorine and with nitrogen on the assumption that each of these gases was composed of diatomic 'compound atoms'.[97] He explained the changes in volume in each of these three reactions by drawing boxes to represent a unit volume and Daltonian symbols to represent the atoms of the gases. For oxygen and hydrogen he used exactly the same symbols as Dalton, but he denoted nitrogen by ⊖ and chlorine by ⊗

Symbols similar to those of Dalton were used to illustrate the structural formulae of similar compounds.[98] In organic chemistry A. W. Hofmann used the same type of symbols to explain certain cases of substitution[99] and the graphic formulae used by Kekulé[100] were really a compromise between Daltonian and Berzelian symbolism. It is certainly true that organic

94. *History of Chemistry*, London, 1830, 31, vol. ii, pp. 304–5. Thomson's argument was, however, based on a false premiss, since the respective formulae of these acids are $C_2H_4O_2$ and $C_4H_6O_4$.

95. *Précis de chimie organique*, Paris, 1844, 45, vol. i; p. 13.

96. C. Daubeny, *An introduction to the atomic theory*, 2nd edn., Oxford, 1850, p. 99.

97. *Annales de Chimie et de Physique*, 52 (1833), 113–33.

98. Daubeny, op. cit., pp. 202–3.

99. According to W. Henry, op. cit., pp. 126–7.   100. See p. 334.

chemists were forced to accept Dalton's view of the importance
of the relative position of atoms in a compound, and it might
well be said that modern chemistry has adopted Berzelius' symbols but uses them in the manner advocated by Dalton. There
is a slight irony in the fact that even Berzelius, whose symbols
were preferred to those of Dalton, made use of Daltonian symbols in at least one publication. He represented the compound
Fe_3O_4 by a cluster of circles, $\bigcirc$ denoting oxygen and $\oplus$
iron.[101] He numbered each atom and remarked how it was
possible for particular atoms of iron to be replaced by atoms of
another metal.

An interesting postscript bearing on the value of Dalton's
symbols is contained in a German obituary notice printed in
1844.[102] The author claimed that Dalton's symbols had the
advantage over those of Berzelius, in that they were even more
international since, for the most part, they did not depend on
initial letters in any one language. Thus the formula $\oplus\bigcirc^3$
could be recognized the whole world over as representing sulphuric acid.[103]

101. Berzelius, *Jahresbericht*, *15* (1835), p. 249.
102. A German translation of Dalton's *New System* by Wolf had appeared
in Berlin in 1812, 14.
103. i.e., the anhydride of sulphuric acid (Du Menil. *Archiv der Pharmacie*, *90* (1844), 324).

CHAPTER FOUR

The Symbols of Berzelius

The Early Use of Abbreviations

The essence of the system of symbols used by Berzelius was simply the use of the initial letters of the Latin names of the elements; when these letters were joined with a plus sign, or were merely adjacent, they denoted the formula of a compound. Before describing the details of Berzelius' scheme and its reception by other chemists, it is proposed to consider to what extent abbreviations had been used in chemistry before Berzelius.

A large proportion of the symbols found in the Greek alchemical manuscripts were either themselves abbreviations or were derived from abbreviations, as Zuretti has clearly shown. In the western alchemical tradition, abbreviations were not quite so common, if we exclude the manuscript abbreviations which were not confined to alchemy. In the *Practica*[104] and the *De Secretis Naturae*,[105] attributed to Raymond Lull, they were used in a mystical way rather arbitrarily. There is no agreement between the meaning assigned to the letters in the former and the latter work respectively:

A *significat Deum*	A *significat Chaos*
B *significat Mercurium*	B *significat Materia*
C *significat Salus Petrum*	C *significat Forma*
D *significat Vitriolum*	D *significat Coelum*
etc.	etc.

To add to the confusion in the latter work, each letter was given two distinct meanings, and Thorndike[106] has noted that the alphabets vary somewhat in different manuscripts. Lull's alphabets and others equally mystical would not be worth mentioning,

---

104. *Th. Ch.*, iv, folding plate opp. p. 156
105. Op. cit., Cologne, 1567.
106. *A History of Magic and Experimental Science*, New York, 1923–41, vol. iv, pp. 41–2.

if it were not for the fact that Lull clearly states that his purpose in using letters was 'to render the art compendious'.[107]

A similar purpose of abbreviation led the more rational author of the *Liber Laureatus* to use the initial letters of the word *Ignis*, *Aqua*, *Aer* and *Terra* to denote these respective Aristotelian elements.[108] In the seventeenth century the letters A. F. were sometimes used as an abbreviation for *aqua fortis* and the abbreviations B.M. (*balneum Mariae*), S.S.S. (*stratum super stratum*), C.C. (*cornu cervi*), etc. are often found among tables of chemical symbols published in the seventeenth and eighteenth centuries. Geoffroy used the abbreviations $\sqrt{y}$ (*esprit de vin*), S.M. (*substances métalliques*), P.C. (*pierre calaminaire*) and Z (zinc) (see Fig. 2). Other recently discovered metals were denoted in the eighteenth century by their initial letters, so that in a German work bismuth (*Wismuth*) and cobalt (*Kobold*) were represented by W and K respectively.[109] These letters were often carried over into French and English works (e.g. translations from the German), where their meaning was not so obvious.

Bergman did not favour the extensive use of letters as chemical symbols, but he did make use of initial letters for a particular purpose and in an original manner. He used these abbreviations to calculate the total possible number of species of compound earths, etc. As a mineralogist, Bergman was concerned to calculate not so much the number of pure compounds as the number of different minerals possible, in which one substance was associated with one, two or more other substances:

> In order to determine with accuracy the species of earths ... let the five primitive earths be indicated by five initial letters, the ponderous by p, calcareous by c, magnesian by m, argillaceous by a, and siliceous by s.[110]

He went on to mention the possibility of applying letters to

---

107. 'Ut inde artem compendiosam reddamus' (*De Secretis Naturae*, Cologne, 1567, Distinctio tertia, p. 152). For a better perspective of Lullian applications of letters of the alphabet see W. Pagel, *Paracelsus*, Basel and New York, 1958, pp. 241–2.

108. These abbreviations occur at least four times: f. 4r, 8r., 10r., 15r. according to Carbonelli, *Sulle Fonti Storiche delle Chimica e dell' Alchimia in Italia*, Rome, 1925, p. 49.

109. e.g. Gellert, *Anfangsgründe zur metallurgischen Chymie*, 2nd edn., Leipzig, 1776, pp. 228–9.

110. *Nova Acta Reg. Soc. Scient. Upsaliensis*, 4 (1784), 99.

denote metals, in order to calculate the number of possible permutations which might occur. In point of fact he confined himself to another calculation using the symbols S = salt, T = earth (*terra*), I = 'phlogistic substance' (*inflammabilia*?). Bergman concluded:

Formulae indeed point out to us what may be done, but whether and where they are employed, must be learned from a faithful analysis.

Although Bergman (who had been a mathematician before he was a chemist) was thinking algebraically, it is interesting in the light of subsequent controversy over the details of Berzelius' symbolism, that Bergman denoted a compound of A and c by merely writing the letters next to each other: Ac.[111]

Another mineralogist who used letters as symbols was the Russian Prince Dimitri de Gallitzin. He denoted nine earths by the first nine letters of the alphabet and commented,

Perhaps I would have done better to use as symbols for these earths the initial letters of their names; but several of them begin with the same letter[112] and it would then be necessary to add a second letter of their name. Now, the least complication causes typographical mistakes and I thought that by simplifying, I would avoid this inconvenience.[113]

We should not forget that the scheme of symbols published by Hassenfratz and Adet in 1787 had included (albeit reluctantly) the use of initial letters to indicate simple substances and radicals. In England, Dalton's system, published in 1808 and 1810, made some use of the initial letters of the English names of the elements. William Higgins, best known perhaps for his claim to have anticipated Dalton's Atomic Theory, might nevertheless be given credit for denoting particles of substances by initial letters. In his *Comparative View of the Phlogistic and Anti-phlogistic Theories* (1789) he used such abbreviations as C = copper, M = mercury, S = sulphur, d or D = dephlogisticated air (oxygen) and I = iron or inflammable air (hydrogen) according to

111. *Disquisitio de attractionibus electivis, Nova Acta Reg. Soc. Scient. Upsaliensis*, 2 (1775), 161.
112. e.g. silica, strontian.
113. Golitsuin, *Recueil de noms . . . apropriés en minéralogie*, Brunswick, 1801, p. 298.

the context.[114] He even wrote formulae for compounds using these symbols, e.g. I——D (water). Using abbreviations of the new nomenclature, Grotthus in 1805 represented a molecule of water by the formula oh, which he later changed to oho.[115] That the use of initial letters as abbreviations for chemical substances was not uncommon in the early nineteenth century is further emphasized by their use by Thomas Young in a 'Table of Double Decompositions'.[116] In this, Young referred to the acids and bases by their initials, e.g. Nitric Acid = N, Sulphuric Acid = S, Sulphurous Acid = SS, Potash = PT, Magnesia = ME, Alumina = AL, etc.

Yet in his general application of letters as chemical symbols, Berzelius was indebted not so much to any of these chemists already mentioned as to Thomas Thomson. Thomson's first published use of symbols seems to have been in 1802, when he made use of them to describe the composition of minerals in the first edition of his *System of Chemistry*.[117] He denoted each of the following twelve constituents of minerals by their initial letters: alumina, silica, magnesia, lime, barytes, glucina, zirconia, yttria, iron (oxide), chromium (oxide), nickel (oxide) and potash. To construct a formula, Thomson arranged the letters representing these substances in the order of their proportions in a particular mineral. Thus 'SAWL' denoted a mineral (zeolite), which had been shown by analysis to contain 53% silica, 27% alumina, 10% water and $9\frac{1}{2}$% lime. Thomson acknowledged that this system of using initial letters to denote minerals had been taken from Bergman. When Berzelius, in his turn, used mineralogical formulae in 1814, he admitted that he was following Thomson's example, with the exception that Berzelius insisted that the intials used should be those of the Latin names.[118]

There is, however, a considerable difference between a decision to use initials to make up for the deficiencies of mineralogical nomenclature[119] and the use of letters in

114. T. S. Wheeler and J. R. Partington, *The Life and Work of William Higgins Chemist*, Oxford, London and New York, 1960, pp. 89, 90.

115. *Ann. chim.*, *58* (1806), 68; *63* (1807), 19–20.

116. *An Introduction to Medical Literature*, London, 1813, p. 494.

117. Op. cit., 1st edn., Edinburgh, 1802, vol. iii, pp. 431–513.

118. Berzelius, *Attempt to establish a system of mineralogy*, London, 1814, p. 44.

119. Thomson, op. cit., vol. iii, p. 431: 'I have not imposed names on these genera of minerals but, in imitation of Bergman, have denoted each by a symbol.'

chemistry to denote definite weights of a particular element. For this reason it is worth quoting from a paper by Thomson on oxalic acid published in 1808. It should be noted that he read this paper sometime after a conversation with Dalton on the atomic theory and its symbolism.

Let an atom of oxygen be w, an atom of carbon c, an atom of hydrogen h. An integrant particle of oxalic acid may be represented by 4w + 3c + 2h. We may represent the composition and weight of an integrant particle of each of the substances into which oxalic acid is decomposed by heat, by the following symbols and numbers:

Carbonic acid	2w + c	weight	16·5
Carburetted hydrogen	c + 2h		6.5
Carbonic oxide	w + c		10·5
Water	w + h		7
Charcoal	c		4·5 [120]

There seems no obvious reason why Thomson should have denoted oxygen by w instead of o, but in any case he used the latter symbol in a paper on the theory of definite proportions printed in his own journal, the *Annals of Philosophy*, in July 1813. The following are some of the formulae he suggested in that paper:

Water	10 + 1h
Carbonic oxide	10 + 1c
Carbonic acid	20 + 1c
Ammonia	2h + 1a
Magnesia	1m + 10 [121]

Although there was no ambiguity in the context, Thomson might have taken more trouble about the symbols for substances with the same initial letters. Thus c stands variously for carbon, copper, cobalt and cerium, while a is used to denote azote (as above), antimony and arsenic, although Thomson did use the symbol st for strontian to avoid confusion with s for soda. In case the reader should be in any doubt as to the meaning of these formulae, Thomson had a plate engraved showing Dal-

---

120. *Phil. Trans.*, *98* (1808), 89.
121. *Annals of Philosophy*, *2* (1813), 43–52. Thomson continued to make use of these symbols and others (e.g. pl = platinum, si = silver) in subsequent issues of the *Annals*, even after Berzelius had published his own scheme (*Annals of Philosophy*, *3*, 135–8, 375–7; *4*, 13–17; *5*, 185–9; *12*, 436–441).

ton's symbols for a selection of compounds. Thomson's reasons for not adhering completely to Dalton's symbols may have been typographical, but it is also possible that Thomson appreciated that his own symbols had the advantage of simplicity.

Berzelius' Symbols

It is against this background that we now turn to examine the contribution of Berzelius to chemical symbolism. Berzelius' first publication in which he used chemical symbols is sometimes dated as January 1814, but it is quite clear from a study of the *Annals of Philosophy*, that Berzelius' symbols were first introduced to the British public in 1813. The relevant paper was entitled *Experiments on the Nature of Azote, of Hydrogen and of Ammonia and upon the Degrees of Oxidation of which Azote is susceptible*. This paper was dated 22 April 1813, but, according to Thomson, it did not reach him till the end of August and was finally printed in November of that year. In his paper Berzelius used the symbols Az = azote, N = nitric, O = oxygen and P = lead (*plumbum*). In a footnote he explained that his method of using symbols was based on Dalton's atomic theory, and it is important to note Berzelius' quantitative approach:

Let us express by the initial letters of the name of each substance a determinate quantity of that substance; and let us determine that quantity from its relation in weight to oxygen, both taken in the gaseous state, and in equal volumes; that is to say the specific gravity of the substances in their gaseous state, that of oxygen being considered as unity . . . .

When two bodies have the same initial letter, I add the second letter, and should that also be the same, I add to the initial the first consonant of the word that differs. In the class of combustibles which I call metalloids, I use only the initial letters. For example S = sulphur, Sn = tin (*stannum*), St = antimony (*stibium*), C = carbon, Cu = copper (*cuprum*), M = muriaticum, Ms = magnesium, Mn = manganese, etc. This is all that is necessary to understand these formulae. The only thing that remains to render the use of them more general is to determine correctly the specific gravity of the gases.[122]

Berzelius returned to the subject of symbolism and dealt with it more fully in his paper of January 1814.[123] He began by

122. *Annals of Philosophy*, 2 (1813), 359n.
123. 'On the Chemical Signs and the Method of employing them to express Chemical Proportions', *Annals of Philosophy*, 3 (1814), 51ff.

referring to the symbols of Hassenfratz and Adet which he himself had been in the habit of using till then.[124] Although the latter's signs were very ingenious, their use was restricted, because, in order to be legible, the characters had to be larger than ordinary writing. The main reason why they were not more widely used, said Berzelius, was that it was easier to write an abbreviated word than to draw a figure. The symbols proposed by Berzelius did not suffer from these disadvantages. Their purpose also was different, since Berzelius was primarily interested in the proportions of the constituent elements of compounds:

They are destined solely to facilitate the expression of chemical proportions, and to enable us to indicate, without long periphrases, the relative number of volumes of the different constituents contained in each compound body. By determining the weight of the elementary volumes, these figures will enable us to express the numeric result of an analysis as simply, and in a manner as easily remembered, as the algebraic formulas in mechanical philosophy.

Berzelius went on to explain again his choice of the initial letter of the Latin name of each element. To denote simple compounds he joined the elementary symbols with a plus sign, e.g.

$$Cu + O = \text{oxidum cuprosum}$$
$$Cu + 2O = \text{oxidum cupricum}$$
$$2H + O = \text{water}$$

To denote more complex compounds an index number was placed above any atom of which there was more than one, e.g.

$$\text{copper sulphate} = CuO + S\overset{3}{O} \quad [125]$$

$$\text{alum} = 3\,(Al\overset{2}{O} + 2S\overset{3}{O}) + (Po + 2S\overset{3}{O})$$

In 1814 Berzelius had devised symbols for nearly 50 elements then known to chemists.[126]

124. *J. Berzelius' Bref*, Uppsala, 1912–35, Part 8, pp. 11–26; Part 9, pp. 38, 118–19.

125. This formula was consistent with the current nomenclature, according to which this salt was 'sulphate of deutoxide of copper'. In a letter written in 1831 Berzelius suggested that it might be an advantage to re-group such formulae with all the electro-negative elements on one side comprising a group analagous to the chloride group. Thus we could write $Fe + SO^4$ instead of $FeO + SO^3$ (*J. Berzelius' Bref*, Uppsala, 1912–35, Part 7, p. 282).

126. These were printed together with their atomic weights in an appendix to Berzelius' *Försök att genom användandet ... grundlägga ett rent vetten skapligt system för mineralogien*, Stockholm, 1814.

Berzelius made further use of symbols in his *Attempt to establish a . . . system of mineralogy*, published in Swedish in the spring of 1814 and translated into English later in the same year. In this small book Berzelius explained how, by using suitable symbols, he was able to dispense with explanations of the results of every mineralogical analysis. His mineralogical formulae used initial letters to denote the earths and other natural compounds and were printed in italics. Thus S = Silica, M = Magnesia, Mg = 'Peroxide of manganese', F = 'Peroxide of iron', f = 'Ferrose Protoxide of iron', etc. Berzelius realized that if he were to use the chemical symbols to express these naturally occurring compounds the resulting formulae would be unwieldy. His 'simplified' formula for hyssolite $(MS + CS + Mgs + F^2S)$[127] might emphasize this point.

Berzelius was, however, prepared to discuss his chemical symbols in an appendix to this book. Here one or two amendments to his previous system are revealed. The small number, denoting the number of atoms of an element, was now placed to the right 'like an algebraical exponent'. He now wrote copper sulphate, therefore, as $SO^3 + CuO$.[128] The reason for this displacement was that he had decided that the presence of oxygen in a compound could be denoted even more briefly by dots placed above the appropriate symbol. Thus instead of writing 'persulphate of copper' $2SO^3 + CuO^2$, it could be abbreviated even further to $\overset{\cdots\;\cdot\cdot}{S^2Cu}$. The shortening of the formula was even more marked in the case of double salts; thus he now wrote alum as $\overset{\cdots\cdots}{K\,S^2} + 3\overset{\cdots\cdots}{Al\,S^3} + 24H^2O$. One might think that Berzelius' reason for reserving a special method of notation for oxygen was that, like Lavoisier, he considered oxygen to be an element of unique importance. Berzelius himself, however, implied that by the use of these dots, he was able to bring his mineralogical and chemical formulae closer together and it was only because of the doubt as to the number of parts of oxygen in many oxides, that Berzelius continued to use the mineralogical formulae, which avoided this question.

127. This formula is taken from the original (*Försök*, Stockholm, 1814, p. 31), since in the English translation by John Black it provides a striking example of inaccurate copying, a common feature in this translation, despite Thomson's assurance in the preface that he had compared it with the original.

128. *Attempt*, London, 1814, p. 123.

In 1818 Berzelius compiled a table[129] based on his own analysis of some 2,000 simple and compound substances. In his list of formulae Berzelius made two changes intended to abbreviate his symbols even further. He proposed the use of the letters Aq. to denote water of crystallization and his (revised) formula for alum now became:

$$\overset{..}{K}\ \overset{...}{S^2}\ +2\overset{...}{Al}\ \overset{...}{S^3}+48Aq.$$

Of more importance was his decision to denote the organic acids by the first letter of their Latin name with a line over the top 'to distinguish them from inorganic atoms'. Thus $\overline{C}$ was citric acid, $\overline{A}$ acetic acid, etc. He also used $\overline{P}$ for Prussic acid instead of the formula based on his own analysis, $C^2\overset{.}{N}H^2$.

A further modification by Berzelius of his original scheme was the introduction of barred symbols:

> There is now apparent the need for a sign for a double atom, for example in the case where an oxide is built up of two atoms of a radical and one of oxygen. The simplest would indeed be the doubling of the letter, but this would often be difficult to read in the formulae; accordingly I have preferred to draw a stroke through the bottom third of the letter which represents an atom if it is intended to represent two atoms, e.g. $\bcancel{H} = H^2O$, water; $\bcancel{NH}^3 = N^2H^6$, ammonia, etc.[130]

The use of barred symbols was to increase the confusion of symbolism for the student of chemistry later in the nineteenth century. The original use of such symbols to denote a double atom was adopted by several chemists and was used by Kolbe, for example, up to about 1850. Other chemists considered barred symbols a useful means of distinguishing between rival systems of atomic weights. Kekulé and Wurtz, for example, used barred symbols with the same meaning as the ordinary symbols of to-day.

Another ill-chosen refinement to Berzelius' original plan was to extend the system by which oxygen was represented by a dot to other electronegative elements. Sulphides were denoted by

---

129. First published in Sweden: *Tabell . . . Bihang till tredje delen of Lärboken i Kemien*, Stockholm, 1818. All the formulae are reproduced in Berzelius' *Essai sur la théorie des proportions chimiques*, Paris, 1819. His remarks on the organic acids are on p. 113 of the latter work.

130. Berzelius, *Jahresbericht*, 7 (1828), 72.

commas, selenides by dashes, and tellurides by crosses, as in the following examples.[131]

$\overset{\cdot\ \ \cdots}{\text{K Mo}}$	potassium oxy-molybdate
$\overset{,\ \ ,,,}{\text{K Mo}}$	potassium sulpho-molybdate
$\overset{-\ \ ---}{\text{K Mo}}$	potassium seleni-molybdate
$\overset{+\ +++}{\text{K Mo}}$	potassium telluri-molybdate

Apart from errors due to faulty analysis, there were several weaknesses in Berzelius' system. In the first place he did not consider the halogens and nitrogen—both important and common substances—as elements but as oxides and he denoted them as such in symbols. Starting from M, the hypothetical radical of spirit of salt, he denoted related compounds as follows:

		modern notation
Acidum muriaticum	$\overset{\cdot\cdot}{\text{M}}\ (=\text{MO}^2)$	HCl
Superoxidum muriatosum	$\overset{\cdot\cdot\cdot}{\text{M}}\ (=\text{MO}^3)$	Cl_2
Murias natricus	$\text{Na}\overset{\cdot\cdot}{\text{M}}{}^2\ (=\text{NaO}^2+2\text{MO}^2)$	NaCl

Similarly, starting from N = *nitricum*:

		modern notation
Nitrogenium	$\overset{\cdot}{\text{N}}\ (=\text{NO})$	N_2
Oxidum nitrosum	$\overset{\cdot\cdot}{\text{N}}\ (\text{NO}^2)$	NO
Ammoniacum	$\overset{\cdot}{\text{N}}\text{H}^6\ (=\text{NOH}^6)$	NH_3

Berzelius also made a misleading analogy between salts containing water of crystallization and what we now call hydroxides, denoting both by the symbol Aq. Thus what we now represent as NaOH, Berzelius wrote as $\overset{\cdot\cdot}{\text{Na}}+2\text{Aq.}\ (=\text{NaO}^2+2\text{H}^2\text{O})$.

Over the years Berzelius made only minor alterations to the symbols themselves. In 1814 he had written Pl for palladium, but, no doubt to avoid confusion with platinum, he changed this to Pa and finally to Pd.[132] By 1827 he was prepared to

---

131. *Théorie des proportions chimiques*, 2nd edn., Paris, 1835, p. 91.

132. *Théorie des proportions chimiques*, Paris, 1819, and 2nd edn., Paris, 1835.

recognize the advantage of speaking of the 'muriatic radical' and he accordingly replaced M by Cl.[133] The 'fluoric radical' (i.e. hydrofluoric acid minus oxygen in Berzelius' opinion) continued to be denoted as F. Iodine was given the symbol I, so that iridium, which had originally been denoted by that letter, became Ir. To complete the symbolism of the halogens, bromine was denoted by Br.

A difficulty which arose in denoting the elements by initial letters was a lack of agreement on the names to be adopted for certain elements. In particular Berzelius favoured certain names current in Germany, but different from those used in France or England. Thus he insisted on using the Latin names *Wolframium* (tungsten), *Beryllium* (the *glucinum* of Vauquelin), *Kalium* (potassium) and *Natrium* (sodium), since he considered these names superior on etymological grounds to the alternative names. Berzelius also disagreed with the British chemists who, loyal to their compatriot Hatchett, preferred to call *columbium* what Berzelius referred to as *tantalum*, a name bestowed on a similar metal by the Swede Ekeberg who had first examined it in the metallic state.

Berzelius was very annoyed[134] when Thomson, in a translation of one of his papers for the *Annals of Philosophy*, substituted the term *columbium* for *tantalum* and *glucinum* for *beryllium*. Thomson had also used the terms *sodium* and *potassium* for what Berzelius called *natrium* and *kalium*; and he added insult to injury to Berzelius when he used the symbols Cb (or Cl), Gl, So, and Po for these elements respectively.[135] To Berzelius' criticism Thomson replied that neither Berzelius nor he were able to change the accepted chemical nomenclature. Time has shown, however, that as far as the symbols are concerned, the international authority of Berzelius was decisive. It has already been pointed out that Thomson often continued to use his own symbols in the *Annals* in preference to those of Berzelius. Sometimes he adopted symbols like F (for Fe), C (for Cu), P (for Pb)[136] which, although they agreed with Berzelius in being based on the Latin names, can hardly be considered to be Berzelian symbols.

133. *Lehrbuch der Chemie*, Dresden, 1825–31, vol. 3, p. 109.
134. *J. Berzelius' Bref*, Part 6, pp. 18–21. See also pp. 24–5.
135. *Annals of Philosophy*, *3* (1814), 250, 360, 362–3.
136. *Annals of Philosophy*, *5* (1815), 187.

The General Adoption of Berzelius' Symbols

Although Berzelius' symbols were accepted fairly readily in France, and Thenard introduced them in his text-book published in 1824,[137] not all French chemists were willing to submit to the use of symbols based on Latin names. Beudant in his *Traité Élémentaire de Minéralogie* (1824) accepted the idea of the symbols of Berzelius with the modification that Beudant's symbols were based on the French names. Thus he wrote E (*Étain*), M (*Mercure*), O (*Or*), Ox (*Oxigène*) etc. Berzelius took exception to this display of nationalism and pointed out that, if it were copied by English, German and Italian authors, all the advantages of precision and ease of communication would be lost.[138] Beudant changed his symbols in the second edition of his text-book,[139] so as to be in conformity with those of Berzelius, but the lack of agreement on terminology still bedevilled the symbols. As long as beryllium was known as *glucinum*, 'wolfranium' as *tungstène* and nitrogen as *azote*, it was natural that the respective symbols G, Tu and Az should be used in France. It is remarkable that, despite the criticisms of azote by the very men who had coined the term,[140] its use has persisted in France to this day and the symbol Az had only recently been replaced by N for the sake of international conformity.

In Germany Berzelius' main work on chemical symbols was published in 1820 under the title *Versuch über die Theorie der chemischen Proportionen* and the third volume of his *Lehrbuch*, containing the explanation of symbols appeared in 1827. Berzelius also had an influential position as the editor of a yearly report on progress in the physical sciences and in his *Jahresbericht*, which appeared in German translation from 1822 onwards, he made full use of his symbols. One of the first German

137. L. J. Thenard, *Traité de chimie*, 4th edn., Paris, 1824, vol. i, pp. 34–7.
138. *Lehrbuch der Chemie*, Dresden, 1825–31, vol. 3, p. 110.
139. *Traité Élémentaire de Minéralogie*, 2nd edn., Paris, 1830–2, vol. i, p. 382.
140. In the first place Fourcroy had preferred the term *alkaligène* to *azote*, but he had been overruled by his colleagues who had pointed out that the gas was also related to *acide nitrique* (*Méthode*, 1787, pp. 35–6). Yet after the publication of the *Méthode* the inconsistency of the terms *azote* and *acide nitrique* was admitted by Lavoisier (*Traité élémentaire*, Paris, 1789, pp. 78–9), Berthollet (in a letter to Gadolin dated April 1789—*Acta Societatis Scientiarum Fennicae, 39* (1910), lxxviii) and Guyton (*Annales de Chymie, 22* (1797), 96).

chemists to use Berzelius' symbols was J. W. Döbereiner, who made use of the formulae $\overset{2}{HO}$, $\overset{3}{NH}$, $\overset{2}{C}\overset{2}{H}\overset{4}{O}$ (oxalic acid) in a book published in 1821.[141] It was only in the 1830's, however, that any general use was made of the symbols in Germany. In 1831 the German analytical chemist Rose made full use of Berzelius' symbols in the second edition of his *Handbuch der analytischen Chemie*.[142] Mitscherlich, although formerly a pupil of Berzelius, employed symbols very infrequently in the first volume of his *Lehrbuch* (1831), but he did make considerable use of them in the second volume published four years later. In some cases Mitscherlich abandoned the use of indices in chemical formulae and preferred to write the number of atoms continuously with the symbols for the atoms, e.g. $14ClOH2O2Ch$. Berzelius' comment on this was that it would make formulae unnecessarily unwieldy, especially in the case of double salts like alum.[143] The symbols of Berzelius were used by Wöhler and Liebig in 1832,[144] but in 1834[145] Liebig took the important step of refusing to accept the barred symbols because it was easy for the printers and the reader to make mistakes because of them. Liebig also considered it preferable to indicate numbers of atoms by a subscript. Thus he wrote C_4H_8 for the C^2H^4 of Berzelius and CO_2 instead of CO^2.

Considering that the first publication of Berzelius' symbols had been in a British journal, the acceptance of these symbols in Britain was very long delayed. The English translator of Berzelius' book on the use of the blowpipe rejected the symbols outright, preferring to use long explanations than write formulae with symbols. The following remarks give a foretaste of the hostility with which many British chemists regarded the new symbols:

141. P. Walden, '*Zur Entwicklungsgeschichte der chemischen Zeichen*', *Studien zur Geschichte der Chemie*, Festgabe E. O. von Lippmann, ed. J. Ruska, Berlin, 1927, pp. 94–9. Walden refers to Döbereiner's *Zur pneumatischen Chemie* Theil 1, Jena, 1821, p. 71. A copy of this book has not been available to the present writer.

142. Op. cit., 2nd edn., vol. ii, Berlin, 1831, pp. 605–709; see especially p. 608.

143. *Jahresbericht*, *15* (1836), 203.

144. '*Untersuchungen über das Radical der Benzoesäure*', *Annalen der Pharmacie*, *3* (1832), 261.

145. '*Ueber die Constitution des Aethers und seiner Verbindungen*', *Annalen der Pharmacie*, *9* (1834), 3n. This modification was also introduced into the *Handwörterbuch der reinen und ungewandeten Chemie*, ed. J. von Liebig and J. C. Poggendorff (see op. cit., vol. i, Braunschweig, 1837, p. ix).

These formulae I have omitted *in toto* . . . . I have taken this
liberty (and I here beg to assure my author, with any feeling rather
than disrespect), because I do not think the introduction of these, or
any other symbols at all necessary; it requires some time and patience
to make oneself thoroughly master of them and, as it strikes me, to
little purpose. Why are the symbols of the old chemists abolished, but
from experience having proved them unnecessary . . . . I have taken
this liberty because these signs and formulae are little known in
England, and consequently without an elaborate and tedious explanation would be perfectly unintelligible to most of my readers. I will
candidly own too, that thinking them rather calculated to perplex
than facilitate our progress, I do not wish to see them used in this
country, and therefore I could not honestly add my mite towards
their introduction, by adopting them.[146]

In a review of this book, William Brande, the successor to Sir
Humphry Davy at the Royal Institution, agreed wholeheartedly with the decision to avoid the use of symbols.[147]
Brande considered that 'common language is amply sufficient
for every purpose these symbols can be applied to' and, in his
opinion, their use as abbreviations would create unnecessary
difficulties and cause confusion.

In 1831 the question of the use of chemical symbols was raised
by William Whewell, then professor of mineralogy at Cambridge
and later a prominent figure in the British Association for the
Advancement of Science (founded 1831). Whewell favoured the
use of symbols, particularly in mineralogy,[148] but also in
chemistry, as a useful means of overcoming difficulties in the
application of chemical nomenclature.[149] Whewell's early
mathematical training led him to compare Berzelius' symbols
with algebraic symbols and he proposed altering the former to
conform to the conventions of the latter.[150] Thus he proposed that
chemical symbols were to be invariably joined with a plus
sign[151] and brackets were to be used as in algebra. Whewell's

146. Berzelius, *The use of the Blowpipe*, trans. J. G. Children, London,
1822, pp. viii–ix.

147. *Quarterly Journal of Science, Literature and the Arts, 13* (1822), 322.

148. *Report of the British Association for the Advancement of Science, 1832*, p. 345.

149. *Journal of the Royal Institution, 1* (1831), 438–9.

150. Whewell's only objection to the dots used by Berzelius to represent
oxygen atoms was that they were 'not consistent with the algebraical rule'
(ibid., p. 449).

151. This criticism was repeated as late as 1858 by Sir John Herschel,
Report of the British Association, 1858, p. 42.

system was far enough removed from the needs of chemists to ensure its general rejection, although Brande made some use of it in his own text-book of chemistry.[152]

Although Whewell had travelled on the continent of Europe, he retained an insularity of outlook (not uncommon in Britain in the nineteenth century) which made him regard anything foreign as necessarily inferior. This is clearly shown in his concluding remarks on his proposed modifications of Berzelius' symbolism:

I should hope that what I have said may tend to induce our chemists to purify and improve the foreign system, before it is admitted to a familiarity and circulation among us.[153]

Berzelius took offence at this remark and made some acid comments on the insularity and conservatism of learned men in Britain.[154]

Not all British chemists, however, despised the symbols of Berzelius and they were being used in 1833 by Edward Turner, Professor of Chemistry at University College London and also by Thomas Graham, then lecturer in chemistry at the Andersonian Institution in Glasgow.[155] The decisive move was taken when Turner decided to adopt the symbols of Berzelius in his text-book. In the third edition of his *Elements of Chemistry* (1831) Turner had not made any use of symbols, but when he was preparing a fourth edition of this work, he found difficulty in describing the results of the research of Liebig and Wöhler on cyanic acid without resorting to symbols. For this reason Turner only used symbols in the latter half of the book. He soon became enthusiastic about their general use in chemistry:

Having once employed them advantageously, I was soon tempted to introduce them again; and this speedily led to the discovery that chemical symbols are not only fitted to be a convenient abbreviation among educated chemists but may be made a powerful instrument of instruction by teachers of chemistry.[156]

---

152. W. T. Brande, *A Manual of Chemistry*, 4th edn., London, 1836, Part 1, e.g. p. 352.

153. *Journal of the Royal Institution*, *1* (1831), 453.

154. *Jahresbericht*, *12* (1833), 168–70.

155. On Turner's death in 1837 Graham was appointed to the chair of chemistry at University College, London.

156. *Elements of Chemistry*, 4th edn., London, 1833, p. vii.

In the following year Turner brought out another edition of his *Elements*, in which he clearly stated his allegiance to the original symbols of Berzelius, rather than any modification, such as had been suggested by Whewell:

The present state of chemistry renders the use abbreviated or symbolic language almost unavoidable; and the question now is, not so much whether they should be used, as whether they shall be generally understood. To ensure this it is essential that a uniform system be adopted; and I have felt the necessity of strictly conforming to the method introduced by Berzelius and adopted on the Continent.[157]

A report to the British Association, printed in 1833, referred to Turner's use of symbols in the fourth edition of his *Elements* and agreed that the state of chemistry 'makes their adoption now imperative'.[158] The author of this part of the report was J. F. W. Johnston, who soon used the symbols in his own publications. Johnston, like Liebig, brings us closer to the symbolism of to-day by writing the number of atoms as a subscript instead of as an index, e.g. MnO_2, P_2Cl_3, P_2Cl_5.[159]

For Johnston it was the rate at which organic compounds were being discovered, without any coherent system of nomenclature to describe them, which made the adoption of symbols and formulae imperative. For Graham, it was the deficiencies of the nomenclature of inorganic chemistry which led him to adopt the use of chemical symbols. Graham's first published work containing chemical symbols was his paper entitled 'Researches on the Arseniates, Phosphates and Modifications of Phosphoric Acid', which he wrote in January 1833 and which was read at a meeting of the Royal Society later the same year.[160] Graham later remarked that he had been unable to express the results of his researches on the acids of phosphorus and their salts with the current nomenclature. He continued,

It is certainly one great advantage of chemical formulae that they may be made to compensate to a certain extent for the increasing deficiencies of the nomenclature. From new light thrown upon the constitution of some familiar salt, its name ceases to indicate its received constitution, or even belies it. In such cases where it may be

157. Ibid., 5th edn., London, 1834, p. x.
158. Op. cit., p. 447.
159. *Chemical Tables*, Part 1, Edinburgh, 1836, p. iv. The latter two compounds mentioned would, of course, now be written PCl_3 and PCl_5.
160. *Phil. Trans.*, *1833*, 253–84.

expedient to change the name, it may well be qualified when used by subjoining in parentheses the correct formula of the salt. I confess that I underrated the advantages of chemical notation till its use was forced upón me in the study of the phosphates. But now I am satisfied that to neglect it would be voluntarily to forgo a most valuable aid in the conception and exhibition of chemical relations.[161]

This striking testimony of the value of chemical symbols both in research and teaching is a fitting conclusion to this section.[162]

161. *Phil. Mag.*, 3rd series, *4* (1834), 404.
162. For the use of symbols in organic chemistry see Part 5, Chapter 3.

Part 5

THE LANGUAGE OF ORGANIC CHEMISTRY

When we reflect on the absence of all system and of all nomenclature to classify and name this multiplicity of bodies, one may ask with anxiety whether it will be possible in a few years to find one's way in the labyrinth of organic chemistry.

LAURENT, *Méthode de chimie*, Paris, 1854, p. 9

CHAPTER ONE

The Beginnings of Organic Chemistry

In the opening years of the nineteenth century, when the broad principles of nomenclature of inorganic compounds had been established, organic chemistry was still in its infancy. Only a comparatively small number of definite chemical compounds derived from vegetable or animal sources were known and it was not even certain if these followed the laws established in mineral chemistry. Yet the number of compounds known steadily increased and Gmelin, when compiling his *Handbuch* in 1827, realized that by the time it was published several new organic compounds would have been discovered. In 1829 it was found that the acids known as 'pyro-uric' and 'cyanuric' were identical and Wöhler humorously wrote to Liebig that Gmelin's reaction to the news would be 'Thank God that there is one acid less'.[1]

Early Organic Chemistry

Although it was not until the nineteenth century that organic chemistry became a science, several important substances which would now be classified as 'organic' were known before that time. The only acid known to the ancient world was vinegar (Lat. *acetum*), from which the word 'acid' was derived as a general term to describe other similar substances which were later prepared. Vinegar was, of course, only a dilute solution of acetic acid, but by the eighteenth century pure or glacial acetic acid was well known as the product of distillation. Similarly the wine familiar to the ancients was prepared in more concentrated solutions in mediaeval times and was called 'spirit of wine'. In the metaphorical language of the alchemists it had

1. J. von Liebig, *Briefwechsel*, ed. A. W. Hofmann, Brunswick, 1888, vol. i, pp. 4–5.

been known as *aqua ardens*, the burning liquid, but after Paracelsus had described it as *alcohol*, this name gradually replaced the others. The first definite mention of ether was made by Valerius Cordus in his posthumously-published *De artificiosis extractionibus* (1540). He obtained it by the action of oil of vitriol on spirit of wine and he considered it simply as a 'sweet oil of vitriol' (*oleum vitrioli dulce*).[2] Blaise de Vigenère (d. 1596) described the preparation of several products in the distillation of gum benzoin. These included a 'salt' of benzoin[3] (benzoic acid), more commonly known in the seventeenth century as 'flowers of benzoin'. Another organic acid described in similar terms was *flos succini* obtained from amber. Both these substances were recognized as acids by Lemery.[4] Acetone was prepared by Beguin in the early seventeenth century by the distillation of verdigris,[5] but it was some time before it was recognized as a distinct compound not related to the metal used in its preparation. Robert Boyle obtained by the destructive distillation of wood an acid spirit (acetic acid) and a neutral liquor. The latter (methyl alcohol and acetone) he termed an 'adiaphorous (i.e. neutral) spirit', saying that it was easier to give it a negative name than one based on any positive property.[6]

In 1749 Marggraf described a new acid which he had obtained by the distillation of red ants.[7] He referred to it simply as *l'acide des fourmis* but it was later called *formic acid* (Lat. *formica* = ant). Scheele's experiments between the years 1780 and 1785 led to the preparation of several new organic acids: that from milk (*lactic acid*), from milk sugar (*mucic acid*), from lemons (*citric acid*), from sorrel (*oxalic acid*) and from apples (*malic acid*) as well as that from tartar (*tartaric acid*) which he had discovered earlier. Scheele did not concern himself with naming these acids, however, and their present names were derived from the Latin or Greek names of their sources. Acetic acid, however, had long been the only known acid of vegetable origin and some chemists refused to believe that these new vegetable acids were anything more than modifications of acetic acid.[8]

---

2. Op. cit., Argentorati, 1561, Pars 3, cap. 10. Frobenius later called it *spiritus vini aethereus* (*Phil. Trans.*, *36* (1729–30), 283).

3. *Traicté du feu et du sel*, Paris, 1618, pp. 91–2.

4. *Cours de chymie*, Paris, 1697, pp. 431, 608.   5. See p. 89.

6. Boyle, *Works*, ed. Birch, London, 1744, vol. i, p. 390.

7. *Histoire de l'Académie Royale des Sciences . . . de Berlin, 1749*, 38–45.

8. e.g. Black, *Lectures*, ed. Robison, Edinburgh, 1803, vol. i, pp. 482–3.

A further chapter in the history of organic chemistry was begun in 1794 when four Dutch chemists, J. R. Dieman, A. van Troostwyck, N. Bondt and A. Lauwerenburgh, described a new gas which they had obtained from alcohol and concentrated sulphuric acid.[9] They recognized it as a compound of carbon and hydrogen (ethylene) and they called it *gaz hydrogène carboné huileux* from its remarkable property of forming an oil when combined with oxymuriatic acid (chlorine). Hence the name *olefiant gas* became established[10] and the oily liquid was known for most of the nineteenth century as 'oil of Dutch chemists'.

The number of organic compounds known in the early nineteenth century made a comprehensive classification and nomenclature desirable, but it was not until the last decade of the century that any nomenclature was formulated which could be compared in its scope and influence with the French reform of inorganic nomenclature of 1787. It is tempting to draw a comparison between the methods of naming substances in these two branches of chemistry. The French chemist Chevreul, whose prolific work entitles him to be considered as one of the fathers of organic chemistry, gave names to the various compounds he discovered in accordance with their appearance or their source. In 1813 he isolated from animal fat a substance which he called *margarine* and later *margaric acid*, because both it and several of its compounds looked rather like mother of pearl ($\mu\alpha\rho\gamma\check{\alpha}\rho\acute{\iota}\tau\eta\varsigma =$ pearl). Chevreul also gave the name *oleic acid* to another compound he had discovered because of its oily appearance and the fact that it occurred in many oils (Lat. *oleum* = oil). Among the many other substances isolated and named by Chevreul were *butyric acid* from butter (Lat. *butyrum* = butter) and *capric* and *caproic acids* from goats milk (Lat. *capra* = she-goat).[11] Quite a number of substances of vegetable origin understandably were given names reminiscent of their source. The Latin word for apple (*malum*) alone gave rise to the names *malic acid* (Scheele, 1785), *maleic acid* (Pelouze, 1834) and *malonic acid* (Dessaignes, 1858).

As descriptions of new compounds taste and smell were rather

9. *Journal de Physique, 45* (1794), 178–91.

10. Fourcroy, *Ann. chim., 21* (1797), 49.

11. *Ann. chim., 88* (1813), 231. *Recherches chimiques sur les corps gras d'origine animale*, Paris, 1823; see especially pp. 71, 80–1, 119, 137, 146.

limited, but Berzelius did suggest the names *picramyl* ($\pi\iota\kappa\rho\acute{o}s$ = bitter) and *cacodyl* ($\kappa\breve{\alpha}\kappa\acute{\omega}\delta\eta s$ = stinking) to describe two different radicals which formed compounds justifying the etymology.[12] The system of naming a substance after a place, although acceptable for elements, was not desirable for compounds and was seldom attempted.[13] Although one does not expect to find the fantasies of alchemical terminology in nineteenth-century chemical names, one is forcibly reminded of Paracelsus on finding that, when all other inspiration failed them, chemists occasionally resorted to the practice of changing round the letters in a name to denote a related compound. Examples of this are Braconnot's *acide éllagique* (from *galle*)[14] and Wöhler's *cotarnin* (from *narcotin*).[15] Generally speaking, however, the more fanciful of the early chemical names had no parallel in the more rationally constituted body of nineteenth-century organic chemistry. Even personal associations are very much less in evidence and it is difficult to find more than a few organic compounds given a generally-accepted name after their discoverer. Occasionally a proper name might be used as a temporary label, but this type of name was superseded as soon as a more systematic name was found.[16] There are, however, numerous important reactions in organic chemistry which even to-day are associated with the names of individual chemists.

The Place of Organic Chemistry in the 1787 Reform of Nomenclature

The authors of the *Méthode de nomenclature chimique*, who had so brilliantly conceived a nomenclature for compounds of mineral origin, were able to do little for the more complex vegetable and animal substances. Guyton was content to regard the following as 'natural chemical compounds': sugar, mucus, gluten, starch, resins, extracts, fixed oils, volatile oils, etc. Most of the suggestions by the French chemists about the naming of organic compounds are contained in an appendix to the *Méthode*.[17] The

---

12. Berzelius, *Jahresbericht*, *22* (1843), 328; *20* (1841), 527.

13. Braconnot's *acide nancéique* (after Nancy in France) was immediately criticized by Guyton (*Ann. chim.*, *86* (1813), 99–100).

14. *Ann. chim. phys.*, [2], *9* (1818), 189.　　　15. *Ann. Chem.*, *50* (1844), 19.

16. The few compounds still sometimes referred to by proper names (e.g. Michler's ketone, Tröger's base and the naphthylamine sulphonic acids: Laurent's acid, Cleve's acid, etc.) nearly all have a complex enough structure to explain the persistence of trivial rather than systematic names.

17. Op. cit., pp. 71–4; see also pp. 50–1.

most important concerned the nomenclature of the 'ethers'. The authors had decided that each of the aetherial compounds obtained by the reaction of alcohol with various acids should be known as 'ether' qualified by an adjective according to the acid used to prepare it, e.g. *éther acétique* (i.e. ethyl acetate). Most of these 'ethers' were what we should now call esters and as such their nomenclature was quite sound. Unfortunately, true ether was to be called *éther sulfurique* and it was only several decades later that the unsuitability of this name was shown when it was demonstrated that sulphuric acid had no part in the composition of this compound.

Another important decision of the French chemists concerned the naming of pyro-acids. These had previously been known as 'empyreumatic spirits'[18] and included the products obtained by strongly heating tartar and wood. The latter fluid was now to be known as *pyroligneous acid* and substances prepared in a similar way were soon to constitute a formidable group of 'pyro-acids'. An experiment of Berthollet[19] had suggested that the acid obtained by distillation of verdigris contained more oxygen than the acid from ordinary vinegar. This led the authors of the *Méthode* to make a futile distinction between *acide acétique* and *acide acéteux*.

In his *Traité*, Lavoisier made some attempt to extend the principles of nomenclature of mineral chemistry to vegetable compounds containing carbon, hydrogen and oxygen.[20] The difficulty was that, unlike inorganic compounds, which could be simply described by names related to their constituents, nearly all organic compounds contained the same basic elements. Lavoisier tried, nevertheless, to coin a series of terms from the names of the elements carbon, hydrogen and oxygen. Hs distinguished between oxides and acids and by placing the words 'hydrogen' or 'carbon' first in the name according to which was in excess and by varying the suffixes of the terms, Lavoisier was able to set down ten distinctive names of the type: *oxide hydro-carboneux, oxide carbone hydrique, acide hydro-carbonique oxygéné*, etc. Lavoisier, however, laid himself open to the charge that he was merely playing with names. As one critic said, who described Lavoisier's terms in Linnaeus' phrase as *sesquipedalia verba*,

18. Empyreumatic = tasting or smelling of burnt organic matter.
19. *Mém. Acad., 1783*, 403–7.
20. *Traité élémentaire de chimie*, Paris, 1789, pp. 126–31.

Little real or useful knowledge is likely to be gained from spelling over a list of names of difficult pronounciation and perhaps of doubtful signification.[21]

Lavoisier, usually so conscious of the imperfections of the science of his time, concluded with the optimistic statement that the above variations in terminology would probably be sufficient to distinguish all the varieties to be found in nature! He did realize, however, that before any known compounds could be fitted into this framework, it would be necessary to carry out a quantitative analysis of vegetable compounds. For the time being, therefore, Lavoisier was prepared to accept the current names for the vegetable acids. Compounds derived from animals were even more complex, since they appeared to contain not only carbon and hydrogen but also nitrogen and phosphorus. Even if a systematic nomenclature were possible for these compounds, it would be very clumsy and Lavoisier was therefore content to keep temporarily such trivial names as formic acid, prussic acid, etc.

The Quantitative Analysis of Organic Compounds

The authors of the *Méthode de nomenclature chimique* cannot be blamed for their failure to arrive at any useful new system of naming vegetable and animal substances. Organic chemistry was not yet a science and, as Lavoisier had foreseen, little progress could be made until some general technique of quantitative analysis had been devised and applied to the few dozen naturally-occurring substances concerned.

Lavoisier himself had carried out some primitive analyses of organic compounds when, under controlled conditions, he had burned spirit of wine, olive oil and a candle separately in excess of oxygen. From the carbonic acid gas and water produced he was able to calculate the percentages of carbon, hydrogen and oxygen in each of these compounds.[22] In 1810 a method of analysis was devised by Gay-Lussac and Thenard which was not only more accurate but of more general application.[23] It

21. (Anonymous), *Critical examination of the first part of Lavoisier's Elements of Chemistry*, London, 1797, p. 28.

22. Lavoisier, *Oeuvres*, Paris, 1862–93, vol. ii, pp. 586–600.

23. Gay-Lussac and Thenard, *Recherches physico-chimiques*, Paris, 1811, vol. ii, pp. 265–350.

consisted of oxidising the substance to be analysed by mixing it with potassium chlorate and dropping it into a red hot tube. The gases produced (e.g. carbon dioxide and nitrogen) were collected and analysed. Gay-Lussac and Thenard examined by this method several acids, resins and also a group of six neutral substances: sugar, gum, starch, milk-sugar, oak wood and beech wood. They found that this last group contained carbon combined with hydrogen and oxygen in the same proportions as in water. In 1844 these compounds were distinguished by C. Schmidt as the class of *carbohydrates*.[24] Berzelius went further than Gay-Lussac and Thenard, not only by weighing the carbon dioxide and water produced in combustion, but, more important, by his application of the atomic theory to his results.[25] The fact that every organic analysis was a major undertaking is emphasized by Berzelius' own statement that it took him about twelve months to analyse fourteen vegetable substances.[26]

As the new chemistry of Lavoisier was founded on a more complete appreciation of the role of gases in chemical combination, it is not surprising that chemists were not slow to investigate the composition of gases, including those which we should classify as 'organic'. Dalton, for example, knew that olefiant gas and marsh gas both contained only carbon and hydrogen and after exploding them separately in a eudiometer with oxygen, he reached the conclusion in 1804 that 'if we reckon the carbon in each the same, then carburetted hydrogen gas[27] contains exactly twice as much hydrogen as olefiant gas'.[28] In his *New System of Chemical Philosophy* (1808), Dalton represented olefiant gas as composed of one atom of carbon and one atom of hydrogen, whereas 'carburetted hydrogen' was considered to consist of one atom of carbon and two atoms of hydrogen. Nearly twenty years later Faraday discovered a further compound of carbon and hydrogen (benzene) and he called it 'bi-carburet of hydrogen' as he believed it contained twice as many atoms of carbon as of hydrogen.[29]

24. *Ann. Chem.*, *51* (1844), 30.
25. *Ann. chim.*, *94* (1815), 1–28, 170–90, 296–323; *95*, 51–90.
26. Berzelius, *Bref*, ed. Söderbaum, Uppsala, 1912–35, Part 1, p. 47.
27. The English translation of Lavoisier's *gaz hydrogène carboné* (methane).
28. T. Thomson, *History of Chemistry*, London, 1830, 31, vol. ii, p. 291.
29. *Annals of Philosophy*, [2], *11* (1826), 46, 49.

The Pyro-Acids and Destructive Distillation

One of the few examples of names based on the method of preparation of a compound is that of the group of 'pyro-acids'. By giving their blessing to the use of the prefix *pyro-*, the French reformers of 1787 had created a useful method of naming compounds obtained by the action of heat on a wide variety of substances including the organic acids. By heating gallic acid, citric acid or mucic acid etc. under suitable conditions, chemists obtained new acids which they called 'pyrogallic acid', 'pyrocitric acid' and 'pyromucic acid'.

A neutral substance, obtained by the distillation of calcium acetate, was described as 'pyro-acetic spirit'. It was an important advance when, in 1833, the French chemist Bussy, at the suggestion of Thenard and Chevreul agreed to abandon this name in preference for the shorter term *acetone*.[30] This change in nomenclature did much to establish the class of ketones as a separate group of compounds, laying stress on their common properties without emphasizing one method of preparation, yet it did little to help the nomenclature of the ever-increasing number of pyro-acids.

In 1834 Pelouze, pursuing his investigations of the pyro-acids, announced the discovery of two isomeric acids obtained by the dry distillation of malic acid. Ampère suggested using variations of the term 'malic' to describe them; one would be called *acide maléique* and the other *acide para-maléique*.[31] This would avoid using such a clumsy phrase as 'pyro-para-malic acid'.[32] The term 'maleic acid' won acceptance, but chemists have preferred to call its isomer 'fumaric acid', a name given by Winckler denoting its most common source, the plant *Fumaria officinalis*.[33]

The difficulties of nomenclature were increased when it was realized that, even apart from isomers, one organic acid might give rise to more than one pyro-acid according to the conditions under which it was heated.[34] It is not surprising that Berzelius in one of his annual reports on the progress of chemistry re-

30. *Ann. chim. phys.*, [2], *53* (1833), 408–9n.
31. *Ann. chim. phys.*, [2], *56* (1834), 74.
32. Pelouze, however, did make use of such expressions (ibid., pp. 302–3).
33. *Repertorium für die Pharmacie*, *39* (1831), 368.
34. e.g. gallic acid formed not only pyrogallic acid but also a second acid which Pelouze called *acide métagallique* (*Ann. chim. phys.*, [2] *54* (1833), 352–3). The behaviour of citric acid on heating is particularly complicated.

marked on the necessity of a reform of the nomenclature of the pyro-acids.[35] At least one such reform, based on the use of successive letters of the alphabet to denote the chronological order of the discovery of each modification of a 'parent' acid, was suggested, but it never came into use.[36]

In the 1830's many new compounds were prepared by the distillation of such complex substances as coal tar. Runge, in the course of one paper, announced the discovery of six important new compounds and devised a nomenclature largely based on the colours of these compóunds or the colours they produced in characteristic reactions.[37] They included aniline (*Kyanol*) and phenol (*Carbolic acid*) as well as the heterocyclic compound *Pyrrol*. Generally speaking, it may be said of many of the compounds prepared about this time that their structure was complex, their identity often uncertain and their nomenclature arbitrary. Although chemists were 'discovering' new compounds, an understanding of these compounds had to wait for several decades. Liebig considered that efforts in the whole field had been misdirected and he expressed the wish that chemists would direct their labours to more useful objects.[38]

The Vague Use of the Term 'Ether'

Probably the vaguest term in general use in organic chemistry in the first half of the nineteenth century was 'ether'. The chemical compound now known as diethyl ether had been called an 'etherial spirit' but it became more generally known simply as 'ether'. As it had been prepared by heating together alcohol and oil of vitriol, chemists naturally tried the effect of using other acids in this experiment, and by the end of the eighteenth century such names as *sulphuric ether, phosphoric ether, nitric ether* and *acetic ether* had entered chemical nomenclature. Unfortunately the relationship of these compounds was not understood. Of the four compounds mentioned the first two are identical and are formed by the dehydrating action of the acid on the alcohol, whilst the two latter compounds would now be classified as esters. The term 'ether' was, therefore, used to denote at least two distinct classes of compounds: true ethers,

---

35. Berzelius, *Jahresbericht*, *13* (1834), 231–2.
36. S. Baup, '*Sur un nouvel acide citrique pyrogéné et sur la nomenclature des corps pyrogénés en général*', *Ann. chim. phys.*, [2], *61* (1836), 182–92.
37. *Ann. Phys. Chem.*, *31* (1834), 66.   38. *Ann. Chem.*, *38* (1841), 203.

sometimes called 'simple ethers' and esters which were referred to as 'compound ethers'.

In a more general sense 'ether' denoted any neutral volatile liquid. When the Derosne brothers, who were pharmacists in Paris, prepared an etherial substance (acetone) by repeating the old experiment of distilling copper acetate, they suggested that it should be called *éther pyro-acétique* to denote its relationship to acetic acid, and at the same time to distinguish it from *éther acétique* (ethyl acetate).[39] Chenevix, however, objected to this name on the grounds that it was too specific for a substance the chemical nature of which was still uncertain and he therefore suggested the more general term 'pyro-acetic spirit'.[40] Yet Chenevix, spoke only for himself and the majority of chemists continued to find 'ether' a very convenient label to describe newly-isolated neutral compounds. When 'spirit of wood' (methyl alcohol) was prepared in 1812 it was called 'pyroligneous ether',[41] and twenty years later, when chloroform was discovered it was described as 'chloric ether'.[42] When Döbereiner obtained two new colourless liquids from alcohol he too described them as 'ethers'; acetaldehyde of low boiling point was 'light oxygen ether' and acetal was 'heavy oxygen ether'.[43]

The vague application of the word 'ether', and in particular the uncritical attitude of many chemists regarding any clear distinction between 'simple' and 'compound' ethers was criticized by Daubeny, professor of chemistry at Oxford, at a meeting of the British Association for the Advancement of Science held in 1851. Daubeny considered that 'a considerable confusion has been created by placing under the same head bodies connected together by a very vague analogy'.[44]

Different Names for the Same Compound

In an ideal nomenclature of a science there is obviously a one-to-one correspondence between names and the things named. In a historical survey of the nomenclature of organic chemistry we find that this was not always the case. Due to the imperfect description of a particular compound or, perhaps, to

39. *Ann. chim.*, *63* (1808), 279.   40. Ibid., *69* (1809), 10.
41. P. Taylor, *Phil. Mag.*, *60* (1822), 315–17.
42. S. Guthrie, *American Journal of Science and Arts*, *21* (1832), 64.
43. *Journal für Chemie und Physik*, *32* (1821), 269–70; *34* (1822), 124–5.
44. *Report of the British Association*, *1851*, p. 130.

ignorance of published work, the same compound might occasionally be 'discovered' more than once, leaving later workers a choice of synonyms for a particular compound. One case where a compound was prepared by quite different processes by chemists largely unaware of previous work on the same compound was that of aniline. The story of the discovery of aniline began in 1826 when Unverdorben, while investigating indigo, discovered an oil which readily formed crystalline compounds with acids and he therefore called it *Crystallin*.[45] In 1834 Runge reported among the products obtained by the distillation of coal tar a certain basic compound which produced a violet-blue colouration with chloride of lime and which he consequently named *Kyanol* (κύανος =dark blue).[46] Six years later Fritzsche, starting from indigo, obtained a compound which he named *Anilin* after the Spanish word for indigo.[47] Erdmann, the editor of the journal in which this work appeared, did, however, point out the identity of *Crystallin* and *Anilin*. Finally in 1842 the Russian chemist Zinin, having discovered a method of reducing nitro- compounds, succeeded in preparing from nitrobenzene a basic compound which he called *Benzidam*. In the following year Hofman pointed out that these four names denoted one and the same compound, for which he favoured the first name *Crystallin*.[48] Yet, as Berzelius remarked, this name depended on a property which was by no means uncommon: he preferred the name *Anilin*[49] and the compound has since been known by this name.

Propionic acid had a rather different history, the successive names given to it corresponding with an increase of knowledge of its properties and composition.[50] The acid was first mentioned by Gottlieb as *metacetic acid*. It was later observed by Noellner that in certain reactions an acid was formed which, though not identical with acetic acid, was similar to it and he therefore called it *pseudo-acetic acid*. It was then investigated by Nicklès who found that its properties were in some ways intermediate between those of two well-known acids: acetic acid and butyric acid. He therefore called it *butyro-acetic acid*. Further

45. *Ann. Phys. Chem.*, *8* (1826), 398.   46. Ibid., *31* (1834), 65–6.
47. *Journal für praktische Chemie*, *20* (1840), 453.
48. *Ann. Chem.*, *47* (1843), 37–87.
49. Berzelius, *Jahresbericht*, *24* (1845), 595.
50. See the historical account given by Dumas, *Comp. rend.*, *25* (1847), 781–3.

investigations of this acid was carried out by Dumas in collaboration with Malaguti and F. Leblanc, this work being published in 1847. They considered that in the series of acids starting from formic and acetic acids and going up to the well-known fatty acids, it was the first acid of a fatty nature, and they therefore proposed to call it *propionic acid* (πρῶτος = first). This name became so well established that no attempt was later made to change it for a more systematic term based on the number of carbon atoms.

There was seldom any confusion in organic chemistry due to the same word being applied to different compounds. Perhaps the only example worthy of mention is that of *acetyl*, which was the name Liebig gave to the radical (modern notation) C_2H_3.[51] The same name was used by Gerhardt to denote the group C_2H_3O,[52] a meaning which it has kept despite the attempts of Williamson[53] and[54] Kekulé to describe this latter group as *othyl* (i.e. oxygen-ethyl) and despite the criticisms of ambiguity levelled by Kolbe.[55] It is true that occasionally chemists who were out of touch with each other would give a similar name to different newly-discovered compounds, as happened with Berzelius and Laurent.[56] Generally speaking, however, although chemical names were often badly chosen, their meanings were not in dispute and their most important change, that of the generalization of words like 'alcohol' and 'sugar' to denote classes of compounds was carried out in such a way that there was little ambiguity.

The Naming of Compounds by Word Contractions

One of the requirements of a nomenclature is that terms should be reasonably short. It is also important that in the early years of the development of a science the terms used should not attempt to say more about the thing denoted than was actually known. Both these requirements were met in the early history of organic chemistry by a method of nomenclature based on the contraction of the names of related compounds.

51. *Ann. Chem., 30* (1839), 139.
52. Gerhardt, *Traité de chimie organique*, Paris, 1853, vol. i, p. 656.
53. *J. Chem. Soc., 4* (1852), 238.   54. *Ann. Chem., 90* (1854), 312n.
55. Kolbe, *Lehrbuch der organischen Chemie*, Brunswick, 1854, vol. i, pp. 53–4.
56. Berzelius, *Jahresbericht, 18* (1839), 311–12, 293; *24* (1844), 483–4.

This should be considered as a temporary expedient rather than a method of nomenclature, although many of the terms coined according to this system are still in use to-day.

The practice of naming new compounds by this method of abbreviation was introduced by Chevreul. He gave the name *éthal* to the compound now known as cetyl alcohol and explained:

I have formed the name *éthal* from the first two syllables of the words ether and alcohol after the analogy of composition which exists between the three substances.[57]

This precedent was followed by Liebig in order to assign a name to a new compound containing carbon, oxygen and chlorine which he had prepared by the action of chlorine on alcohol. Being unable to suggest a systematic name, he proposed to call it *Chloral*, a term which, he said, was based on the same principles as *éthal*.[58] Liebig was also responsible for the name *Acetal*.[59] The most famous of these contracted names was *Aldehyde*, a contraction of '*Alcohol dehydrogenatus*'.[60] Although abbreviation as a system of nomenclature may seem a crude way of solving the problem, it avoided some of the pitfalls of alternative methods. This is well illustrated by the case of chloroform. When Soubeiran investigated this new etherial spirit, his analysis led him to regard it as containing one atom of carbon and two atoms each of hydrogen and chlorine. Accordingly he called it *éther bichlorique*.[61] Liebig's analysis was even worse, since he failed to recognize that it contained hydrogen; for him, therefore, it was a chloride of carbon, '*ein neue Chlorkohlenstoff*'.[62] Dumas was more successful and if he had used symbols as we do to-day he would have written its formula correctly as $CHCl_3$. In the absence of any recognized nomenclature based on substitution (a concept which had yet to be explored by Dumas and Laurent) the compound was called *chloroform*. Dumas, bearing in mind Liebig's term *Chloral*, proposed this name to suggest the relationship of the compound to formic

57. *Recherches chimiques sur les corps gras d'origine animale*, Paris, 1823, p. 169.
58. *Ann. Pharm.*, *1* (1832), 32.
59. *Berzelius and Liebig. Ihre Briefe von 1831–1845*, Munich and Leipzig, 1893, pp. 34, 40.
60. *Ann. chim. phys.*, [2], *59* (1835), 290.
61. Ibid., [2], *48* (1831), 137.   62. *Ann. Phys. Chem.*, *23* (1831), 444.

acid and chlorine. The analogous compounds formed from bromine and iodine were called *bromoform* and *iodoform*.[63]

From the above, it is clear that the leading chemists of both the German and French schools accepted this method of naming compounds. A further example is provided by the names *mercaptan* (*corpus mercurium captans*) and *mercaptum* (*corpus mercurio captum*) proposed by Zeise.[64] Although Berzelius took exception to the etymology of these terms,[65] it is more surprising that Dumas, who had coined the term '*chloroform*' should be critical of expressions suggested by other chemists such as *aldehyde* and *mercaptan*. Dumas said that he considered that such a nomenclature was only justified if the resulting name indicated the derivatives of a compound rather than its origin.[66] Despite advances in chemical theory and technique, names based on contractions continued to be formed. Wurtz, for example, introduced the word *glycol* to denote a compound he had discovered with properties intermediate between those of glycerine and alcohol.[67]

Names based on contractions were themselves regarded as a legitimate source of new names. Thus Dumas and Stas gave the name *acide éthalique* to the acid related to *éthal*.[68] The process came near to absurdity, however, when names were suggested which were abbreviations of abbreviations. Such a term was *aldol*, proposed by Wurtz to denote the compound still known by this name which has the properties of both an aldehyde and an alcohol.[69]

63. *Ann. chim. phys.*, [2], *56* (1834), 120–5.
64. Ibid., *88*, 93.
65. Berzelius, *Jahresbericht*, *14* (1835), 334n.
66. *Leçons de philosophie chimique*, Paris, 1837, pp. 355–7.
67. *Comp. rend.*, *43* (1856), 200.
68. *Ann. chim. phys.*, [2], *73* (1840), 125.
69. *Comp. rend.*, *74* (1872), 1362.

Nomenclature based on Systems of Classification and Theories of Organic Chemistry

Systematic Word-endings

One symptom of progress in the nomenclature of organic chemistry in the early nineteenth century was the development of names with deliberately chosen suffixes, so that compounds which reacted in a similar way were not only assigned to the same class but their very name was a constant reminder of some of their characteristic properties. If the method of nomenclature based on word-contractions was a landmark in pre-scientific organic chemistry, the method of systematic word-endings, based on a knowledge of the chemical properties of the compounds concerned may be considered as the first successful attempt to bestow names of permanent value to the science of organic chemistry.

The first class of compounds to be distinguished in this way was the alkaloids. The history of this important group of compounds began when Sertürner examined a new substance extracted from opium. In 1817 he announced that the new substance was an alkali, the first alkaline compound of vegetable origin to be isolated. Sertürner called it *morphium*,[70] but when the original paper written in German was translated into French, it was called *morphine*.[71] The next group of alkaloids to be isolated were all discovered in France and it was the French name which was taken to establish their nomenclature. The second vegetable alakli was discovered by Pelletier and Caventou in 1818 and they eventually gave it the name *strychnine* from

70. *Annalen der Physik*, *55* (1817), 56–90.
71. *Ann. chim. phys.*, [2], *5* (1817), 21–41. The paper was translated by M. Rose, but the term *morphine* may well have been suggested by Gay-Lussac who edited the *Annales* at that time.

its source (*Strychnos nux vomica*).[72] Even a critic of this name, who considered that such substances which exhibited a high degree of physiological activity should be named after their medical properties, agreed that it was desirable to keep the suffix *-ine*. Pelletier and Caventou also isolated several other alkaloids to which they gave the names *brucine*, *veratrine* and *quinine*. They suggested that the principle which Gomez had called *cinchonin* should be known as *cinchonine*, so that its name would conform with those of the other alkaloids.[73] Although these names were universally accepted and the suffix *-ine* was adopted to denote the hundreds of alkaloids subsequently discovered, its use was not exclusive since it came to be applied to a variety of compounds of uncertain classification. Vauquelin and Robiquet, for example, had already described an apparently neutral compound extracted from asparagus shoots as *asparagine*[74] and later Laurent gave the name *isatine* to a product of oxidation of indigo.[75] Even worse, in view of their importance were the names *glycerine* and *naphthaline*.[76]

Another group of compounds with a recognized nomenclature was the class of ketones. In 1833 Bussy, as a result of his experiments on the dry distillation of the salts of acetic, stearic and oleic acids, decided not to refer vaguely to the products as 'spirits'; instead each was to receive a name related to the acid from which it was derived, together with the common suffix *-one*. Accordingly, he proposed using the terms *acétone*, *stéarone*, and *oléone*.[77] When in the following year Péligot isolated a similar compound by the distillation of a salt of benzoic acid, he decided to conform to this nomenclature by calling it *benzone*.[78] This became the established nomenclature and Chancel in a paper published in 1845 referred to all similar compounds as *acétones*.[79] In the fourth edition of his text-book of chemistry Gmelin used the term *ketone* for 'acetones in general'.[80]

Some chemists had more of a sense of responsibility in matters of nomenclature than others. Among those who chose their

72. *Ann. chim. phys.*, [2], *10* (1819), 145; see also p. 176n.
73. Ibid., [2], *12* (1819), 117; *14* (1820), 75; *15* (1820), 348 and 294–5.
74. *Ann. chim.*, *57* (1806), 88.   75. *Comp. rend.*, *12* (1841), 538.
76. Proposed by J. Kidd, Professor of Chemistry at Oxford, *Phil. Trans.*, *1821*, 209–21.
77. *Ann. chim. phys.*, [2], *53* (1833), 408–9n.
78. Ibid., [2], *56* (1834), 60.   79. *Comp. rend.*, *20* (1845), 1580–7.
80. *Handbuch der organischen Chemie*, Heidelberg, 1848, vol.i, p. 181.

terms with some deliberation were Berzelius, Liebig and Wöhler. Berzelius' vigilance in matters of nomenclature included criticisms of some of his contemporaries who disregarded suffixes when coining new names for their discoveries.[81] When Liebig and Wöhler published their work on the benzoyl radical, they said that they had originally intended to call it 'benzoin', but as this name resembled that of the vegetable alkalis, they decided to avoid any possibility of confusion by calling it *benzoyl*.[82] When Woskresensky discovered a new compound (quinone) which he proposed to call *Chinoyl*, Wöhler pointed out that the suffix *-yl* had come to be recognized as denoting a radical and must therefore be changed.[83] Berzelius approved Wöhler's suggestion of *Chinon* by analogy with acetone which it resembled.[84] Liebig too was critical of the names given to some compounds by other chemists although, in the case of his criticism of Mitscherlich's *Benzin*,[85] his own *Benzol*[86] was to prove at least as confusing as the term it was to replace.

The suffix *-ol* was recognized in the Geneva nomenclature as the standard termination of the names of alcohols and phenols. Its early history shows that it was applied to several quite distinct classes of compounds. In the first place it was used in the name of certain hydrocarbons, particularly by German chemists who spoke of *Benzol*, *Toluol* (toluene), etc. Kolbe even tried to extend this system so that marsh gas, for example, would have had the systematic name *Methylol*.[87] The habit of denoting hydrocarbons by the suffix *-ol* also crept into the English language, as such names as *xylol* and *cymol* testify. When Runge announced the preparation from coal tar of three basic oils he gave them names based on the colours formed in characteristic reactions and called them *Kyanol* (aniline), *Leucol* (quinoline) and *Pyrrol* (pyrrole), using the termination *-ol* as a contraction of the Latin word *oleum* (oil).[88] These names were not very popular, however,

81. Berzelius, *Jahresbericht*, *19* (1840), 347; *22* (1843), 411; *24* (1845), 595. Concern with systematic suffixes had previously been expressed by J. E. Herberger, who also attempted a classification and nomenclature of organic compounds ('*Versuch einer Nomenklatur der chemischorganischen Gebilde, nach einfachen Grundsätzen entworfen*', *Repertorium für die Pharmacie*, *44* (1833), 34–59).

82. *Ann. Phys. Chem.*, *26* (1832), 483n.   83. *Ann. Chem.*, *51* (1844), 145n.

84. Berzelius, *Jahresbericht*, *19* (1840), 407.

85. *Ann. Phys. Chem.*, *29* (1833), 233.   86. *Ann. Pharm.*, *9* (1834), 43n.

87. Kolbe, *Lehrbuch der organischen Chemie*, Brunswick, 1854, vol. i, p. 56.

88. *Ann. Chem.*, *31* (1834), 65–8.

and only the last has survived. The fact that the ending *-ol* now came to denote certain aromatic alcohols was largely through the influence of Gerhardt. He used this suffix deliberately to denote certain 'oxygenated essential oils' including *borneol*. He also spoke of *phenol* (Laurent's *hydrate de phényle*) and this name established the pattern of nomenclature of analogous compounds which were later isolated.[89]

By the time Gerhardt wrote his *Précis* in 1844–5, he was able to quote a further example of systematic names. This was the use of the suffix *-ene* to denote hydrocarbons. Not only had the French chemists begun to use such terms as *benzène* and *ethérène* (ethylene) but they also denoted all newly-discovered hydrocarbons in this way. Dumas and Péligot, for example, gave the name *cétène* to the unsaturated hydrocarbon related to cetyl alcohol[90] and Laurent's extensive research enabled him to announce the discovery of other hydrocarbons including *anthracène*, *pyrène*, *chrysène* and *stilbène*.[91]

The Radical Theory

One of the more important theories mentioned in any history of organic chemistry is the radical theory and in a study of the nomenclature of organic chemistry it is particularly important, since it provided a basis for the systematic naming of organic compounds. In 1832 Liebig and Wöhler published their notable work on the benzoyl radical. In a series of experiments on the oil of bitter almonds they had found that various compounds derived from it could be considered simply as derivatives of a group of atoms which remained intact throughout these reactions and functioned as a whole. Such a group of atoms was well known in inorganic chemistry and Guyton de Morveau had used the word *radical* to describe it.[92] Lavoisier had recognized the existence of organic radicals such as tartrates and acetates and Hassenfratz and Adet had even devised symbols for about eighteen such radicals. Berzelius in his turn contributed to the establishment of the radical theory by proposing the use of special symbols to denote radicals. Having previously suggested the use of the symbol Am to denote the composite

89. *Revue scientifique, 10* (1842), 179, 210.
90. *Ann. chim. phys.,* [2], *62* (1836), 10.
91. Ibid., [2], *66* (1837), 149, 146, 136. *Comp. rend., 16* (1843), 857.
92. *Encyclopédie méthodique, Chimie,* Paris, 1786, vol. i, p. 142.

'metal' ammonium,[93] he proposed that the benzoyl radical should be written, not as Liebig and Wöhler had done as $C^{14}H^{10}O^2$, but simply as Bz. He further proposed that the group of atoms present in olefiant gas (described as *Aetherin*) should be represented by the symbol Ae:[94]

From the moment we know with certainty of the existence of ternary atoms [i.e. molecules] of the first order, which combine in the same way as simple bodies, it will greatly facilitate the expression in the language of formulae to denote each radical by a particular symbol.[95]

Berzelius was able to write oil of bitter almonds as BzH, benzoic acid as the oxide of benzoyl, etc. He added a warning, however, that formulae based on such symbols should not be extended without good reason.

Liebig and Wöhler had derived the name 'benzoyl' from benzoic acid and the suffix ὕλη (matter). When Liebig found that he could explain the composition of certain simple organic compounds such as ordinary alcohol and ether by considering them to be derived from a hypothetical radical C_4H_{10} (i.e. C_2H_5), he called this *ethyl* and denoted it by the symbol E.[96] Berzelius extended this system to the newly-discovered radical from wood spirit, which he proposed to call *methyl*.[97] The radical theory was now well established and chemists became preoccupied with the searching out of new radicals.

A rival school in France led by Dumas postulated the existence of rather different radicals. Gay-Lussac had previously carried out experiments on the densities of ethylene gas and the vapours of ether and alcohol, from which he concluded that alcohol could be considered as a compound of 'one volume of olefiant gas and one volume of water vapour', whereas ether consisted of 'two volumes of olefiant gas and one volume of water vapour'.[98] Dumas and Boullay extended this idea and considered alcohol and ether as hydrates of olefiant gas denoted by the formulae $H^2C^2 + \frac{1}{2}HOH$ and $2H^2C^2 + \frac{1}{2}HOH$ respectively.[99] This might

93. Berzelius, *Jahresbericht*, *2* (1823), 57.   94. Ibid., *13* (1834), 192.
95. *Ann. Phys. Chem.*, *26* (1832), 483–5.
96. *Ann. Pharm.*, *9* (1834), 18. See also ibid., *30* (1839), 139 for Liebig's use of the symbol Ad for amide.
97. Berzelius, *Jahresbericht*, *15* (1836), 381.
98. *Ann. chim.*, *95* (1815), 313, 315.
99. *Ann. chim. phys.*, [2], *36* (1827), 309. These formulae were based on the atomic weights C = 6, H = 1, O = 16. In the original paper the oxygen atom was denoted by a dot.

be considered as the first theory of organic radicals, although Dumas did not describe the group H^2C^2 by this name. It was Berzelius who later referred to it as the 'Aetherin radical'. When Dumas and Péligot found that spirit of wood contained a compound similar to alcohol, they proposed the name *methylène* (μέθυ =wine, ὕλη =wood) to denote the hypothetical radical from which it was derived.[100] They called the alcohol itself *bihydrate de methylène*, the present name methyl alcohol not being used till some years later. Regnault, who carried out an important series of investigations on halogenated organic compounds, proposed the radical *aldehydène* to explain their formation[101] Liebig later suggested that this radical, C_4H_6 (i.e. C_2H_3) should be considered after his own pattern of nomenclature as the '*Acetyl*' radical with the symbol Ac.[102]

Although Liebig and Dumas differed in what they considered to be the fundamental radicals and they gave them names according to two distinct patterns, these radicals could be simply related to each other and the important fact was that both schools agreed that organic compounds were composed of compound radicals. In 1837 Dumas and Liebig therefore decided to co-operate to try to establish a 'natural' classification of organic compounds based on a study of their component radicals. In their joint paper entitled 'Note on the present state of organic chemistry'[103] they compared the role of the elements in inorganic chemistry with that of the radicals in organic chemistry:

> In mineral chemistry the radicals are simple; in inorganic chemistry they are compound; that is all the difference.

In the following year Liebig formally defined a radical. He laid down three conditions, two of which must be fulfilled by any group of atoms if it was to be considered as a radical: it must occur unchanged in a series of compounds, it must be replaceable in these by single elements and in its compounds with a particular element the latter must be able to be separated and replaced by equivalents of other elements.[104]

If, as Dumas and Liebig claimed, the radicals played the same part in organic compounds as the elements did in in-

100. Ibid., *58* (1835), 9.   101. Ibid., *59* (1835), 374–5.
102. *Ann. Chem., 30* (1839), 139.   103. *Comp. rend., 5* (1837), 567–72.
104. *Ann. Chem., 25* (1838), 3.

organic chemistry, it followed that it should be possible to build up a binomial nomenclature in organic chemistry not entirely dissimilar to that which had been successfully established in inorganic chemistry. Such names as 'chloride of benzoyl' had the advantage of being reasonably short yet fully informative of the nature of the atoms contained in the compound. In 1837, when Berzelius was compiling a new edition of his text-book he wrote to Liebig that in the chapter on ether he had found Liebig's nomenclature ('oxide of ethyl', etc.) quite indispensable.[105] Even after the introduction of the type theory the idea of radicals was still useful in organic chemistry. A. W. Hofmann's investigation of what we now call quaternary ammonium compounds led him to postulate the existence of a radical which he called *tetraethylammonium* and, having isolated a compound which he regarded as the iodide of this radical, he remarked:

> The view I have taken of the new compound . . . has the great advantage of closely assimilating these substances to the compounds of mineral chemistry, whereby the nomenclature is essentially facilitated.[106]

If the radical theory was a valuable aid to nomenclature, the reverse was also true and Wurtz claimed that the advantages of this nomenclature greatly contributed to the success of the theory.[107]

Yet the systematic application of the radical theory to all organic compounds often had unfortunate results. Hydrocarbons, for example, were considered as hydrides of a related radical and Kolbe referred in his *Lehrbuch* (1854) to ethylene as 'hydride of vinyl'. Such names were not only bizarre but misleading, since they obscured the similarity of related compounds. Ethane was first isolated by Kolbe as *Methyl*[108] and was later called 'dimethyl'. These names hardly suggested that it was a homologue of methane ('hydride of methyl'). Perhaps the most serious defect of such a nomenclature was the rather arbitrary way in which some radicals were arrived at. To make

105. *Berzelius und Liebig. Ihre Briefe von 1831–1845*, Munich and Leipzig, 1893, p. 118.
106. *Phil. Trans., 1851*, ii, 361–2.
107. Wurtz, *Dictionnaire de chimie pure et appliquée*, Paris, 1869–78, vol. ii, p. 573.
108. *Ann. Chem., 69* (1849), 257–94.

use of a radical in chemical theory there was no obligation to isolate it in the laboratory. As far as Gerhardt, for example, was concerned, radicals were merely convenient means of establishing relationships between various compounds. It was even possible to consider the same compound to be a derivative of several quite different radicals and thus having several different names. Not all compounds could be reduced to radicals and the radical theory could do nothing for this large group of substances. A final defect of the radical theory as a basis for nomenclature was the vast number of radicals which came to be known and the names of these were most likely at first to be derived from the source of one of its compounds rather than any more systematic consideration which could be more easily remembered.

The Type Theory

The radical theory, having contributed a useful concept to the study of organic chemistry, had become fairly well established in the late 1830's, but just at this time a new theory was put forward which also had a useful contribution to make to organic chemistry and its nomenclature. This was the type theory and it was closely linked with the idea of substitution in organic compounds.

Gay-Lussac in the course of a lecture which he delivered in 1828 pointed out that when chlorine combines with oils, hydrochloric acid is formed as well as a new substance in which 'a part of the chlorine . . . takes the place of the hydrogen which has been removed'.[109] This was a clear statement of the principle of substitution. Ten years later Dumas confirmed that atoms of chlorine could be substituted for atoms of hydrogen in acetic acid and the product, which he called *acide chloracétique* (i.e. trichloracetic acid), retained the chemical properties of the original compound.[110] The theory of substitution, based on the work of Dumas and Laurent, implied a rejection of Berzelius' dualism which distinguished between two types of elements the electropositive and the electronegative, since it had been shown

109. Gay-Lussac, *Cours de Chimie*, Brussels, 1829, vol. ii, Leçon 28 (16 juillet 1828), p. 12.
110. *Comp. rend.*, 7 (1838), 474; 8 (1839), 612. As Dumas later pointed out, 'the chlorine not only takes the place of the hydrogen, but it plays the same part' (*Ann. chim. phys.*, [3], 49 (1857), 496).

that the electronegative chlorine could replace the electropositive hydrogen without essentially altering the character of
an organic compound. According to the new theory many
reactions were now regarded as simple cases of substitution of
one element for another in a parent compound and a nomenclature based on this parent compound was a logical consequence.

Once the type theory had proved its value, a bitter controversy arose between Dumas and Laurent, each claiming
priority. Laurent could claim that in 1835 he had made the
following statement in connection with his experiments on
derivatives of naphthalene:

I shall call naphthalene the fundamental radical and the compounds
which result from its transformation the derived radicals.[111]

Laurent was using the term 'radical' in a new sense and to make
this clear he later changed it for 'nucleus' (*noyau*).[112] He therefore suggested[113] that Dumas' only claim to be the author of
the type theory was that Dumas had been the first to use the
expression 'chemical type'.[114] Dumas, on the other hand, belittled Laurent's work on naphthalene and considered that the
theory of substitution dated from his own work on acetic acid.
The effect of the dispute was that Dumas, a powerful figure in
scientific circles in Paris, was able to use his influence against
his former pupil and Laurent was never able to take his just
place in Paris. This is all the more regrettable because, apart
from his large output of experimental work, Laurent had many
constructive proposals to make towards the establishment of a
systematic nomenclature for organic chemistry.

Dumas' Nomenclature

Dumas gave some consideration to the subject of nomenclature in a paper on the theory of types published in 1840.[115]
He was prepared to admit that the nomenclature of Lavoisier
was admirably suited to the task of naming inorganic compounds. The dualism implied in this nomenclature and subsequently justified by the electrochemical theory of Berzelius

111. *Ann. chim. phys.*, [2], *59* (1835), 389.
112. *Comp. rend.*, *19* (1844), 1093.
113. Ibid., *10* (1840), 410.
114. Ibid., *8* (1839), 621–2; *10* (1840), 149ff.
115. *Comp. rend.*, *10* (1840), 168–70.

could not, however, be extended to organic compounds. Every organic compound should, on the contrary, be regarded as a modification of a particular type. Dumas continued:

It is necessary that every type should have a name and that this name should occur in the numerous forms which it can assume; this name should be kept as long as the type itself is not destroyed.

Lavoisier's nomenclature had placed emphasis on the constituent elements of a compound; Dumas wished to emphasize the common features of groups which, though containing different elements, could be considered as coming from the same mould. Dumas pointed to his own nomenclature which had been based on this principle. By the action of chlorine on olefiant gas Dumas had obtained what he called *gaz chloroléfiant* and his terms 'chloracetic acid', 'chloraldehyde' and 'chlorether' were formed on the same principle.

Dumas considered that chloracetic acid belonged to the same *chemical type* as acetic acid. He also adopted Regnault's idea of a *mechanical type* by which he meant substances having a similar formula and related by substitution, but essentially different in many of their important chemical properties, e.g. marsh gas and chloroform. This idea led logically to the view that most chemical compounds could be reduced to a few basic types.

Laurent's Nomenclature

Probably Laurent first felt the need of a systematic nomenclature in 1833 when he was reporting the isolation of two different compounds of naphthalene with chlorine. At that time, however, he distinguished them merely as 'the oily chloride' and 'the solid chloride'.[116] Two years later, however, a further study of compounds derived from naphthalene led him to consider the latter as a fundamental radical or group common to all compounds and he began to use a nomenclature based on this concept. The compound formed by the action of cold nitric acid on naphthalene he called *nitronaphthalase* (α-nitronaphthalene), whereas the product when boiling nitric acid was used (a mixture of dinitronaphthalenes) was *nitro-naphthalèse*.[117] Laurent extended this system of using vowels to

116. *Ann. chim. phys.*, [2], *52* (1833), 275–85.
117. Ibid., [2], *59* (1835), 376–97. Laurent gave due credit to Dumas for the idea of using the vowels to denote the number of atoms of chlorine

denote the successive degrees of substitution in a 'nucleus' to the substitution of chlorine atoms for hydrogen in naphthalene:

	Modern formula
chloronaphtalase or *chloronaphtase*	$C_{10}H_7Cl$
chloronaphtalèse	$C_{10}H_6Cl_2$
chloronaphtalise	$C_{10}H_5Cl_3$ etc.

Thus Laurent's name for picric acid (*trinitrophenol*) was *acide nitrophénisique*,[118] a name intended to indicate clearly the presence of three nitro groups in the benzene nucleus (*phène*).[119] Laurent could claim that his nomenclature had the advantage that the formula of a compound could be readily deduced from its name and vice-versa. The nomenclature was, however, limited by the five vowels to the first five substitution products. To indicate the presence of 6, 7, or 8 atoms of chlorine in naphthalene a second series was necessary so that hexachloro-naphthalene would be *chloronaphtalase A*, etc. Laurent developed his ideas on nomenclature in his posthumously-published *Méthode de chimie* (1854).

Laurent was quite fearless and uncompromising in his use of these new terms and he introduced them into his publications without apology and often without explanation. Berzelius, who had been a constant critic of Laurent's terminology, wrote to him in 1843[120] pointing out how very slight was the difference involved in changing a vowel so that in speech it was easy to mistake one name for another. Furthermore nearly all the names proposed by Laurent had been connected with naphthalene and by retaining this common stem all the names became too much alike. Laurent replied by a defence of his nomenclature, although he was prepared to admit his eccentricity which he attributed to his exile in the provinces. It is certainly true that in Bordeaux Laurent had not the same opportunities which he would have enjoyed in Paris. This fact, together with his

substituted in a nucleus (Laurent, *Chemical Method*, London, 1855, p. 37). This dates back to 1834 when Dumas and Péligot made implicit use of the principle in a paper on cinnamic acid (*Ann. chim. phys.*, [2], *57* (1834), 316–317. *Comp. rend.*, *10* (1840), 517–18) and Dumas continued to use this system of naming substitution compounds in 1840 (*Ann. chim. phys.*, [2], *73* (1840), 136, 139).

118. *Ann. chim. phys.*, [3], *3* (1841), 195.

119. Derived from φαίνω = I light, since benzene was first prepared from illuminating gas. Laurent introduced this root to avoid confusion with benzoyl compounds, ibid., [2], *63* (1836), 44.

120. Berzelius, *Bref*, Uppsala, 1912–35, part 7, pp. 192–3, 204–6.

embitterment because of the hostility of his most influential contemporaries do much to account for Laurent's independent attitude in matters of nomenclature where co-operation was so desirable.

Laurent's nomenclature may appear as no more than a curiosity, but it definitely contributed to the systematizing of nomenclature. His ideas were later adopted by others, particularly Gerhardt and Hofmann. Yet his terminology, which Hofmann described as 'commendable'[121] was used by only a few of his contemporaries. To-day we are hardly in a position to scorn his method of naming compounds by changing the vowels in their names, since we have accepted the term *imide*, coined by Laurent from *amide* according to the same principles.[122]

Gmelin's Nomenclature

Another nomenclature based on the theory of substitution and which drew inspiration from the ideas of Dumas and Laurent was that proposed by Leopold Gmelin in the fourth edition of his *Handbuch*.[123] For inorganic compounds he suggested synthetic names indicating both the elements present and their number. For organic compounds this principle had to be modified if for no other reason because the number of atoms involved would be too great to express simply. Gmelin therefore suggested a nomenclature founded on the type theory. Each 'primary nucleus' was to have a distinct name, and in forming these names he put brevity before all other considerations. Thus methylene was to be called by the one syllable *forme*, ethylene by *vine*, benzene by *bunze*, etc. When other elements or groups were substituted in these nuclei, they were denoted by a consonant (e.g. chlorine $=k$) or a monosyllable, and the number of atoms of the element substituted up to a maximum of five by one of the vowels. Accordingly the compounds represented by Gmelin's formulae $(C=6)$ C_4H_3Cl, $C_4H_2Cl_2$, C_4HCl_3, C_4Cl_4 were denoted respectively by the terms *Vinak*, *Vinek*, *Vinik*, and *Vinok*. Gmelin went no further than introducing these curious expressions in parentheses in his text-book. He could hardly

---

121. *Ann. Chem.*, *53* (1845), 14.
122. *Ann. chim. phys.*, [2], *59* (1835), 397; Berzelius, *Jahresbericht*, *16* (1837), 245-7.
123. Gmelin, *Handbuch der organischen Chemie*, 4th edn., Heidelberg, vol. i, 1848, pp. 133-5.

have expected such an arbitrary synthetic language which made no concessions to euphony, etymology or current usage to win general acceptance.

The 'New Type Theory'

The type theory provided not only a nomenclature but a classification, according to which organic compounds were considered to be derived from one of a few basic types. Wurtz's discovery of the amines in 1849 led to Hofmann's idea of an 'ammonia type', whilst a suggestion of Laurent, extended by Williamson provided a 'water type'. Taking these two types together with a 'hydrochloric acid type' and a 'hydrogen type', Gerhardt attempted to derive all organic compounds from them.[124] Alcohols, ethers, acids, salts, etc. were considered to belong to the water type. Halogen compounds were derived from the hydrochloric acid type; amines, amides, etc. were related to the ammonia type and hydrocarbons and aldehydes (both considered as hydrides) belonged to the hydrogen type. Williamson and Gerhardt considered that acetic acid belonged to the water type $\left.\begin{array}{c}H\\H\end{array}\right\}O$ and they therefore wrote its formula as $\left.\begin{array}{c}C_2H_3O\\H\end{array}\right\}O$. If this is the formula for acetic acid it should be theoretically possible to prepare a compound $\left.\begin{array}{c}C_2H_3O\\C_2H_3O\end{array}\right\}O$. This would be an acid anhydride and it was actually prepared by Gerhardt. This illustrates that, despite its limitations, the type theory did have a certain predictive value.

Gerhardt had earlier used the idea of types as the basis of an essentially binomial nomenclature. There was, after all, a certain similarity between a chemical type and a genus in natural history:

> As the name of every organic substance should express at once the genus and the species to which it belongs, it would be very convenient in our opinion to apply the binomial nomenclature of Linnaeus to the nomenclature of organic substances.[125]

124. *Ann. chim. phys.*, [3], *37* (1853), 285–342.
125. *Précis de chimie organique*, Paris, 1844, 45, vol. i, pp. 66–8. M. J. G. Hunt, Professor of Chemistry at Montreal brought out 12,000 copies in the U.S. and Canada of an abridged version of Gerhardt's *Precis* and the book must have had considerable influence in America in the mid-nineteenth century.

Among examples of this strictly binomial nomenclature Gerhardt cited *acétate trichloré* (trichloracetic acid) and *formène trichloré* (chloroform). Gerhardt did not, however, make any serious attempt at a comprehensive nomenclature on these lines.

In conclusion it may be said that the type theory made a valuable and permanent contribution to nomenclature, notably in cases of substitution by chlorine. If we compare the modern application of the theory of substitution with that of the radical theory for the same compounds, the former often has certain advantages. Three compounds which can be produced by substitution of atoms of chlorine for hydrogen in methane can be simply described as mono-, di-, tri-chloromethane according to the substitution theory. According to the radical theory, three different radicals must be invoked to describe them and they become methyl chloride, methylene chloride and methenyl chloride respectively. Further extension of the substitution method can be seen in the carbinol nomenclature which was introduced by Kolbe.

Systems of Classification

The earliest classification in organic chemistry was the distinction made between substances of vegetable and those of animal origin. A further division was made in each class. Fourcroy, for example, divided substances of vegetable origin into twenty principles into which they could be resolved[126] and animal matter was similarly subdivided. In 1827 the London physician William Prout made the suggestion that

The principal alimentary matters might be reduced to three great classes, namely the saccharine, the oily and the albuminous.[127]

The 'saccharine class' was later denoted by the term *carbohydrate*.

The first method of classifying organic compounds according to their chemical properties was that based on their acidity or alkalinity. A fair number of organic acids were known in the late eighteenth century and by 1820 the contrasting group of alkaloids had been established. According to this simple classi-

126. Fourcroy, *Philosophie chimique*, 3rd edn., Paris, 1806, pp. 305–6.
127. *Phil. Trans., 1827*, 357.

fication any neutral liquid discovered was likely to be described as an 'ether'.

When a larger number of organic compounds had been subjected to both qualitative and quantitative analysis, there were two useful ways in which they could be classified. All compounds with the same function (e.g. alcohols) could be grouped together; alternatively, all compounds of the same complexity (e.g. containing the same number of carbon atoms) could be grouped together. These two methods may be considered as taking vertical and horizontal sections respectively. This simple analysis of classification would, however, be misleading if one were to think that it was obvious to all organic chemists in the mid-nineteenth century. There were many systems of classification favoured by chemists and Laurent remarked that, according to the various theories proposed 'there is scarcely a single body which cannot be arranged successively in every class'.[128]

The former method of classification led to the fruitful concept of the homologous series. In 1835 Dumas and Péligot in their researches on 'spirit of wood' discovered that it had many properties in common with ordinary alcohol.[129] In the following year they recognized that what Chevreul had called 'ethal' was also an alcohol. They remarked that as the complexity of the molecule increased (i.e. methyl, ethyl and cetyl alcohol) the boiling point of these alcohols also increased; the same was true for the chlorides of the series.[130] As these compounds contained one, two and sixteen carbon atoms respectively, it is obvious that many more compounds would have to be included before a convincing series with a regular gradation in properties could be formed. In 1842, however, Dumas extended this idea to a series of acids from formic acid to margaric acid[131] and a few months later J. Schiel contributed further to the concept of a series of compounds with similar chemical properties. Using the symbol R to denote the increment CH_2, Schiel extended the series of alcohols to include seven radicals and he commented on the regular increase of boiling points of the alcohols from methyl to amyl.[132] Propyl and butyl alcohols, however, were not known and Schiel mistakenly included glycerine among the monohydric alcohols.

128. Laurent, *Chemical Method*, trans. Odling, London, 1855, p. 34.
129. *Ann. chim. phys.*, [2], *58* (1835), 10.   130. Ibid., [2], *62* (1836), 22–3.
131. *Comp. rend.*, *15* (1842), 935.   132. *Ann. Chem.*, *43* (1842), 107–8.

The expression 'homologous series' was coined by Gerhardt,[133] who pointed out its usefulness not only as a means of systematizing the study of organic chemistry but also as an aid to the discovery of new compounds:

It is a kind of dictionary where all the words are arranged according to a methodical order; it cannot help gaining as the science develops, for there are still gaps to be filled.

Gerhardt's enthusiasm for classifying compounds according to the homologous series was so great that he subordinated everything else to it and he admitted that his passion for the concept of series had often earned him the reproach that he was studying algebra rather than chemistry.[134] Gerhardt represented all members of a homologous series such as the fatty acids as derivatives of the same type (i.e. formic acid) and was able to express this idea in a systematic nomenclature. Acetic acid became 'methyl formic acid', propionic acid was 'ethyl formic acid', etc. Kekulé adopted similar names and referred to the toluic acids, for example, as 'methyl-phenyl-formic acids'.[135]

Early studies of organic acids could make little progress until there was some insight into their different degrees of acidity. It was Liebig who, extending Graham's concept of polybasic acids to organic acids, established the basis of their classification in terms of their basicity.[136] An understanding of the oxidation products of the alcohols and a formulation based on Kolbe's version of the type theory enabled the latter chemist to distinguish alcohols as primary, secondary or tertiary although he did not call them such. The recognition by Berthelot[137] that glycerine was a 'triatomic' (i.e. trihydric) alcohol marked the beginning of an understanding of polyhydric alcohols. The classification of amines depended largely on Hofmann's work, although it was Gerhardt who was responsible for their formal classification in modern terms:

One might call the nitrogen compounds *primary*, *secondary* or *tertiary* according as they represent the ammonia type with substitution of one of two, or of three atoms of hydrogen.[138]

133. *Revue scientifique, 14* (1843), 580ff.
134. *Traité de chimie organique*, Paris, 1853–6, vol. i, pp. iii, 124–5.
135. *Bulletins de l'Académie Royale des Sciences de Belgique*, [2], *19* (1865), 564.
136. *Ann. Chem., 26* (1838), 138.
137. *Ann. chim. phys.*, [3], *52* (1858), 428.
138. Gerhardt, op. cit., vol. iv, p. 592.

A second general method of classifying organic compounds was to place together all compounds with a common nucleus. This was the method adopted by Laurent who, for example, considered acetic acid, acetaldehyde, ethyl alcohol, ether, ethylene, ethylene dichloride, etc. as belonging to the same class. This was an improvement on the classification of Liebig who had considered acetic acid and alcohol separately as derivatives of different radicals; Dumas too had failed to see the relation between these two compounds. When Gmelin was compiling the fourth edition of his important *Handbuch*, he decided that the previous arrangement of organic compounds was unsatisfactory and he adopted a classification based on Laurent's nucleus theory. The classification adopted in Beilstein's *Handbuch* was in turn based on that of Gmelin.

Once it was realized that organic compounds formed themselves into groups of the same complexity but different functions, chemists began to consider a particular type of compound as a 'parent' compound from which all the others were derived. As regards the historical order of discovery, the organic acids had an overwhelming claim to be considered as 'parent' compounds. Benzene, for example, was first prepared from a salt of benzoic acid, acetone from a salt of acetic acid, etc. The names of the acids were not unnaturally used in the nomenclature of their derivatives and in the mid-nineteenth century the name of the corresponding acid was still used as the basis of the name of the newly-discovered 'butyl alcohol'.[139] When Gerhardt coined the expression 'homologous series' it was the acids which he considered as the foundation of each series and he referred to compounds containing one carbon atom as belonging to the *série formique*, those with two carbon atoms to the *série acétique*, etc.[140]

A second group of compounds with a claim to be regarded as the head of a family of compounds was the class of alcohols. This at least was the opinion of Dumas, who compared the discovery of a new alcohol in organic chemistry to the discovery of a metal in inorganic chemistry.[141] Somewhat later Berthelot claimed that the alcohols should be taken as the

139. Wurtz, *Ann. chim. phys.*, [3], *42* (1854), 129.
140. Gerhardt, op. cit., vol. i, pp. 123-7.
141. Dumas and Stas, *Ann. chim. phys.*, [2], *73* (1840), 114.

starting point of a nomenclature.[141a] His main reason for choosing the alcohols was their fair reactivity which meant that related compounds could actually be prepared simply from the alcohol instead of being merely related to it theoretically.

A third possibility was to relate organic compounds to the corresponding hydrocarbon. This was finally achieved in the Geneva nomenclature of 1892, but it had been attempted much earlier in the century. In 1830 R. Herrmann had tried with little success to classify organic compounds by regarding them as formed by the union of hydrocarbons with various other compounds such as carbonic acid, water and ammonia.[142] Six years later Laurent made a new attempt to group organic compounds round the hydrocarbons. His work on the compounds of naphthalene had led him towards a theory of types according to which naphthalene formed a common nucleus. He accordingly made the following generalization:

All organic compounds are derived from a hydrocarbon, a fundamental radical, which often does not exist in its compounds but which may be represented by a derived radical containing the same number of equivalents.[143]

It was not until 1865, however, that Hofmann showed that a nomenclature and classification based on the hydrocarbons was practicable.

Related to the classification based on the number of carbon atoms in the molecule of a compound was a very useful distinction made by Kekulé between aliphatic and aromatic compounds. In 1858 Kekulé grouped together benzene and its homologues and naphthalene as a class of bodies with a relatively high carbon content compared with the other compounds such as ethylene, propylene, etc. He referred to the former group as *kohlenstoffreichere Verbindungen* (i.e. compounds richer in carbon).[144] Two years later, in the course of a paper on salicyclic and benzoic acids which he presented at a meeting of the Belgian Royal Academy of Sciences, Kekulé made explicit a distinction between 'fatty bodies' (*corps gras*) and 'aromatic bodies' (*corps*

141a. Berthelot, *Chimie organique fondée sur la synthèse*, Paris, 1860, vol. i, p. 179.

142. Berzelius, *Jahresbericht*, *11* (1831), 210–14.

143. *Ann. chim. phys.*, [2], *61* (1836), 126.

144. *Ann. Chem.*, *106* (1858), 156–7.

aromatiques).[145] Kekulé never gave a rigid definition of what he meant by aromatic compounds and even declined responsibility for this, since the compounds in question 'had long been described as aromatic'[146] It is certainly true that many such compounds which occurred naturally were found in essential oils and other bodies having an aromatic odour, e.g. oil of wintergreen, (methyl salicylate), oil of bitter almonds (benzaldehyde), gum benzoin (containing benzoic and cinnamic acids).[147]

The other class of compounds described by Kekulé in German as *Fettkörper* (fatty bodies) were compounds in which the carbon atoms were said by Kekulé to be arranged in a simple manner.[148] He later used the term 'open chain' (*chaine ouverte*) to describe the structure of these compounds, as opposed to the closed chain (*chaine fermée*) configuration of aromatic compounds.[149] The historical justification for the term 'fatty body' was that among the first members of this group to be studied by chemists were the acids derived from fats and it was these which Kekulé was considering when he began to make use of the term. Although the expression 'fatty acid' is still sometimes used in organic chemistry, chemists have generally preferred the term 'aliphatic' (ἄλειφαρ = fat) to denote the class.[150]

The 'Copula' in organic chemistry

A review of the place of language in the development of organic chemistry should not pass without mention of the introduction of the term 'copula' (or 'conjunct') into organic chemistry and its subsequent vicissitudes. Gerhardt introduced the term into chemistry in 1839 when he was investigating the reaction of sulphuric acid with certain compounds like benzene. In Gerhardt's opinion this was neither the familiar addition reaction nor that of substitution but a third method of forming

145. *Bulletins de l'Académie Royale des Sciences de Belgique*, [2], *10* (1860), 347, 348.
146. *Zeitschrift für Chemie*, N. F., *3* (1867), 215.
147. Kolbe, who in 1860 distinguished 'aromatic acids' from 'fatty acids', remarked on the smell of the aldehydes of the former as a justification for this name (*Lehrbuch der organischen Chemie*, Brunswick, 1860, vol. ii, p. 52).
148. Kekulé, *Lehrbuch der organischen Chemie*, Erlangen, 1861, vol. i, p. 361.
149. *Bulletin de la Société chimique de Paris, Nouvelle série, 3* (1865), 100.
150. The term 'aliphatic' was coined by A. W. Hofmann (according to Graebe, *Geschichte der organischen Chemie*, Berlin, 1920, p. 277n.). The class name 'Acyclic' is now often used instead of 'Aliphatic'.

compounds which he described as *'forme d'accouplement'*.[151] He was later to develop this concept with considerable success as the process of double decomposition,[152] but other chemists applied it rather differently. It was eagerly grasped by Berzelius as a device by which he could 'explain' organic reactions without abandoning his cherished dualism. All kinds of compounds could form copulae, whether they were acidic, basic or neutral. Acetic acid became oxalic acid 'conjugated' or 'copulated' (*gepaart*) with methyl[153] and by this face-saving device Berzelius was able to make less obvious the fact that the electronegative element chlorine replaced the electropositive element hydrogen in acetic acid. Berzelius considered organic bases as ammonia copulated with hydrocarbons and Hofmann at one time hoped to see aniline split up into ammonia and the copula $C_{12}H_4$ (i.e. $C_6H_4 + NH_3$ in modern notation). Hofmann considered that the concept of copulae would simplify nomenclature.[154] Laurent pointed out, however, that each copula arbitrarily introduced into a formula for a particular compound would make a new name necessary. He commented scathingly:

A word let fall from the pen of Gerhardt was thus transformed into a luminous idea for dualism. From this time everything was copulated. Acetic, formic, butyric, margaric, etc. acids, alkaloids, ethers, amides, anilides, all became copulated bodies. So that to make acetanilide, for example, they no longer employed acetic acid and aniline, but they recopulated a copulated oxalic acid with a copulated ammonia . . . .
What then is copula? A copula is an imaginary body, the presence of which disguises all the chemical properties of the compounds with which it is united.[155]

Laurent's irony was justified at the time, since Berzelius had used this concept as a device to account for atoms which would not otherwise fit into his scheme. Even for Kolbe, who made a valuable contribution to an understanding of molecular structure, the acceptance of copulae was a weakness.

151. *Ann. chim. phys.*, [2], *72* (1839), 198.
152. e.g. Gerhardt, *Traité de chimie organique*, Paris, 1853–6, vol. iv, pp. 566ff.
153. Berzelius, *Lehrbuch der Chemie*, 5th edn., Dresden and Leipzig, vol. i, 1843, p. 709.
154. *J. Chem. Soc.*, *1* (1849), 317.
155. Laurent, *Chemical Method*, London, 1855, pp. 37, 204.

CHAPTER THREE

The Representation of Organic
Compounds by Formulae

In the 1830's the chemical symbols of Berzelius offered a new aid to organic chemistry. Even some of the more conservative British chemists, who were slow to make any general use of Berzelius' symbols, saw their value in organic chemistry.[156] Yet chemical symbolism proved to be a double-edged sword, since different chemists, interpreting experimental data in different ways used the same symbols to mean quite contrary things. The confusion of language in organic chemistry towards the mid-nineteenth century was due not so much to the names used as to the formulae which were ascribed to organic compounds. In any case many chemical names were no more than attempts to translate formulae into spoken language. Some chemists opposed the introduction of names based on formulae. Dumas, for example, considered that there were two quite distinct nomenclatures, one spoken and the other written. The spoken nomenclature should be

a clear, simple and even elegant language that may be spoken without effort and which can be easily understood. It must be exact but it must also be concise and harmonious.[157]

This French demand for elegance excluded a literal translation of formulae into words.

Confusion in the Use of Chemical Symbols

To understand why there should have been so much confusion in writing formulae we must remind ourselves of the steps by which a chemist arrives at a formula, once he knows

156. Daubeny remarked that a chemist who is 'engaged in the analysis of organic compounds will be more sensible of the use of such symbols' (*Report of the British Association, 1837*, p. xxx).
157. *Leçons de philosophie chimique*, Paris, 1837, p. 353.

what elements are present. Having estimated the percentage composition of a compound he has at once to make assumptions about the weights of the atoms of the constituent elements before any kind of formula can be arrived at. The molecular weight of the compound must then be determined; without this only the ratio of the number of atoms in a compound can be known. Thirdly, even when the actual number of each kind of atom present in a molecule is known, the different possible arrangements of these atoms must be taken into account.

The first difficulty, that of agreement on atomic weights, was to bedevil organic chemistry for more than half a century. The first list of atomic weights was drawn up by Dalton in 1803. Dalton's list, however, was really one of equivalents selected to give the simplest possible formulae to chemical compounds; it was, moreover, very innacurate. For an accurate list of atomic weights we must wait for the work of Berzelius who, by 1830 had compiled a list of atomic weights the values of which were almost the same as those accepted to-day. Yet by 1840 the majority of chemists no longer made any use of them. The distrust of atomic weights which developed in the 1830's was very largely due to the work of Dumas, whose method of determining molecular weights showed anomalies for various compounds. As it was not understood that these anomalies were due to factors now known as association and dissociation, discredit was thrown on the values of the atomic weights.

Many chemists, seeing the uncertainty of any system of atomic weights, abandoned them in favour of equivalents, since the latter were based directly on experimental evidence. Confusion resulted, however, when they continued to use the same symbols to denote equivalents as had been used to denote atomic weights. In the case of elements with more than one equivalent, the smallest value was usually selected as the standard. Leopold Gmelin, professor of chemistry at Heidelberg was one of the more influential figures who advocated the use of the simplest combining weights. In practice, most of the equivalent weights proposed by Gmelin were one half of those of Berzelius, but this was a poor consolation for the lack of unity. In 1839 Liebig remarked that the study of chemistry would be made infinitely easier if all chemists decided to return to equivalents.[158]

158. *Ann. Chem.*, *31* (1839), 36.

During the next decade, however, further ideas on atomic weights seemed to make the hope of unity even more remote. In 1843 Gerhardt proposed formulating organic compounds according to a system in which water was represented as H_2O (instead of H_4O_2). The practical consequences of this were that Gerhardt's proposed atomic weights became the same as those of Berzelius except for certain metals. The result of the disagreement about atomic weights was that even the simplest formula of a compound could be written in several different ways. Berthelot pointed out the four different empirical formulae which had been assigned to acetic acid:[159]

$C_4H_4O_4$ (Equivalent weights: $C=6$, $H=1$, $O=8$)
$C_8H_8O_4$ ('4 volume' theory and $C=6$, $H=1$, $O=16$)
$C_2H_4O_2$ ('2 volume' theory and $C=12$, $H=1$, $O=16$)
$C_2H_4O_4$ (Assuming: $C=12$, $H=1$, $O=8$)

The difficulties of studying the chemical literature of the period become even more evident when the same author used different systems in the same work. Odling, who translated Laurent's *Méthode de chimie* into English, warned the reader that in the course of the book he would encounter four different systems of proportional weights. Gerhardt, though convinced of the superiority of his own system of atomic weights, used the old notation in most of his *Traité* in order to find a public for the book. He explained:

I have kept the usual nomenclature, preferring to modify the sense of names rather than their form; I have even sacrificed my notation and have kept to the old formulae in order to show more clearly by example how irrational the use of the latter is; time alone will sanction a reform which chemists have not yet generally adopted.[160]

In the fourth volume, however, he changed to his own notation, adding a foot-note explaining to the reader how to translate this back into the old system.

The futility of discussions between chemists using different languages (i.e. different notations) was pointed out by Gerhardt:

Such discussions are always futile, either because each, without

159. Berthelot, *Chimie organique fondée sur la synthèse*, Paris, 1860, vol. i, p. 187.
160. Op. cit., vol. i, p. i. See also vol. iv, p. 561n.

realizing it, express the same facts in a language which is not understood by his opponent or because both attribute to the language of
formulae a meaning which it does not have, that of expressing the
molecular arrangement. The same chemists would understand each
other perfectly if they translated for each other the words they used
into precise terms.[161]

When Gerhardt wrote this, the confusion of notation had
reached its zenith but even twenty years earlier Edward
Turner, as the chairman of a British committee appointed to
consider chemical symbols, had pointed out that much confusion
would be avoided if every chemist were to state explicitly the
exact quantities which he intended to represent by his symbols.[162]

'Rational' Formulae

The confusion about atomic weights can explain some apparent anomalies in nomenclature. When Faraday analysed
the new hydrocarbon he had discovered in compressed illuminating gas, he found that it contained carbon and hydrogen
in the ratio of approximately 12:1. For Faraday 12 was equal
to two equivalents of carbon and, had he favoured the symbols
of Berzelius, he might have written this as C_2H. This explains
why he gave it the name *bicarburet of hydrogen*.[163] Any quantitative nomenclature was necessarily hypothetical as long as
there was doubt about atomic weights. Yet it was important
that organic chemists should know not only the ratio of the
number of each kind of atom in a compound but also the
number of atoms per molecule. Progress depended not so much
on knowing that Faraday's hydrocarbon had the empirical
formula CH as in establishing that its molecular formula was
C_6H_6 and so relating it to compounds containing the C_6H_5-
group. If it is known that the formulae of alcohol and ether are
C_2H_6O and $C_4H_{10}O$ respectively, it can be deduced that they
are related compounds, since a molecule of ether consists of two
molecules of alcohol minus one of water, or:

$$2C_2H_6O = C_4H_{10}O + H_2O$$

161. Ibid., vol. iv, p. 565.
162. *Report of the British Association, 1835*, p. 207.
163. *Annals of Philosophy*, [2], *11* (1826), 46, 49.

By doubling the formula for alcohol, however, Berzelius obscured this relationship.[164] Even when Gerhardt wrote what we now regard as the correct molecular formulae for alcohol and ether, by placing these two obviously related compounds in different classes, he alienated many chemists who might otherwise have regarded his atomic weights more favourably.[165]

The terms 'empirical formula' and 'rational formula' were introduced by Berzelius in 1833.[166] The 'rational formula' indicated how the atoms were grouped together in the molecule. Such formulae had already been used in organic chemistry by Dumas and Boullay to represent the composition of 'compound ethers'[167] and by Mitscherlich for benzoic acid and some of its derivatives. If Liebig and Wöhler had gone beyond writing an empirical formula for benzoic acid, it was only to illustrate the concept of the benzoyl radical of which they regarded it as the oxide. Mitscherlich, however, interpreted the formula for benzoic acid as:

$$12C + 12H + 2C + 4O^{168} \text{ (i.e. } C_6H_6 + CO_2)$$

Berzelius would not accept a formula of this kind, since it conflicted with his experience of inorganic compounds, but he had to admit that to arrive at the 'true' rational formula for an organic compound would be a very difficult problem.

Berzelius' almost Platonic conception of a rational formula may be contrasted with that of Gerhardt, for whom a formula was acceptable if it helped to explain any of the reactions of a compound.[169] The same compound could often be given more than one formula. In some reactions, for example, an aldehyde might seem to behave as a hydride and in others as an oxide and it could therefore be represented by two formulae. Gerhardt's position may be summed up by his own phrase:

Autant de réactions, autant de formules rationelles.[170]

Gerhardt's pragmatic attitude to rational formulae was reflected in the opinion expressed by the body of French chemists

164. *Ann. Phys. Chem.*, *26* (1832), 484.
165. Laurent, *Chemical Method*, London, 1855, p. 76.
166. Berzelius, *Jahresbericht*, *13* (1834), 186.
167. *Ann. chim. phys.*, [2], *37* (1828), 15–53.
168. *Ann. Phys. Chem.*, *32* (1834), 229–30.
169. Gerhardt, op. cit., vol. iv, pp. 577–81.
170. Grimaux and Gerhardt, *Charles Gerhardt, sa vie*, etc., Paris, 1900, p. 490.

who in 1889–92 considered the problem of a nomenclature for organic chemistry. They demanded that any reform of nomenclature should not lay down one name for each compound; instead they suggested that it should concern itself with the rules according to which the different names applicable to a particular compound should be constructed.

Although it was necessary for the progress of organic chemistry that the way in which the atoms are grouped together in a compound should be considered, the inevitable result was an even greater diversity in the formulae given to any particular compound. To accept the principle that a compound could have more than one formula itself laid the way open for anarchy. As Laurent remarked:

> Every chemist follows his own particular course and changes his formulae as often as he obtains a new reaction.[171]

As an illustration of the confusion Kekulé managed to collect 18 rational formulae which had been given to acetic acid.[172]

The type theory gave encouragement to the conjectural writing of formulae. The following examples $(C = 6, O = 8)$, based on the ammonia type, illustrate type formulae at their best:

$$\left.\begin{array}{l}H\\H\\H\end{array}\right\}N \qquad \left.\begin{array}{l}C_4H_5\\H\\H\end{array}\right\}N \qquad \left.\begin{array}{l}(C_4H_5)\\(C_4H_5)\\H\end{array}\right\}N \qquad \left.\begin{array}{l}C_{12}H_5\\H\\H\end{array}\right\}N \qquad \left.\begin{array}{l}C_4H_3O_2\\H\\H\end{array}\right\}N$$

ammonia ethylamine diethylamine aniline acetamide

As an American writer[173] remarked in 1863,

> At the present time, not to understand this method of writing formulae is to be excluded from following the course of modern chemical progress.

Unfortunately the process of writing formulae did not stop here. Finding that many compounds could not be reasonably reduced to one of the established types, Kekulé introduced the idea of mixed types.[174] By this means chemical classification became a little less arbitrary, but it led to the writing of formulae grotesque in their complexity, and it was in this connection that Kolbe

171. Laurent, op. cit., p. 23.
172. Kekulé, *Lehrbuch der organischen Chemie*, Erlangen, 1861, vol. i, p. 58.
173. C. M. Wetherill, 'A Brief Sketch of the Modern Theory of Chemical Types', *Annual Report of the Smithsonian Institution, 1863*, 153–68.
174. *Ann. Chem.*, *104* (1857), 133–42.

remarked that chemistry had become an empty game of formulae.[175]

Despite Gerhardt's theoretical speculations, in one sense he represented a movement back from the prejudices of both the radical and the dualistic theories towards empiricism. In Gerhardt's unitary system alcohol was given the formula C_2H_6O. This empirical formula may be contrasted with other contemporary formulae for the same compound: $C_4H_8 + H_4O_2$ of Dumas, $(C_2H_6)O$ of Berzelius, $C_4H_{10}O + H_2O$ of Liebig and $C_4H_{10}O_2 + H_2$ of Mitscherlich. There was, nevertheless, much to be said for a rational formula provided it was based on an accumulation of experimental evidence. Laurent, for example, did not agree with the movement back to empirical formulae and he wrote to Gerhardt saying that a system of empirical formulae was too absolute and if it were adopted it would prevent the discovery of a host of interesting relationships between compounds.[176] Gerhardt's own preparation of acid anhydrides was one example of a successful prediction which could hardly have been made on the basis of the empirical formula of a related compound and Kolbe's predictions of the existence of what we now call secondary and tertiary alcohols was another.[177] Kolbe wrote formulae for carboxylic acids in which they were represented as derivatives of carbonic acid. By recognizing that all the oxygen atoms were not equivalent he was able to explain the nature of alcohols and their behaviour on oxidation. In the case of ethyl alcohol he clearly showed its relation to aldehyde and acetic acid and he postulated the existence of compounds similar to alcohol but with different oxidation products. When Friedel had prepared what he considered was 'probably propyl alcohol',[178] Kolbe[179] thought it more likely to be 'singly methylated ethyl alcohol', for which he then wrote the formula $(C = 6, O = 8)$:

$$\left.\begin{array}{l} C_2H_3 \\ C_2H_3 \\ H \end{array}\right\} C_2O \cdot HO$$

175. '*Ein leer Formelspiel*' (*Ann. Chem.*, *113* (1860), 294).
176. Grimaux and Gerhardt, *Charles Gerhardt, sa vie*, etc., Paris, 1900, p. 475.
177. *Ann. Chem.*, *113* (1860), 305–8.   178. *Comp. rend.*, *55* (1862), 53.
179. *Zeitschrift für Chemie*, *5* (1862), 687.

Kolbe suggested that this formula could be confirmed if Friedel's alcohol yielded acetone on oxidation, which it did. Erlenmeyer[180] subsequently re-wrote Kolbe's formula in a manner acceptable to-day as:

$$CH_3$$
$$|$$
$$CH.OH$$
$$|$$
$$CH_3$$

There remained the discovery of what Kolbe's called 'doubly methylated [ethyl] alcohol' (i.e. containing three 'C_2H_3' groups) which was achieved by Butlerow (1864), who called it more aptly 'trimethylated methyl alcohol' or 'tertiary pseudo butyl alcohol'.[181]

Kolbe had referred to ordinary ethyl alcohol as 'normal alcohol', but the use of the term 'normal' in organic chemistry probably began with Gerhardt.[182] The term *isopropyl alcohol* was used by Kolbe,[183] the prefix *iso-* already being in use to denote isomeric compounds. It did not always happen, of course, that the first alcohol of a group to be discovered was the normal alcohol. The 'butyl alcohol' discovered by Wurtz,[184] for example, was really isobutyl alcohol.

Once the distinction between primary, secondary and tertiary alcohols was appreciated, it became necessary to distinguish them by suitable names. Kolbe was able to do this by considering all alcohols to be derived from methyl alcohol and calling the latter *carbinol*.[185] The application of this nomenclature may be seen from the following examples (given in modern notation):

$$\left.\begin{array}{l} CH_3 \\ H \\ H \end{array}\right\} C.OH \qquad \left.\begin{array}{l} CH_3 \\ CH_3 \\ H \end{array}\right\} C.OH \qquad \left.\begin{array}{l} CH_3 \\ C_2H_5 \\ C_5H_{11} \end{array}\right\} C.OH$$

| *methyl carbinol* | *dimethyl carbinol* | *amyl-ethyl-methyl* |
| (i.e. ethyl alcohol) | (i.e. isopropyl alcohol) | *carbinol* |

180. *Ann. Chem.*, *139* (1866), 211.

181. *Zeitschrift für Chemie*, 7 (1864), 385.

182. Gerhardt used the term *normale* in his *Précis* (1844) in his peculiar species method of nomenclature according to which acetic acid was *acétate normal* as opposed to e.g. the potassium salt which was *acétate potassique*. In a similar way he described marsh gas as *formène normal* and ethyl alcohol as *alcool normale*.

183. *Zeitschrift für Chemie*, 5 (1862), 687–90.

184. *Ann. chim. phys.*, [3], *42* (1854), 129.

185. *Ann. Chem.*, *132* (1864), 103–4n.

This nomenclature proved invaluable for secondary and tertiary alcohols and is still used to-day.

Although Kolbe's formulae were purely formal they may be seen as a link between the theory of types and the theory of structure. Before structural formulae are considered, however, the question of isomers and their nomenclature will be discussed.

Isomerism

Since the end of the eighteenth century it had been recognized that a wide variety of organic compounds consisted of the three elements carbon, hydrogen and oxygen. It was at first assumed that differences were due to slight variations in the proportions of these elements but it was later realized that in organic chemistry it was not only the kind of elements present and their proportions but also their internal *arrangement* which effects the properties of the compound. Gay-Lussac made this suggestion in 1814,[186] but it was only ten years later that there was incontrovertible evidence that two simple compounds could exist each with the same number of the same atoms but with quite distinct properties. Wöhler's analysis of silver cyanide was found to agree exactly with an analysis which Liebig had made of silver fulminate. These papers were published in the *Annales de Chimie* and Gay-Lussac, as editor, called attention to the similarity of the results.[187] Further examples of this phenomenon came with Faraday's discovery (1825) of a new hydrocarbon (isobutylene) with the same proportion of carbon and hydrogen as olefiant gas and Wöhler's synthesis of urea from ammonium cyanate (1828).

It was now obvious that this was no isolated phenomenon and in 1830 Berzelius decided that it must have a name:

In order to be able to speak of these bodies easily, we must have a general name for them and it seems to me that this is best taken from the Greek as the usual root of scientific terminologies.[188]

Berzelius suggested that they might be called *homosynthetic* or, alternatively, *isomeric* (ἴσος =equal, μερίς =part) bodies; he decided to use the latter term which was shorter. Berzelius

186. *Ann. chim.*, *91* (1814), 149n.
187. *Ann. chim. phys.*, [2], *27* (1824), 200n.
188. *Ann. Phys. Chem.*, *19* (1830), 326.

defined isomeric bodies as those with the same chemical constitution and molecular weight (*Atomengewicht*) but having dissimilar chemical properties. Faraday's gaseous hydrocarbon
and olefiant gas were not included under the term, since their
molecular weights were not the same. He later coined the
word *polymer* to cover such cases.[189]

It now became necessary to consider an appropriate nomenclature for isomers. Berzelius made the first attempt in 1830
when he suggested the use of the prefix *para-* to suggest a variation from the original. Berzelius admitted, however, that in
practice it would be difficult to decide which of two isomers
should be considered as normal and which as the variation, so
that there was necessarily a certain arbitrariness in this nomenclature. He suggested that racemic acid should be called *para-
tartaric acid* to indicate that it was related to, though not identical
with, tartaric acid. Berzelius extended the use of the term *para-*
to compounds which, though related were not isomers. Thus it
could be applied to describe one of the two phosphoric acids
which differed by a small proportion of water.[190] The prefix
para- came to be used to denote those modifications of organic
acids which had previously been called pyro-acids.[191] Another
application was in Laurent's 'paranaphthalene', a term which
he later changed for the shorter word *anthracène* (ἄνθραξ =coal).[192]

A second prefix intended to denote a modification of an
original compound was introduced by Graham in 1833 in his
classic paper on the relationship of the three phosphoric acids.
Graham distinguished these as 'phosphoric acid', 'pyrophosphoric acid' and 'metaphosphoric acid' and commented:

Although of the opinion that there is only one phosphoric acid, and
that the modifications are entirely due to the quantity of water
combined with the acid, I have still retained the names which have
come into use, and even proposed a third, *meta*phosphoric acid,
implying merely that the acid to which this name is applied is
phosphoric acid with something else, namely with an atom of

189. Ibid., *26* (1832), 320–1. The term *polymer* is used to-day with a rather
different meaning.

190. i.e. [ortho-] phosphoric acid and pyrophosphoric acid. Berzelius
considered the latter the simpler acid and therefore wished to call it 'phosphoric acid' so that phosphoric acid would be called *para-phosphoric acid*.

191. Pelouze suggested calling pyro-malic acid 'para-malic acid' (now
called 'maleic acid') (*Ann. chim. phys.*, [2], *11* (1819), 96; *56* (1834), 429).

192. *Comp. rend.*, *1* (1835), 439.

water . . . . These trivial names . . . may be adopted provisionally till chemists are prepared, by an extended knowledge of the salts, to innovate upon their nomenclature with more advantage than can be done at present.[193]

This suggestion found favour and in a paper presented in February 1834, for example, Pelouze referred to an acid related to gallic acid as *acide métagallique*.[194] Liebig, who considered that the prefix *para-* could only be used to denote strict isomers, found *meta-* a convenient prefix to use in the description of compounds whose relationship was not so close.[195]

The history of the use of the prefix *ortho-* in chemistry is not so clear. It was, however, used in the course of a paper published by William Odling in 1859, in which he distinguished 'common or orthophosphates' from metaphosphates.[196]

Having mentioned the early use of the prefixes *para-*, *meta-* and *ortho-* in general chemistry, we may now turn to their later use to distinguish derivatives of benzene and related compounds. The classification, nomenclature and identification of the derivatives of benzene owes much to the work of Kekulé and his pupil Körner. Kekulé had made a preliminary attempt to explain the structure of aromatic compounds in 1861. In 1865 he was investigating the possible isomeric modifications of compounds of the type $C_6H_4X_2$ and in the same year Kekulé's hexagonal formula for benzene was first published.[197] The positions of the carbon atoms were distinguished by letters as follows:

In the following year, however, he substituted the numbers 1–6 for the letters a–f.[198] By this time several pairs of isomeric derivatives of benzene were known (under such names as

193. *Phil. Trans.*, *123* (1833), 283.
194. *Ann. chim. phys.*, [2], *54* (1833), 352–3.
195. e.g. *acide métaméconique*, *Journal de Pharmacie*, *20* (1834), 21–2.
196. *Phil. Mag.*, 4th series, *18* (1859), 368.
197. *Bulletins de l'Académie Royale des Sciences de Belgique*, [2], *19* (1865), 553.
198. *Lehrbuch der organischen Chemie*, Erlangen, 1866, vol. ii, p. 514. The system of ring-numbering was extended by Graebe in 1869 to derivatives of naphthalene (*Ann. Chem.*, *149* (1869), 26).

'chloraniline' and 'parachloraniline') and, in order to understand the confusion in their nomenclature it is necessary to appreciate that they had received names considered appropriate for isomers before chemists had any idea of their structure. There were at least two cases where three isomers were known: the three dihydroxybenzenes and the hydroxybenzoic acids, known as salicylic acid, 'oxybenzoic acid' and 'para-oxybenzoic acid'.

It was obviously desirable to use systematic names to indicate a relationship between groups of disubstituted benzene derivatives and Körner, following Kekulé, decided to use the three prefixes *ortho-*, *meta-* and *para-* for this purpose.[199] Unfortunately the application of this nomenclature, sometimes based on faulty assumptions, was a slow and difficult process. For his use of the prefix *para-* Körner quoted the precedents of 'paranitroaniline' and 'para-oxybenzoic acid'. It was an unfortunate beginning to place these two compounds in the same class, since they were later found to have a dissimilar structure. The prefix *ortho-* Körner rather naively intended for compounds produced in certain simple reactions,[200] and substances in the third group were to be called *meta-* compounds. According to Körner's use of the terms, resorcinol, hydroquinone and pyrocatechin were typical examples of the *para-*, *ortho-*, and *meta-* groups respectively and he was therefore using these prefixes to denote the 1, 3; 1, 4; and 1, 2 positions. A nomenclature was, however, of little practical use until the question of the absolute configuration of any particular compound was settled. Körner neatly solved this problem by showing on theoretical grounds that each of the three possible disubstituted isomers of benzene could give rise to a different number of trisubstituted derivatives. It now remained for chemists to agree on nomenclature. Graebe showed that in one of the compounds originally designated as *para-* the substituting groups were in the 1, 4 position and he used the terms *ortho-*, *meta-* and *para-* to denote the 1, 2; 1, 3; and 1, 4 positions respectively.[201] Baeyer and Fittig also used the prefixes in this

---

199. *Giornale di Scienze Naturali ed Economichi di Palermo*, 5 (1869), 229 (see Körner, '*Uber die Bestimmung des chemischen Ortes bei den aromatischen Substanzen*, (*1866–74*)', Ostwald's Klassiker No. 174, Leipzig, 1910, pp. 27–8).

200. e.g. the action of nitric acid on phenol or aniline. Körner admitted, however, that in practice these so-called *ortho-compounds* would be formed mixed with other isomers.

201. *Ann. Chem.*, *149* (1869), 27.

way and eventually this usage became established.[202] Ironically enough, in view of his important contribution to the identification of aromatic isomers, Körner had to have his later publications 'translated' into the current nomenclature. This, at least was the case when his work was reported to the British Chemical Society.[203]

Structural Formulae

Until about 1860 the majority of chemists used formulae merely as convenient representations of organic compounds. The formulae based on the type theory, despite appearances to the contrary, were not intended to represent the actual arrangement of the atoms in the molecule. Gerhardt and Chancel had written a paper 'On the constitution of organic compounds',[204] but they made it clear from the outset that by 'constitution' they did not mean the absolute arrangement of the atoms, which they considered it impossible to determine. In 1861 the Russian chemist Butlerow, addressing a meeting of German chemists at Speyer, formally introduced the concept of structure.[205] Formulae should no longer be written according to the type theory. By determining the chemical structure of bodies it should be possible to write true rational formulae and for each compound only one rational formula would be possible. Butlerow did not claim originality for these ideas and in particular he mentioned the formulae of the Scottish chemist A. S. Couper, which were first published in June 1858.[206] Couper was primarily concerned with the force of attraction between the various elements in organic molecules and the lines (at first dotted, but afterwards continuous) that

202. Though not immediately (see e.g., V. von Richter, *Berichte der deutschen chemischen Gesellschaft, 5* (1872), 429 and H. Hübner, ibid., *8* (1875), 474).
203. H. E. Armstrong, *J. Chem. Soc., 1876,* 1, 204–41; see espec. p. 207n. When the third volume of Kekulé's *Lehrbuch* appeared after a long delay in 1882, the author was obliged to point out in the preface that since the publication of the previous volume he had decided to use the terms *ortho-, meta-* and *para-* in the now generally accepted sense.
204. *Comptes rendus des travaux de chimie par Laurent et Gerhardt, 1851,* 65–84
205. '*Einiges über die chemische Structur der Körper*', *Zeitschrift für Chemie, 4* (1861), 549–60.
206. *Comp. rend., 46* (1858), 1157–9. See also *Phil. Mag.,* 4th series, *16* (1858), 104–16 and *Ann. chim. phys.,* [3], *53* (1858), 469–89.

he wrote in various formulae may be taken to represent these forces. Two examples of these formulae ($O = 8$) are:

$$C \begin{Bmatrix} O \dots OH \\ H^3 \end{Bmatrix}$$

$$C \begin{Bmatrix} O \\ H^2 \end{Bmatrix} \dots \begin{Bmatrix} O \\ H^2 \end{Bmatrix} C$$

$$C \dots H^3 \quad H^3 \dots C$$

methyl alcohol
(CH_3OH)

ether
($CH_3 . CH_2 . O . CH_2 . CH_3$)

Couper's formulae became widely known and of particular interest is the influence which they had on Lothar Meyer, who referred to them several times in his *Modernen Theorien der Chemie* (1864).[207] In this book he not only drew bonds between atoms as in

$$O\!\!\diagup^{H}_{\diagdown H} \quad, \qquad N\!\!\diagup^{H}_{\diagdown H}^{-H} \quad \text{and} \quad C\!\!\lessgtr^{H}_{H}{}^{H}_{H}$$

but he also drew the double bond in ethylene.. By means of his formulae he clearly showed its reaction with chlorine:

$$\left.{H \atop H}\right\} C\!\!\bigcirc\!\!C \left\{{H \atop H}\right. \qquad \text{and} \qquad \left.{H \atop H}\right\} \underset{Cl}{\overset{}{C}} \overset{\frown}{} \underset{Cl}{\overset{}{C}} \left\{{H \atop H}\right.$$

Even more interesting are various conjectural ring formulae which he drew to represent various compounds including sulphur trioxide and ozone:

$$O\!\!\diagup^{\textstyle S}\!\!\diagdown\!\!_{\textstyle O}\!\!\diagup O \qquad \text{and} \qquad \overset{\textstyle O}{\underset{O\!-\!\!-\!\!-O}{\diagup\diagdown}}$$

It is not unlikely that these formulae had some influence on Kekulé's idea of the benzene ring.

A brief mention must be made of a booklet published by the Austrian chemist, J. Loschmidt,[208] who drew formulae in which

207. For references to Couper, see op. cit., pp. 68, 87n., 103n.; for double bond, see p. 102 and for ring formulae, see pp. 81-2, 112.

208. *Constitutions Formeln der organischen Chemie in graphischer Darstellung, Chemische Studien, 1,* Vienna, 1861.

carbon was represented by a large circle and hydrogen by a

small circle. His formula for benzene: 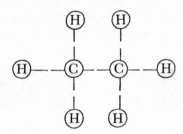 bears at least a

superficial resemblance to the ring structure published by Kekulé four years later. Loschmidt wrote out several hundred structural formulae, many of which suggest that he had a keen insight into the constitution of organic compounds. Unfortunately his work passed unnoticed and it is again to Scotland that we must turn for the next important contribution to structural formulae.

A. Crum Brown published several structural formulae in 1864, although it seems that he had been using such formulae since 1861 independently of Couper and Loschmidt.[209] He showed that these formulae could be used to throw light on certain problems of organic chemistry such as distinguishing between isomers. He wrote the formula:

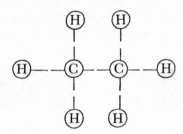

in an attempt to answer the question whether 'hydride of ethyl' (i.e. ethane) and Kolbe's 'methyl' gas were identical, but he drew no positive conclusions.[210] Among other graphic formulae given by Brown and acceptable by modern standards may be mentioned those for ordinary propyl alcohol and isopropyl alcohol ('Friedel's alcohol'). He also drew the following clear representations of double and triple bonds:

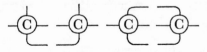

209. Sir J. Walker, 'Symbols and Formulae', *J. Chem. Soc., Transactions* *123* (1923), 942. A. Crum Brown, 'On the theory of isomeric compounds', *Transactions of the Royal Society of Edinburgh*, *23*, 3 (1864), 234.

210. The problem was finally solved by Schorlemmer in the same year (*Ann. Chem.*, *132* (1864), 234).

Crum Brown's formulae gained a considerable reputation. In France they were used immediately by Wurtz.[211] In Britain Frankland made extensive use of them in lectures which he delivered at the Royal College of Chemistry, London during the session 1865–6.[212] Frankland remarked that

Graphic notation affords most valuable aid to the teacher in rendering intelligible the constitution of chemical compounds.

Something must now be said of the graphic formulae used by Kekulé. In the first volume of his text-book of organic chemistry, published in 1861, Kekulé, although writing most formulae after the formal manner of the type theory, made some use of graphic formulae in foot-notes to the text.[213] The size of each atom depicted was proportional to its combining power so that a univalent atom was represented by a small circle containing the appropriate chemical symbol, whereas carbon consisted of a series of four circles fused together, giving rise to formulae reminiscent of sausages. In all the simpler compounds the atoms were arranged in two equal horizontal rows and every point of contact between the rows indicated a linkage, e.g.:

water   marsh gas   ethyl alcohol

Even after the publication of the simpler and more suitable formulae of Crum Brown, Kekulé preferred to use his own formulae and in 1865 he applied them to explain the structure of various aromatic compounds,[214] e.g.:

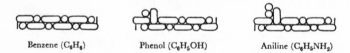

Benzene (C_6H_6)   Phenol (C_6H_5OH)   Aniline ($C_6H_5NH_2$)

211. *Leçons de philosophie chimique*, Paris, 1864; p. 143.
212. *Lecture notes for chemical students*, London, 1866. See especially pp. v–vi and chap. 3.
213. *Lehrbuch der organischen Chemie*, Erlangen, 1861, vol. i, pp. 160n., 162n., 164n., 165n.
214. *Ann. Chem.*, *137* (1865), Table II.

From the above examples it may be seen that Kekulé had modified the delineation of the atoms and it is rather difficult to distinguish between the oxygen atom of length 2 units in phenol and the nitrogen atom of length 3 units in aniline. The dashes in the formulae were intended to denote 'affinity units' (i.e. valency bonds) linking up the opposite ends.[215]

The only one of Kekulé's structural formulae which is of more than historical interest, however, was the famous hexagonal formula for benzene which was published in 1865. In the following year Kekulé justified the conception by drawing a diagram with what amounts to alternate single and double bonds[216] so that the structure was reconciled with the valency of four which he had established for carbon. The actual term 'valency' or 'valence' (*Valenz*) was not used before 1868 when it was introduced by Wichelhaus.[217]

From what has been said it is clear that there was considerable interest in the mid-1860's in the linkages between atoms and numerous methods were devised for representing them. One scheme was proposed by the German chemist Wilbrand[218] and a similar idea was put forward in 1866 by G. C. Foster of Glasgow.[219] Foster represented the 'atomicity' (i.e. valency) of elements by dashes, so that hydrogen, oxygen and carbon would be respectively │ , ⊓ , and ⊓⊓ . In this scheme which subordinated the identity of a particular element to a classification based on valency, the compounds ethane, ethylene and acetylene were written respectively;

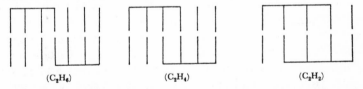

(C_2H_6) (C_2H_4) (C_2H_2)

215. Kekulé admitted, however, that the ring structure could not be clearly shown on paper by means of these formulae and he referred to P. Havrez, *Principes de la chimie unitaire*, 1866, where an attempt had been made to draw his formulae in three dimensions (*Lehrbuch*, Erlangen, 1866, vol. ii, pp. 514–15n).

216. *Lehrbuch*, vol. ii, p. 496; c.f. diagram of structure of mesitylene, *Zeitschrift für Chemie*, *10* (1867), 216.

217. *Ann. Chem., Suppl.*, *6* (1868), 259. Wichelhaus took this term from Hofmann's '*Quantivalenz*' which had been used in the same sense.

218. *Zeitschrift für Chemie*, *8* (1865), 685.

219. Art. 'Classification' in H. Watts, *Chemical Dictionary*, London, 1866, vol. i, pp. 1007–23.

Various models were also constructed to popularize the idea of structural formulae. Hofmann, at a lecture given at the Royal Institution in April 1865 made use of croquet balls of different colours to represent various kinds of atoms (e.g. carbon black, hydrogen white, chlorine green, 'fiery' oxygen red, nitrogen blue).[220] The combining power of the atoms was illustrated by tubes and pins projecting from the croquet balls. Hofmann successfully represented many organic and inorganic compounds on the principle that there must be no arms left not connected with another atom. The limitations of his model were apparent, however, when he tried to apply this principle to unsaturated organic compounds. Another mechanical device was that suggested by Dewar in 1866–7 when he used small circular pieces of brass with two rods fixed at right angles to represent carbon atoms with four valencies and by means of these he was able to illustrate various possible structures of benzene.[221] No-one, however, had yet given serious thought to anything more than two-dimensional models of organic compounds.

A new chapter in organic chemistry was opened in the autumn of 1874 when two chemists van't Hoff in Holland and le Bel in France independently postulated a three-dimensional structure of molecules. Van't Hoff pointed out that the number of isomers known of a particular compound did not agree with what one would expect from the current constitutional formulae; nor could certain cases of isomerism be foreseen by the use of such formulae. Both these difficulties could be overcome by assuming the carbon atom to be tetrahedral.[222] Van't Hoff and le Bel were able to relate their theory to the optical properties of compounds containing an asymmetric[223] carbon atom although le Bel's arguments were more abstract and it was van't Hoff who emphasized the fruitful concept of the tetrahedron.[224] The latter pointed out that if the atoms were ar-

220. 'On the combining power of atoms', *Chemical News*, 12 (1865), 176–9, 189.

221. *Proceedings of the Royal Society of Edinburgh*, 6 (1866–9), 84–6.

222. J. H. van't Hoff, *La Chimie dans l'Espace*, Rotterdam, 1875.

223. This term was used by van't Hoff to denote a carbon atom combined with four different univalent groups. He represented an asymmetric carbon atom by an italic *C* when writing a linear formula.

224. Pasteur (*Leçons de chimie professées en 1860*, Paris, 1861, p. 25) and Kekulé (*Zeitschrift für Chemie*, N.F., 3 (1867), 218.) had both speculated on the tetrahedral structure of certain organic compounds.

ranged in a plane there would be more isomers of the type $CR_1R_2R_3R_4$ than were actually observed. Assuming the tetrahedral structure, he was able to show that there were only two possible isomers related to each other as mirror images. Van't Hoff also showed that, apart from this kind of isomerism depending on an asymmetric carbon atom, there was another kind of isomerism exhibited by certain compounds containing double bonds and he was thus able to explain the long-standing problem of the isomerism of maleic and fumaric acids. The prefixes *cis-* and *trans-* were introduced by Baeyer to denote the relative positions of the groups in maleic and fumaric acids respectively.[225]

The development of stereochemistry[226] was the chief accomplishment in organic chemistry in the last two decades of the nineteenth century. Such fruitful theories as that of steric hindrance (V. Meyer) and the strain theory (Baeyer) were based on the new stereochemistry and by means of it Fischer was able to elucidate the structure of isomeric sugars, thus laying the foundations of carbohydrate chemistry.

225. *Ann. Chem., 245* (1888), 137.
226. The term 'stereochemistry' ($\sigma\tau\epsilon\rho\epsilon\delta s$ = solid) was proposed by Victor Meyer, *Berichte der deutschen chemischen Gesellschaft, 23* (1890), 569.

CHAPTER FOUR

The Development of a Systematic Nomenclature for Organic Chemistry

So far various general methods of naming organic compounds have been mentioned: that based on word contractions and those related to the radical and type theories. In this chapter it is intended to look briefly at one or two schemes of nomenclature associated with particular chemists and to consider in what ways they anticipated the agreement on the nomenclature of organic compounds which was sealed in Geneva in 1892. The Geneva conference is seen as the culmination of a series of events, not the least of which was the congress held in Karlsruhe some thirty years previously.

The Contributions of Berzelius, Gerhardt and Hofmann

The establishment of any system of nomenclature presupposes the authority of an individual or group to impose such a system. One of the first figures in the history of organic chemistry whose authority was recognized almost internationally was Berzelius and this was particularly true in the third decade of the nineteenth century. Apart from his experimental work, which included the discovery of many new compounds and innumerable extremely accurate quantitative analyses, Berzelius had devised a simple system of chemical symbols which chemists were finding increasingly useful. Berzelius was also able to exert some influence on his contemporaries by his yearly reports on the progress of the physical sciences. Berzelius' influential position is illustrated in his wide correspondence, including the many letters which he exchanged with the younger chemist Justus von Liebig. In the years 1832–4 in particular, Liebig wrote several letters to Berzelius in which he asked the latter's advice on questions of nomenclature.[227]

227. *Berzelius und Liebig. Ihre Briefe von 1831–1845*, Munich and Leipzig, 1893, pp. 34, 40, 82; 80, 86, 88.

In his yearly report for 1833 Berzelius had several comments to make about the nomenclature of organic compounds.[228] He suggested that the term *amide* should be the recognized name for compounds containing the -NH_2 group, following the precedent of Dumas, who had called the substance obtained by distilling ammonium oxalate *oxamide* and Liebig and Wöhler who had called a similar compound related to benzoic acid *benzamid*. Berzelius remarked on the term 'spirit of wood' which could only be regarded as a temporary label to be changed as soon as a 'general scientific nomenclature' could be established. Two years later, when Dumas and Péligot had isolated their *bihydrate de methylène*, Berzelius suggested that the time had come to extend the meaning of the word 'alcohol' to cover this compound and any others like it which might be discovered. Alcohol was therefore to become a general term for a whole class of compounds, this particular compound being the alcohol of the radical methyl.[229] He later predicted that the compound known as aldehyde would be found to be only one of a new class of compounds.[230] When this was found to be the case 'aldehyde' was used in the wider sense. This process of generalization was not uncommon in organic chemistry and the use of the terms *olefine*[231] (from 'olefiant gas') and *paraffin*[232] provide later examples of this practice.

Berzelius continued to comment on chemical nomenclature in his *Jahresbericht*.[233] He was often critical of the names coined by other chemists, taken at random from Latin and Greek sources. He criticized haphazard word-endings and suggested a system in which similar compounds and radicals were denoted by similar suffixes. In his criticisms he was particularly severe

228. Berzelius, *Jahresbericht*, *13* (1834), 205–6, 231–2, 328.
229. Ibid., *15* (1836), 380–2.
230. Ibid., *18* (1839), 483. Oil of bitter almonds (benzaldehyde) was then considered as the hydride of the benzoyl radical. Gmelin suggested the term *aldide* to describe compounds similar to aldehyde (*Handbuch*, 4th edn., Heidelberg, 1848, vol. i, p. 162). 'Methyl aldehyde' (i.e. formaldehyde) was described by Hofmann in 1867 (*Proceedings of the Royal Society*, *16* (1867), 156).
231. The term *olefine* was used by Guthrie in *J. Chem. Soc.*, *12* (1860), 109.
232. The term *paraffin* was coined by Reichenbach (from Lat. *parum* + *affinis* = little affinity) to denote a particular substance, a mixture of hydrocarbons (*Journal für Chemie und Physik*, *59* (1830), 455). The term was extended to cover any hydrocarbons of the series C_nH_{2n+2} by Watts (*Dictionary of Chemistry*, 1868, vol. iv, p. 344 and *Supplement*, 1872, p. 705).
233. See especially *Jahresbericht*, *14* (1835), 334n.; *17* (1838), 342–3; *19* (1840), 347; *21* (1842), 374; *22* (1843), 353–4.

with Laurent, whose terms he suggested were almost laughable. His own suggested nomenclature for derivatives of naphthalene was based on an enunciation of the number of carbon and hydrogen atoms in a molecule. The compound, for example, formed by substitution of two chlorine atoms in a molecule of naphthalene, which Laurent had called *chloronaphtalèse*, Berzelius called *Dekahexylchlorur* ($C_{10}H_6Cl_2$). Sometimes Berzelius gave good reasons for preferring a particular name for a compound and it was due to his influence, for example, that the terms *aniline* and *toluene* became generally accepted. Berzelius' interests were not, of course, confined to organic chemistry and he was always prepared to coin a term to meet the growing requirements of general chemistry. Terms like *catalyst* and *allotropy* testify to Berzelius' influence.[234]

The need for the establishment of a definite system of nomenclature for organic chemistry was recognized by the majority of chemists. Dumas, who envisaged such a nomenclature based on the type theory, considered that a complete reform was urgently needed and quite within the limits of possibility in 1840.[235] The question of how organic compounds were to be named was raised by Daubeny at a meeting of the British Association in 1851.[236] Although he recognized that a reform was necessary, Daubeny realized that only one of the 'great masters' of organic chemistry through his influence on his students would have the authority to establish such a system. He, nevertheless, suggested several principles which he considered should be incorporated in a reform. As many organic names were 'extended already to the limits of ready utterance', they should be limited to six or seven syllables. In the case of naturally-occurring compounds and those of unknown composition, he condoned the current habit of giving them a trivial name after their origin or after some characteristic property. Similar compounds should be denoted by similar suffixes, but Daubeny considered that old-established names should be kept. His suggestion that the Chemistry Section of the British Association should consider the whole subject and draw up 'certain definite rules' came to nothing.[237]

234. Ibid., *15* (1834), 243; *20* (1841), Part 2, 13.
235. *Comp. rend.*, *10* (1840), 170.
236. 'On the nomenclature of organic compounds', *Report of the British Association for the Advancement of Science, 1851*, pp. 124–32.
237. See, however, G. C. Foster, 'Suggestions towards a more systematic nomenclature for organic bodies', *Report of the British Association, 1857*, 45–7.

An important step towards a system of nomenclature as opposed to a collection of arbitrary names was the use of terms based on the number of atoms of the elements, particularly carbon, contained in a molecule of the compound concerned. The first system of names in which Latin or Greek numerals were used for this purpose was that of Berzelius, who had suggested such a scheme in his yearly report published in 1838. Gerhardt in his *Traité* (1853, 54) also made use of numbers with the purpose of emphasizing the position of a compound in the homologous series. Thus he referred to propylene as *tritylene* (τρίτος = third), and the radicals containing 4, 6, 7 carbon atoms were called *tetryl*,[238] *hexyl* and *heptyl* respectively after the respective Greek numerals. Gerhardt's suggestion was welcomed in Britain by Henry Watts, the editor of the *Dictionary of Chemistry*, who used some of Gerhardt's names as synonyms, e.g. 'caproylic or hexylic alcohol', 'oenolithic or heptylic alcohol'. For compounds containing more than five carbon atoms the systematic terms seemed preferable, but Watts remarked that such terms as methyl, ethyl and amyl were 'too much consecrated by use to be discarded',[239] an opinion which found support at the Geneva conference of 1892.

The name of the great German chemist A. W. Hofmann is perhaps most naturally linked in the history of organic chemistry with his important work on the amines. Yet it was not any of his work on organic compounds of nitrogen, but a suggestion on the nomenclature of aliphatic hydrocarbons and related radicals which entitles him to be considered as one of the founders of a systematic nomenclature of organic chemistry.[240] Hofmann's proposal's owed something to Laurent, as he was the first to admit. Hofmann suggested that saturated hydrocarbons should be denoted by terms ending in *-an*. The first three paraffins were thus to be called *Methan*, *Aethan* and *Propan* and the higher members of this series were given names based on the Latin numeral corresponding to the number of carbon atoms in the compound, e.g. $C_8H_{18} = Octan$. The groups CH_3, C_2H_5, C_3H_7 were to have parallel names with the suffix *-yl*, e.g.

238. Laurent had previously referred to butylene as *tetrène*, *Ann. chim. phys.*, [2], *61* (1836), 139, 144.
239. Watts, *Dictionary of Chemistry*, London, 1866, vol. i, pp. 97, 98.
240. *Berichte der königlichen Preuss. Akad. der Wissenschaften zu Berlin, 1865*, 652–4n. Hofmann's scheme was extended to cover aromatic compounds by Graebe (*Ann. Chem., 146* (1868), 71–2).

$C_{10}H_{21} = Decyl$. To denote a double bond (or a group with a valency of 2, as he considered it) the ending *-en* was to be used, e.g. $C_2H_4'' = Ethen$. Considering the atoms CH to form a tri-valent group, which he called *Methenyl*, Hofmann used the systematic name *Methenyltrichlorid*, for example, for chloroform $(CHCl_3)$. The way in which Hofmann, relying only on the concept of homologous series, extended this system indefinitely to groups with supposed valencies of 5, 6, etc. may seem rather strange to modern eyes. Yet much of Hofmann's scheme was to form a permanent part of the nomenclature of organic chemistry, although Greek numerals have been preferred to the Latin to denote the number of carbon atoms. Hofmann's suggestions were not accepted immediately, although they were welcomed by Henry Watts who considered that

a systematic nomenclature for the hydrocarbons, which are the fundamental compounds of organic chemistry, is a great desideratum and it would not perhaps be easy to devise a better system.[241]

Beilstein later made some use of Hofmann's scheme in his *Handbuch* (1880–3).

The Karlsruhe Congress

In September 1860 an event occurred which had a double impact on the unification of the nomenclature of organic chemistry. In that year a congress was held in Karlsruhe to discuss various problems of nomenclature and symbolism arising mainly from the lack of agreement on atomic weights.[242] The necessity for such an agreement had been felt for many years and it is noteworthy that the need for stability and standardization was sometimes felt to be even more important than arriving at true atomic weights. Laurent in 1853 had remarked

It is necessary that the proportional numbers of the simple bodies[243] ... should be fixed for a period of at least ten, twenty or thirty years and that all chemists should employ these numbers.[244]

241. Watts, *Dictionary of Chemistry, Supplement*, London, 1872, p. 705.

242. '*Compte rendu des séances du Congrès international des chimistes réuni à Carlsruhe le 3, 4 et 5 Septembre 1860*' (R. Anschutz, *August Kekulé*, Berlin, 1929, vol. i, appendix 8, pp. 671–88; see also ibid., pp. 183–209).

243. i.e. the equivalents or the atomic weights of the elements.

244. *Chemical Method*, trans. Odling, London, 1855, p. 7.

The original idea of the Congress was that of Kekulé who persuaded his friend Carl Weltzien of the *Technische Hochschule* of Karlsruhe to organise it. Weltzien had published a large systematic treatise on organic chemistry in which he had attempted to classify all organic compounds then known. In the preface[245] the author had remarked that one of the difficulties of his task was that of nomenclature. Although it was not difficult to ascribe a formula to a compound according to the radicals which it contained, a name for the compound was often lacking. Weltzien had provided a few new names in the course of the work in what he termed 'a modest attempt at preparing the way towards a more rational nomenclature'. Weltzien had written this only a year before the idea of a Congress was suggested.

In March 1860 Kekulé wrote to Weltzien, suggesting that the object of the conference should be an agreement firstly about which of the current theories was to be preferred and secondly about the standardizing of nomenclature and symbolism. Under the latter heading he proposed a uniform atomic notation and a separate equivalent notation.[246] They should also try to reach agreement on the writing of rational formulae, i.e. they should not discuss the various rational formulae then used for the same compound but rather how the symbols should be arranged to express any particular idea. Kekulé's final aim—'initiation of a systematic and rational nomenclature'—together with his lack of interest in the experimental determination of atomic weights give support to the contention that the primary concern of the conference was nomenclature and notation with particular reference to organic chemistry. This being the case, it may be regarded as the forerunner of the 1892 conference on nomenclature. Kekulé himself foresaw that the Karlsruhe Congress was not likely to make much progress with the direct question of nomenclature. This, he said, would be the task of a future commission consisting of only a few members.

245. Written in December 1858 (*Systematische Zusammenstellung der Organischen Verbindungen*, Brunswick, 1860; see also p. xxv).

246. Separate symbols for equivalents had been used by Gerhardt (*Comptes rendus de travaux chimiques par A. Laurent et C. Gerhardt*, 1849, i–viii), but Kekulé was even more convinced of the utility of such a scheme. In 1871 he devised a scheme in which equivalent weights were denoted by small letters, so that water, for example, was oH, methane cH, etc. (Art. '*Aequivalent*', *Neues Handwörterbuch der Chemie*, ed. H. von Fehling, Brunswick, 1871, vol. i, p. 88).

Having sounded the opinion of other chemists on the proposed conference, Weltzien, Kekulé and Wurtz then drew up a letter addressed to all European chemists in which the aims of the meeting were stated as follows:

Definition of important chemical ideas, such as those expressed by the words: atom, molecule, equivalent,[247] atomic,[248] basic. Examination of the question of equivalents and chemical formulae. Establishment of a uniform notation and nomenclature.

The meeting was arranged for 3 September 1860 and on this date about 140 chemists from nearly every country in Europe met in Karlsruhe. The opening address of the Congress was made by Weltzien and included the remark that,

It is obviously most desirable and necessary to give chemistry a more exact formulation so that it will be possible to teach it scientifically in a relatively short time.

At this first meeting Kekulé suggested that the questions to be submitted to the Congress should be drawn up by a sub-committee. The first question dealt with concerned the precise meaning to be given to the terms 'atom' and 'molecule', which were then used in various senses and even as synonyms. On the second and third days of the Congress the question of chemical nomenclature was discussed. The problem of chemical symbols was perhaps the most far-reaching of difficulties tackled. The same chemical symbol was then being used to denote quite different weights of a particular element. Cannizzaro, who spoke in favour of the system of atomic weights based on the theory of Avogadro and also adopted by Gerhardt, suggested

247. The term 'equivalent' was often used very loosely; for example, Gerhardt often spoke of 'equivalents' of chemical compounds when he was merely referring to comparable quantities. The vagueness of the term is illustrated by Gerhardt's statement: 'Atoms, equivalents and volumes are synonymous. . . . The densities of gases are proportional to their equivalents.' (*Ann. chim. phys.*, [3], *8* (1843), 245).

248. The terms 'monatomic', 'biatomic', 'triatomic', etc. had been introduced by Gaudin in 1833 (*Ann. chim. phys.*, [2], *52* (1833), 115–16) to denote the number of atoms in a molecule, and these terms were accepted and generally used with this meaning. Meanwhile, however, other chemists made use of the same terms to denote what we should now call the valency of a radical or element. Thus when Kekulé in 1858 announced his theory about the combining power of the carbon atom, he said that the latter was 'tetratomic' (*vieratomig oder vierbasisch*) (*Ann. Chem.*, *106* (1858), 153). The terms 'univalent', 'bivalent', etc. originated with Lothar Meyer, *Die modernen Theorien der Chemie*, Breslau, 1864, p. 67.

that the new doubled atomic weights (e.g. $C = 12$) should be distinguished by the barred symbols which had originally been used by Berzelius.

The members of the Congress dispersed without agreement being reached. Perhaps it would have been over-optimistic to expect all differences to be resolved in a few days, particularly as most of the members of the Congress had done little by way of preparation. Although many distinguished chemists attended the Congress, many others stayed away and these included Berthelot, Williamson and Hofmann.[249] Liebig did not come either, but he had written to Kekulé acknowledging the necessity for such a conference and he gave his support, even going so far as to subscribe in advance to any resolutions made by the Congress which included many of his former students. Among those chemists who did attend were six (including Baeyer, Beilstein and Friedel) who, some thirty years later sat on the commission appointed specifically to agree on a nomenclature for organic chemistry. The 1860 Congress not only raised the question of a standard nomenclature for organic chemistry but by its international character established a precedent invaluable for future discussions among chemists all over the world.

Other Steps towards a Reform of Nomenclature

Although the first general agreement on the nomenclature of organic chemistry had to wait till 1892, the need to standardize chemical terms had been felt earlier. The necessity of a uniform nomenclature and notation was particularly great in chemical journals and it is not surprising that the Geneva agreement was anticipated by the Chemical Society of London. In its *Journal* for 1879 rules were laid down for the guidance of contributors and abstractors by the council of the Chemical Society.[250] These general instructions included details related to organic nomenclature. Aliphatic hydrocarbons were to be called by the usual names: methane, ethylene, acetylene,[251] etc. and hydrocarbons with a long side chain were to be considered as derivatives of

249. Williamson and Hofmann had, however, signed the general invitation to the Congress. Hofmann had in any case changed to the revised system of atomic weights earlier in 1860.

250. *J. Chem. Soc., 35* (1879), *Transactions*, 276–81.

251. The term *acetylène* was introduced by Berthelot, *Comp. rend., 50* (1860), 805.

methane (e.g. $CH_3 . CH_2 . CH_2 . CH_3 =$ propyl methane; $CH_3 . CH . (CH_3)_2 =$ isopropyl methane). Derivatives of benzene did not have to be represented by means of the benzene hexagon, since the position of groups could easily be denoted by making use of the figures 1–6 to denote the positions shown in the figure:

The meaning of the prefixes *ortho-*, *meta-*, *para-* to denote the positions 1, 2; 1, 3; 1, 4 was re-stated. Naphthalene derivatives were to be denoted by similar numbers 1–4 and 1′–4′ in each of the two rings. Certain suffixes should be used exclusively to denote compounds of a particular class. The term 'ether' should be restricted to oxides of hydrocarbon groups and alcohols should be called mono-, di-, tri- hydric according to the number of OH groups. The terms sulphonic acid and sulphonamide were proposed for the appropriate compounds.

Three years later these instructions were published again,[252] the remarks on organic nomenclature being substantially the same as before. The publications committee of the Chemical Society hoped that their suggestions might have 'some influence in promoting uniformity of Nomenclature and Notation, especially in papers communicated to this Journal'.

Another sign of the necessity of a reform of nomenclature, although in a more limited way, was the publication of a paper in Germany by J. Denzel on the nomenclature of the halogen substitution products of ethane, ethylene and acetylene.[253] Denzel pointed out the equivocal nature of names based on the substance used to make a particular compound. Thus the same compound C_2Br_2 might be given three quite dissimilar names according to whether it had been prepared from ethane, ethylene or acetylene. The name 'ethylene', however, was also used (together with 'ethylidene'[254]) to distinguish pairs of

252. *J. Chem. Soc.*, *41* (1882), *Transactions*, 247–52.
253. *Ann. Chem.*, *195* (1879), 210–18.
254. The term *ethylidène* was proposed by Lieben to suggest the isomerism of the CH_3—$CH=$ group with ethylene (*Comp. rend.*, *46* (1858), 663).

isomers irrespective of whether they were actually prepared from ethylene; in this sense the name was merely used to denote symmetry. Denzel proposed a nomenclature which would avoid ambiguity and which could be applied to all polyhalogen derivatives of aliphatic hydrocarbons.

Authors were also naturally concerned about nomenclature. Beilstein's *Handbuch*, which became the most famous of all textbooks of organic chemistry and has been called 'the organic chemist's bible', was first published in two volumes in 1880–3. Beilstein set out clearly the nomenclature he intended to use. mentioning the systematically used suffixes, the use of standard abbreviations (e.g. s = symmetrical, m = meta, etc.) and the use of Greek letters to indicate the position of substituting groups. It is not surprising that the Geneva Congress of 1892 expressed the hope that its proposals might be used in the third edition of Beilstein's *Handbuch* which was then in course of preparation.

The Geneva Congress[255]

The first positive move towards an international agreement on the nomenclature of organic compounds was taken in 1889, the year of the great Paris exhibition. An International Congress of Chemistry was also held in Paris in the summer of that year. A special section was appointed to consider the unification of chemical nomenclature, but in the very limited time at their disposal, they could do little more than appoint an International Commission to study the subject more fully. The following chemists agreed to serve on the Commission:

Austria	Lieben		Friedel
Chile	Mourgues		Gautier
			Grimaux
France	Béhal		Jungfleisch
	Berthelot		Schützenberger
	Bouveault		
	Combes	*Germany*	Baeyer
	Fauconnier		Nölting

255. See H. E. Armstrong, *Nature*, 46 (1892), 56–9; A. Pictet, *Archives des Sciences Physiques et Naturelles*, 27 (1892), 485–520; F. Tiemann, *Berichte der deutschen chemischen Gesellschaft*, 26, 2 (1893), 1595–1631.

Great Britain	Armstrong	Spain	Calderon
Holland	Franchimont	Sweden	Cleve
Italy	Paterno	Switzerland	Graebe
Roumania	Istrati		
Russia	Alexejeff	Turkey	Bottkowski-Bey
	Beilstein	United States	Remsen

Each of the above was to send a detailed report to a per-manent sub-committee in Paris, consisting of seven members of the Commission resident in Paris under the presidency of Charles Friedel. This sub-committee met forty-five times al-together over a period of two years. In this time it summarized the reports sent to it and used these to draw up a provisional scheme for standardizing the nomenclature of organic chemistry. Its report was submitted to a further Congress which met in Geneva on Easter Monday 1892. This Congress, held within three years of the first, was less international in its composition and this time no representatives from the United States, Russia, Sweden, Spain, Turkey or Chile were present, although in-vitations had been issued to all members of the Commission listed above as well as to other prominent chemists. Great Britain was represented by Professors H. E. Armstrong and William Ramsay and Dr J. H. Gladstone. Among distinguished chemists from other countries who took part for the first time were Cannizzaro (Italy),[256] E. Fischer and Tiemann (Germany) and le Bel (France). Altogether there were thirty-six chemists present.[257] (See Plate 5.)

The first question which the conference had to deal with was the precise nature of the reform envisaged. The French sub-committee suggested that many compounds could be denoted by different names, each equally valid and each of use in teach-ing, when wishing to describe a particular aspect of the sub-stance concerned. Accordingly, no attempt should be made to find a single name for any compound, but rather the aim should

256. It will be remembered that Cannizzaro had been a prominent mem-ber of the Karlsruhe Congress of 1860.

257. The numbers from each country represented were: Austria (2), Belgium (1), France (11), Germany (5), Great Britain (3), Holland (1), Italy (4), Roumania (1), Switzerland (6). It may be noted that the number of the French chemists again greatly exceeded that of any other country. The comparatively large number of chemists from Switzerland was, of course, due to the location of the Congress.

be to agree on rules by which the various names applicable to a particular compound could be arrived at. The German chemists, led by Adolph von Baeyer did not agree. They considered the question not from the point of view of the teacher but from that of the research worker, who would only be confused by a multiplicity of names. The Germans therefore suggested that the aim of the Congress should be to agree on an official name for each compound. It was this latter view which after much discussion, won the day and the first resolution, agreed by a majority vote of the members of the Congress was as follows:

In addition to the usual name, every organic compound should be given an official name under which it may be found in indexes and dictionaries.

The Congress would like authors to adopt the custom of mentioning the official name in brackets in their publications after the name chosen by themselves.

It may be gathered from the terms of this resolution that the Congress did not consider it its business to reform the existing written or spoken language of organic chemistry, but rather to agree on terms based like formulae on chemical constitution and which would be used in dictionaries and be generally understood. For this reason considerations of brevity or euphony were not of primary importance. The sub-committee had suggested that any reformed nomenclature should be based on the principle of substitution. Each member of a group of compounds should have a name denoting its class together with suitable prefixes and suffixes to indicate the groups present in the molecule. Most important of all the proposals of the sub-committee, perhaps, was the decision to base names on chemical formulae. These principles were implicitly accepted by the Congress, although they could not, of course, be applied to compounds of unknown composition. A consideration of the nomenclature of such compounds was postponed indefinitely.

It was agreed that saturated hydrocarbons (i.e. the paraffins) should be known by names ending in *-ane*. The traditional names of the first four members of the series: methane, ethane, propane, butane were to be kept, but for members of the series containing more than four carbon atoms names derived from the Greek numerals would be used, e.g. *pentane, hexane*, etc. In the case of hydrocarbons with side-chains two different systems

could be used. The compound
$$CH_3-CH-CH_3$$
$$| \atop CH_3$$
, for example, could be given a name indicating that it was an isomer of normal butane or, as was suggested by Lieben (Austria), a name based on the longest straight chain with a substituted group (i.e. 'methyl propane'). The latter suggestion was accepted and it may be said to have had the advantage of being applicable to aromatic hydrocarbons, which it analysed into a nucleus and a side chain. For unsaturated hydrocarbons the endings *-ene* (*-diene*, etc.) and *-ine* were to be used to indicate double and triple bonds respectively. It was, appropriately enough,[258] Baeyer who suggested this and hence the official names for olefiant gas and acetylene became *ethene* and *ethine* respectively. A nomenclature for closed-chain hydrocarbons was proposed by Armstrong. It involved the use of the prefix *cyclo-*. Thus what had been called 'hexamethylene' (C_6H_{12}) was to be known as *cyclohexane*. In all these cases the position of a substituting group was to be indicated by an appropriate number.

Having agreed on the nomenclature of hydrocarbons, the Congress then discussed the nomenclature of other groups of compounds which were regarded as derived from these. Perhaps an extreme case of this nomenclature was that which Beilstein had forwarded to the sub-committee. This was the proposal that ethers should be given names related to the corresponding hydrocarbons together with the particle *-oxy-*. This suggestion, which was provisionally accepted by the Congress, meant that common ether received the official name *ethane-oxy-ethane*.

Of more general importance was the nomenclature of the acids. The Congress was faced with two alternative suggestions, both consistent with the principles already accepted by it and each with certain advantages and disadvantages. The majority of the sub-committee considered that acids should be named after the hydrocarbon containing the same number of carbon atoms with the addition of the suffix *-oic*, *-dioic*, etc. according

258. In view of Baeyer's theory to explain the instability of these compounds (*Berichte der deutschen chemischen Gesellschaft*, *18* (1885), 2278). The alternative proposal by the sub-committee was that published by Hofmann in 1865 in which the supposed valency of groups rather than their structure was considered.

PLATE 5. CHEMISTS AT THE GENEVA CONGRESS, 1892. *Front row* (L. to R.): Barbier (Lyons), Paterno (Palermo), Graebe (Geneva), von Baeyer (Munich), Cannizzaro (Rome), Friedel (Paris), Lieben (Vienna), Gladstone (London), Cosso (Turin), Ramsay (London). *Second row*: Haller (Nancy), Cazeneuve (Lyons), Fischer (Würzburg), Hanriot (Paris), Le Bel (Paris), von Meyer (Leipzig), Istrati (Bucharest), Tiemann (Berlin), Bouveault (Paris), Monnier (Geneva), [Olivier]. *Third row*: Armstrong (London), Nietzki (Basle), Maquenne (Paris), Delacre (Ghent), Béhal (Paris), Arnaud (Paris), Hantsch (Zurich), Combes (Paris), Pictet (Geneva), Skraup (Graz), Guye (Geneva), [Reverdin], Noelting (Mulhouse), Fileti (Turin), Franchimont (Leyden). *Back*: Participants not on the official list are shown in brackets.

to the basicity of the acid. The French chemist Bouveault, however, thought it better to consider the carboxyl group as a substituting group, thus relating the acid to a hydrocarbon containing one, two or three carbon atoms less. According to the former proposal, for example, succinic acid, $\begin{array}{l} CH_2COOH \\ | \\ CH_2COOH \end{array}$, would be called 'butanedioic acid, and according to the second idea, 'ethanedicarbonic acid 1, 2'. Taking a simple example of a name constructed according to the second system, 'methane carbonic acid' for acetic acid might be tolerated in what was, after all, only an official language and moreover, Bouveault's idea (unlike the other) could be applied equally to acids of the aliphatic and aromatic series. When the matter was put to the vote, however, it was the sub-committee's suggestion which was adopted by 24 votes to 10 with the restriction that the method was only to be applied to aliphatic acids. The German chemist Graebe, then working in Geneva, supported by several other chemists, suggested that they should continue to use the names formic, acetic, propionic and butyric acids. It was argued that the traditional names of the first four hydrocarbons had been accepted and the retention of the common names for the acids would make it easier to change from the old to the proposed new system. This proposal was, however, rejected by the Congress.

In order to distinguish various classes of compounds the Congress agreed to make use of appropriate suffixes. The ending *-al*, for example, was to denote an aldehyde, *-one* a ketone and *-ol* an alcohol or phenol. In some instances, however, a different system was adopted for aliphatic and aromatic compounds, e.g. aliphatic compounds containing the -CN group were to be denoted by the suffix *-nitrile*, whereas corresponding compounds in the aromatic series were to be distinguished by the prefix *cyano-*.

Little time had been left to consider aromatic compounds. It was, nevertheless, possible to establish one or two simple principles. Firstly it was agreed to use the names *benzene* and *naphthalene*. These names were commonly in use in the English language, but German chemists had been in the habit of writing *Benzol*,[259] whilst in France *benzine* was equally misleading in its

259. Armstrong had criticized the names *Benzol* and *Naphtalin* in common use among German chemists (*Berichte der deutschen chemischen Gesellschaft*, 15 (1882), 200n.).

suffix. The names of the radicals *phenyl* and *naphthyl* (giving the hydroxy-compounds *phenol* and *naphthol*) had been suggested to the sub-committee by Graebe, but the Congress did not have time to consider this proposal.

Of fundamental importance to aromatic chemistry was the nomenclature of poly-substituted derivatives of benzene. The two alternative methods of naming such compounds were: (i) the use of the prefixes *ortho-*, *meta-* and *para-* with the meanings now established, (ii) the use of the numerals 1–6 to denote the relative positions of the substituting groups. The first method, excellent when used for disubstituted derivatives, was applied with the greatest difficulty to compounds containing more than two substituting groups. Combes, the French member of the sub-committee who had examined this question in detail, therefore decided that only the second method was acceptable. Yet even here there was a difficulty—by taking the substituting groups in a tri-substituted derivative of benzene in a different order, it was possible to write its name in six different ways according to which group was given the number 1 and whether the other groups were numbered in a clockwise or anticlockwise direction. To standardize the nomenclature Combes therefore suggested that in any such compound the number 1 should be given to that substituting group in which the atom linked directly to the nucleus had the least atomic weight. Other substituting groups would be named successively in order of increasing atomic weight of the atom linked directly to the nucleus. All these suggestions were accepted by the Congress, as was one by Graebe that in the case of two benzene nuclei linked either as in naphthalene or as in diphenyl the numbers of the substituting groups in the second nucleus should be marked with a dash. This was, of course, already the practice in the *Journal of the Chemical Society*. At this point Armstrong brought forward a scheme for the nomenclature of heterocyclic compounds but it was disputed by Bouveault who, as a member of the sub-committee, had drawn up an alternative scheme. Lack of time prevented any decisions being reached on this subject by the Congress.[260]

260. Proposals for the nomenclature of the heterocyclic compounds were made by Armstrong in *Proceedings of the Chemical Society*, 8 (1892), 127–30. Armstrong suggested replacing the trivial names by systematic names, e.g. furfuran and indol would become *oxypentaphene* and *phenazopentaphene* respectively.

In seeking an appraisal of the Geneva Congress it is difficult not to make certain criticisms. Two criticisms which might apply to many conferences are that the members were insufficiently prepared for their task and that the time available was too limited. As regards the first point, the members of the Congress were only presented with the report of the French sub-committee on the morning of their first meeting and had not adequate time to study the proposals before discussion of them began. As it is easier to see the faults of a proposed system than to think at short notice of constructive alternatives, it probably happened that more than one resolution was accepted by the Congress, not because the members were completely satisfied with it, but because no better alternative could be found. The report of the sub-committee was, however, regarded by members of the Congress as little more than a basis for discussion and no-one attempted to impose its decisions on the Congress. As regards the second criticism, that of time, it is quite clear that this was a severe limitation to the achievements of the Geneva Congress. The first business meeting of the Congress took place on Tuesday, 20 April 1892 and the final meeting was held on the Friday morning of the same week. The achievement of the Congress was limited particularly by the fact that it was only at its last meeting that the subject of the nomenclature of aromatic compounds was broached. Aromatic chemistry was therefore treated in a hurried and necessarily superficial way.

The twentieth century

At the end of the nineteenth century it was generally agreed that despite the imperfections of the Geneva Congress it had succeeded in laying the foundations of a nomenclature for a large part of organic chemistry, but it remained for a future congress to carry the process to completion. Meanwhile, however, organic chemistry continued to expand and in the early twentieth century it became increasingly difficult to extend the Geneva system to cover more complex compounds and even entirely new classes of compounds which had been discovered. A further international agreement on nomenclature was therefore doubly necessary. In 1922, on the suggestion of Sir William Pope, a committee composed of delegates from the editorial staffs' of the leading chemical journals was appointed by the newly-founded International Union of Chemistry to look further into problems of nomenclature in organic chemistry and a new scheme of nomenclature was drawn up and finally approved at Liège in 1930.[261] The extent of even this reform was limited, however, by the first rule adopted that 'as little change as possible is to be made in terminology universally accepted'. A limitation in another direction was imposed by the exclusion from consideration of compounds like proteins, vitamins and hormones which were considered to come under the heading of biochemistry. The nomenclature of several such important natural substances was already in the hands of a committee on biochemical nomenclature. Nevertheless a valuable contribution was made towards standardizing the whole nomenclature of organic chemistry.

Yet the independent attitude of individual chemists and of several national bodies has made the achievement of a uniform nomenclature only an imperfectly-attained goal. In the English language there is still lack of uniformity of nomenclature in American and British publications.[262] Furthermore, in the case of certain classes of compounds, including cyclic compounds, chemists have been forced to make use of trivial names. It is a sad conclusion to the endeavours of generations of chemists if it is true, as one writer has said, 'that systematic nomenclature is reaching breaking point and that human ingenuity can scarcely cope with it.'[263]

261. See *J. Chem. Soc.*, *1931*, 1, 1607–16 also '*1936*, 2, 1067–78.
262. Particularly in the numbering of various ring systems.
263. A. D. Mitchell, *British Chemical Nomenclature*, London, 1948, p. 37.

Bibliography

I. BOOKS

ADANSON, M., Familles des plantes, 2 vols., Paris, 1763.

ADET, P. A., Leçons élémentaires de chimie, Paris, 1804.

AGRICOLA, G., De ortu et causis subterraneorum, Lib. V. . . .
Interpretatio Germanica vocum rei metallica, Basle, 1558.
De re metallica, Basle, 1556.
—trans. Hoover, London, 1912.

AGRIPPA, H. C., De occulta philosophia, Argentorati, 1531.

AIKIN, A. and C. R., A Dictionary of Chemistry and Mineralogy, 2 vols.,
London, 1807.

ALBERTUS MAGNUS (attrib.) Libellus de Alchimia, trans. Sister V.
Heines, Berkeley & Los Angeles, 1958.

ALBINEUS, N. Bibliotheca Chemica Contracta, Geneva, 1653.

ANSCHÜTZ, R., August Kekulé, 2 vols., Berlin, 1929.

ARISTOTLE, On Marvellous Things Heard (Minor Works), Loeb edn.,
London, 1936.

PSEUDO ARISTOTLE, Meteorologia, Book IV, ed. Düring, Göteborg,
1944.

ARMITAGE, F. P., A History of Chemistry, London, 1920.

ATWOOD, M.A., A Suggestive Inquiry into the Hermetic Mystery, London,
1850.

Auriferae Artis quam Chemiam vocant, Basle, 1572.

AVICENNA (Husain ibn 'Abd Allah or Ibn Sīnā) Avicennae de congela-
tione et conglutinatione lapidum, being sections of the Kitâb al-Shifâ,
trans. with notes E. J. Holmyard & D. C. Mandeville, Paris,
1927.
De Anima in arte Alchemicae in Artis Chemicae Principes, Basle, 1572.

BACON, ROGER, De mirabili potestate artis et naturae, Paris, 1542.
Opus Tertium, ed. J. S. Brewster, London, 1859.
Part of the Opus Tertium of Roger Bacon, ed. A. G. Little, Aberdeen,
1912.

BACON, ROGER, (attrib.) De Arte Chymiae Scripta, cui accesserunt
opuscula alia eiusdem Authoris, Frankfurt, 1603.

BAILEY, D. and K. C. An Etymological Dictionary of Chemistry and
Mineralogy, London, 1929.

BAILEY, K. C. *The Elder Pliny's Chapters on Chemical Subjects*, 2 vols., London, 1932.

BARBA, A. A., *El Arte de los Metales*, trans. R. E. Douglass & E. P. Mathewson, New York, 1923.

BARMA, H. à, *Saturnia regna*, Paris, 1657.

—trans. *Le Règne de Saturne*, Paris, 1780.

BARNER, J., *Chymia Philosophica*, Nuremberg, 1689.

BARROW, J. *Dictionarium Medicum Universale*, London, 1749.

BARTHOLOMEUS ANGLICUS *De Genuinis Rerum Coelestium, Terrestrium et Inferarum Proprietatibus, Libri XVIII . . . . cui accessit Liber XIX de variarum accidentibus*, Frankfurt, 1650.

'BASILIUS VALENTINUS' *Haliographia*, Bononiae, 1644.

Letztes Testament, Strasburg, 1645.

Triumph Wagen Antimonii, Leipzig, 1604.

BATE, G., *Pharmacopoeia Bateana*, 2nd edn., London, 1691.

BAUHINUS, C., *Phytopinax seu enumeratio plantarum*, Basle, 1596.

Pinax theatri botanici . . . . Opus 40 Annorum, Basle, 1623.

BAUMÉ, A., *Chymie expérimentale et raisonnée*, 3 vols., Paris, 1773.

Élémens de Pharmacie, Paris, 1762.

—8th edn., Paris, 1797.

Manuel de Chymie, 2nd edn., Paris, 1765.

Opuscules Chimiques, Paris, 1798.

BECHER, J. J., *Chymischer Glücks Hafen oder Grosse Chymische Concordanz*, Frankfurt, 1682.

Physica Subterranea, Leipzig, 1703.

Tripus Hermeticus Fatidicus, Pandens Oracula Chymica, Frankfurt, 1689.

BECKMANN, J., *A History of Inventions*, trans. W. Johnston, 4th edn., 2 vols., London, 1846.

BEDDOES, T., *Contributions to Physical and Medical Knowledge*, Bristol, 1799.

BEGUIN, J., *Élémens de Chymie*, Paris, 1615.

Tyrocinium Chymicum, ed. J. Hartmann—Hartmann, *Opera Omnia*, vol. 3, Frankfurt, 1690.

Tyrocinium Chymicum, trans. Russell, London, 1669.

BEILSTEIN, F. C., *Handbuch der organischen Chemie*, 1st edn., 2 vols., Hamburg & Leipzig, 1880-3.

—3rd edn., 4 vols., Hamburg & Leipzig, 1893-9.

BERGBÜCHLEIN, *Bergbüchlein*, Worms, 1518.

Bergwerk—und Probierbüchlein, trans. A. G. Sisco & C. S. Smith, New York, 1949.

BERGMAN, T. O., *A Dissertation on Elective Attractions*, trans. [T. Beddoes], London, 1785.

Traité des affinités chymiques ou attractions électives, trad., Paris, 1788.

Dissertatio de Magnesia Alba sistit C. Norell, Uppsala, 1775.

Opuscula Physica et Chemica, 6 vols., Uppsala, 1779-90.

Physical and Chemical Essays, trans. E. Cullen, 2 vols., London, 1784.
—another edn., 3 vols., Edinburgh, 1788, 91.
Opuscules Chymiques et Physiques, trans. Guyton, 2 vols., Dijon, 1780, 85.
Kleine Physische und Chemische Werke, 6 vols., Frankfurt, 1782–90.
Sciagraphia regni mineralis, Lipsiae et Dessaviae, 1782.
Outlines of mineralogy, trans. W. Withering, Birmingham, 1783.
Manuel de Minéralogiste, trad. Mongez, Paris, 1784.
—2nd edn., 'considérablement augmentée par J. C. De La Métherie', 2 vols., Paris, 1792.
BERTHELOT, P. E. M., *Chimie organique fondée sur la synthèse*, 2 vols., Paris, 1860.
Collections des anciens alchimistes grecs, 3 parts, Paris, 1887–8.
La Chimie au moyen-âge, 3 vols., Paris, 1893.
Introduction à L'Étude de la chimie des anciens et du moyen-âge, Paris, 1889.
Les Origines de l'Alchimie, Paris, 1885.
La Révolution Chimique, Lavoisier, Paris, 1890.
BERZELIUS, J. J., *Jöns Jacob Berzelius, Autobiographical notes* published by the Royal Swedish Academy of Sciences through H. G. Söderbaum, trans. O. Larsell, Baltimore, 1934.
Bref, ed H. G. Söderbaum, 15 parts, Uppsala, 1912–35.
Berzelius und Liebig. Ihre Briefe von 1831–1845, ed. J. Carrière, Munich & Leipzig, 1893.
An Essay on Chemical Nomenclature, prefixed to the treatise on Chemistry by J. J. Berzelius, trans. A. D. Bache, Philadelphia, 1833?
Essai sur la théorie des proportions chimiques et sur l'influence chimique de l'électricité, ... Traduit... sous les yeux de l'auteur, Paris, 1819.
—2nd edn., Paris, 1835.
Försök att genom användandet af den electrokemiska theorien och de kemiska proportionernz, grundlägga ett vettenskapligt system för mineralogien, Stockholm, 1814.
An attempt to establish a pure scientific system of mineralogy by the application of the electrochemical theory and the chemical proportions, trans. J. Black, London, 1814.
Jahresbericht über die Fortschritte der physichen Wissenschaften—see Periodicals.
Lärbok i kemien, 2nd edn., 6 vols., Stockholm, 1817–30.
Lehrbuch der Chemie, trans. Wöhler, 4 vols., Dresden, 1825–31.
—3rd edn., 10 vols., Dresden & Leipzig, 1833–41.
Traité de Chimie, trans. Jourdan (tom. 2–8 by Esslinger), 8 vols., Paris, 1829–33.
Tabell, som utvisar vigten af större delen vid den oorganiska kemiens studium märkvärdiga atomer, jemte deras sammansättning, räknad i procent. Bihang till Tredje Delen af Lärboken i kemien, Stockholm, 1818.

The use of the Blowpipe in Chemical Analysis and in the Examination of Minerals, trans. J. G. Children, London, 1822.

BEUDANT, F. S., *Traité élémentaire de minéralogie*, Paris, 1824.
— 2nd edn., 2 vols., Paris, 1830, 32.

BIRCH, T., *History of the Royal Society*, 4 vols., London, 1756–7.

BIRINGUCCIO, V., *The Pirotechnia of Vanoccio Biringuccio*, trans. C. S. Smith and M. T. Gnudi, New York, 1942.

BLACK, J., *Experiments upon Magnesia Alba, Quicklime and some other alcaline substances* (1756)—Alembic Club Reprint No. 1, Edinburgh, 1910.

Lectures on the Elements of Chemistry, ed. J. Robison, 2 vols., Edinburgh, 1803.

BOEHME, J., *Concerning the three principles of the Divine Essence*, trans. J. Sparrow, London, 1910.

BOERHAAVE, H., *Elementa Chemiae*, 2 vols., Leyden, 1732.
Elements of Chemistry, trans. Dallowe, 2 vols., London, 1735.

BONNOT DE CONDILLAC, E., *Oeuvres Complètes*, 23 vols., Paris, 1798.

BORN, I. VON., *Index Fossilium*, 2 parts, Prague, 1772, 75.

BORRICHIUS, O., *Hermetis, Aegyptiorum et chemicorum sapientia . . . vindicata*, Hafniae, 1674.

BOSTOCK, J., *Remarks on the nomenclature of the New London Pharmacopoeia*, Liverpool, 1810.

BOUILLON LAGRANGE, E. J. B., *Manuel d'un Cours de Chimie*, 1st edn., 2 vols., Paris, 1799.
— 5th edn., 3 vols., Paris, 1812.

BOWMAN, J. E., *An Introduction to Practical Chemistry*, London, 1848.

BOYLE, R., *Experiments touching colour*, London, 1664.
Experiments, Notes, etc. about the Mechanical Origine or Production of divers particular Qualities . . . together with some reflections upon the hypothesis of alcali and acidum, London, 1676.
The Philosophical Works of the Hon. R. Boyle, ed. P. Shaw, 3 vols., London, 1725.
The Sceptical Chymist (Everyman edn.), London, 1911.
The Works of the Hon. Robert Boyle, ed. T. Birch, 5 vols., London, 1744.

BRANDE, W. T., *A Manual of Chemistry*, 4th edn., London, 1836.
— 5th edn., London, 1841.

BRASAVOLA, A. M., *Examen omnium simplicium medicamentorum*, Lugdini, 1537.

BRONGNIART, A. L., *Tableau analytique des combinaisons et des décompositions de différentes substances*, Paris, 1778.

BROUAULT, J. *Abrégé de l'Astronomie Inférieure*, Paris, 1644.

BROWN, J. C., *A History of Chemistry*, 2nd edn., London, 1920.

BRUGNATELLI, L., *Elementi di Chimica*, 3 vols., Pavia, 1795-8.
Avvertimento sopra la nomenclatura chimica from *Annali di Chimica*, *18*(1800?)
BUCQUET, J. B. M., *Introduction à l'étude des corps naturels tirés du règne minéral*, 2 vols., Paris, 1771.
Introduction à l'étude des corps naturels tirés du règne végétal, 2 vols., Paris, 1773.
BUDGE, SIR E. A. W., *An Egyptian Hieroglyphic Dictionary*, 2 vols., London, 1920.
BUFFON, LE CLERC, Conte de Buffon, *Correspondence Inédite de Buffon*, ed. H. N. de Buffon, 2 vols., Paris, 1860.
Histoire Naturelle des Minéraux, 5 vols., Paris, 1783-8.
Histoire Naturelle, Supplément, 7 vols., Paris 1774-89.
BUGGE, G. (ed.) *Das Buch der Grossen Chemiker*, 2 vols., Berlin, 1929, 30.
BUNSEN, C. C. J., *Egypt's Place in Universal History*, 2nd edn., 5 vols., London, 1867.

CADET, C. -L., *Dictionnaire de Chymie*, 4 vols., Paris, 1803.
CAPPELLI, A., *Dizionario di Abbreviature Latine ed Italiana*, 5th edn., Milan, 1954.
CARBONELLI, G., *Sulle Fonti Storiche della Chimica e dell' Alchimia in Italia*, Rome, 1925.
CAVALLO, T., *Essay on the Medicinal Properties of Factitious Airs*, London, 1798.
A Treatise on the Nature and Properties of Air, London, 1781.
CAVEN, R. M. and CRANSTON, J. A., *Symbols and Formulae in Chemistry*, London and Glasgow, 1928.
CAVENDISH, H., *The Scientific Papers of the Hon. Henry Cavendish*, vol. 2 ed. Sir E. Thorpe, Cambridge, 1921.
CAVENTOU, J. B., *Nouvelle nomenclature chimique d'après la classification adoptée par M. Thenard*, 2nd edn., Paris, 1825.
CHAPTAL, J. A. *Élémens de Chimie*, 3 vols., Montpellier, 1790.
CHAUCER, G., *The Chanouns Yemannes Tale—Works*, ed. Skeat, 2nd edn., Oxford, 1900.
CHENEVIX, R., *Remarks upon Chemical Nomenclature*, London, 1802.
CHESTER, A. H., *A Dictionary of the Names of Minerals*, New York, 1896.
CHEVREUL, M. E., *Recherches chimiques sur les corps gras d'origine animale*, Paris, 1823.
CLARKE, W., *The Natural History of Nitre*, London, 1670.
COELHO DE SEABRA SILVA TELLES, V., *Elementos de Chimica*, 2 parts, Coimbra, 1788, 90.
COLEBY, L. J. M., *The Chemical Studies of P. J. Macquer*, London, 1938

CONDORCET, J. M. CARITAT DE, *Esquisse d'un tableau historique des progrès de l'esprit humain*, [Paris], 1795.

CONTI, NATALE, *Mythologiae, sive Explicationum Fabularum*, Venice, 1568.

CORDUS, V., *Dispensatorium Pharmacorum omnium tam Galenicorum quam chymicorum*, 4th edn., Nuremberg, 1666.

In hoc volumine continentur Valerii Cordi Simesusii Annotationes in Pedacii Dioscoridis . . . de Medica materia libros V . . . De artificiosis extractionibus liber . . . Omnia summo studio atque industria . . . Conri Gesneri . . . collecta, Argentorati, 1561.

Critical Examination of the first part of Lavoisier's Elements of Chemistry, London, 1797.

CROLLIUS, O., *Basilica Chymica . . . De Signaturis*, Frankfurt, 1609.

CRONSTEDT, A. F., *Försök til mineralogie*, Stockholm, 1758.

An Essay towards a System of Mineralogy, trans. G. von Engenstrom . . . with notes by E. Mendes da Costa, London, 1770.

DALTON, J., *A New System of Chemical Philosophy*, vol. i, part i, Manchester, 1808; part ii, Manchester, 1810; vol. 2, part i, London, 1827.

—2nd edn., part i, London, 1842.

On a new and easy way of analysing sugar, Manchester, 1840.

On the Phosphates and Arsenates, Manchester, 1840.

DARMSTAEDTER, E., *Die Alchimie des Geber*, Berlin, 1922.

DAUBENY, C., *An Introduction to the Atomic Theory*, Oxford, 1831.

—2nd edn., Oxford, 1850.

DAUMAS, M., *Lavoisier, théoricien et expérimentateur*, Paris, 1955.

DAVY, SIR H., *Collected Works*, 9 vols., London, 1839–40.

Elements of Chemical Philosophy, London, 1812.

A Syllabus of a Course of Lectures on Chemistry delivered at the Royal Institution of Great Britain, London, 1802.

DEMACHY, J. F., *Instituts de Chymie*, 2 vols., Paris, 1766.

Recueil de dissertations physico-chimiques, Amsterdam & Paris, 1774.

DESCARTES, R., *Discourse on Method*, trans. (Everyman edn.), London, 1912.

DICKSON, S., *An Essay on Chemical Nomenclature, in which are comprised observations on the same subject by Richard Kirwan*, London, 1796.

DICTIONNAIRE HERMETIQUE par un Amateur de la Science, Paris, 1695.

DIDEROT, D. and D'ALEMBERT, *Encyclopédie*, 17 vols., Geneva, Paris, Neufchastel, 1754–76.

—*Supplément*, 4 vols., Amsterdam, 1776–7.

DIERGART, P. (ed.), *Beiträge aus der Geschichte der Chemie dem Gedächtnis von G. W. A. Kahlbaum*, Leipzig & Vienna, 1909.

DIOSCORIDES, *Herbal,* ed. R. T. Gunther, Oxford, 1934.
DOBBIN, L., *Occasional Fragments of Chemical History,* Edinburgh, 1942.
DORN, G., *Dictionarium Paracelsi,* Frankfurt, 1583.
DOSSIE, R., *The elaboratory laid open, or the secrets of modern chemistry and pharmacy revealed,* London, 1758.
DUMAS, J.-B., *Leçons sur la philosophie chimique,* Paris, 1837.
Traité de Chimie, 8 vols., Paris, 1828–46.
DURANDE, J. F., *Notions Élémentaires de Botanique,* Dijon, 1781.
DUVEEN, D. and KLICKSTEIN, H. S., *Bibliography of the Works of A. L. Lavoisier,* London, 1954.

ENCYCLOPAEDIA BRITANNICA, 3rd edn., 18 vols., Edinburgh, 1791, etc.
ENCYCLOPAEDIA OF ISLAM, ed. M.Th. Houtsma & M. Seligsohn, 5 vols., Leyden & London, 1908–38.
ENCYCLOPÉDIE MÉTHODIQUE, *Chymie, Pharmacie et Métallurgie,* 6 vols., Paris, 1786 etc.
—*Botanique,* 13 vols., Paris, 1789, etc.
ERXLEBEN, J. C. P., *Anfangsgründe der Chemie,* Göttingen, 1775.
ETTMUELLER, M., *Chimia rationalis ac experimentalis curiosa,* Leyden, 1684.
—trans. *Nouvelle Chymie Raisonée,* Lyon, 1693.

FARBER, E., *The Evolution of Chemistry,* New York, 1952.
FERGUSON, J., *Bibliotheca Chemica,* 2 vols., Glasgow, 1906.
FINAR, I. L., *Organic Chemistry,* Vol. 1, The Fundamental Principles, 3rd edn., London, 1959.
FLAMEL, N.—*His exposition of the hieroglyphical figures which he caused to be painted upon an arch in St. Innocents Church Yard in Paris by Eirenaeus Orandus,* London, 1624, reprinted with introduction by W. W. Westcott, London, 1889.
FLUDD, R., *Medicina Catholica,* 5 parts, Frankfurt, 1629–31.
FORBES, R. J., *Metallurgy in Antiquity,* London, 1950.
Short History of the Art of Distillation, Leyden, 1948.
FOURCROY, A. F. DE, *Leçons élémentaires d'histoire naturelle et de chimie,* 2 vols., Paris, 1782.
Éléments d'histoire naturelle et de chimie; Seconde édition des Leçons élémentaires sur ces deux sciences, publiées en 1782, 4 vols., Paris, 1786.
—trans. *Elements of natural history and of chemistry,* 4 vols., London, 1788.
Supplement to the Elements of natural history and chemistry.... Carefully extracted from the edition of 1789 and adapted to the English, London, 1789.
Elements of natural history and chemistry ... with an alphabetical comparitive view of the ancient and modern names of chemical substances, 3 vols., London, 1790.

Elements of chemistry and natural history, 4th edn., 4 vols., London, 1796.

Philosophie chimique, 1st edn., Paris, 1792.
—3rd edn., Paris, 1806.

Mémoires de Chimie, Paris, 1784.

Système des connaissances chimiques, 4to edn., 6 vols., Paris, 1801–2.

FOWNES, W., *Manual of elementary chemistry*, 1st edn., London, 1844.
—6th edn., London, 1856.
—10th edn., London, 1868.
—13th edn., London, 1883.

FRANKLAND, E., *Lecture Notes for Chemical Students*, London, 1866.

FREITAG, J., *Aurora Medicorum Galeno-Chymicorum*, Frankfurt, 1630.

GADOLIN, J., *Animadversiones in novam nomenclaturae chemicae methodum*, Aboae, Nov. 1788.

GANZENMUELLER, W., *Die Alchimie im Mittelalter*, Paderborn, 1938.

GARLANDIA, J. DE, *De Alchimia—Laurentii Venturae de ratione conficiendi Lapidis philosophico . . . huic accesserunt eiusdem Argumenti Joan. Garlandii liber unus*, Basle, 1571.

GAY-LUSSAC, J. L., *Cours de chimie*, 2 vols., Brussels, 1829.

GAY-LUSSAC, J. L., and THENARD, L. J., *Recherches physico-chimiques*, 2 vols., Paris, 1811.

GEBER, *Alchemiae Gebri Arabis*, Berne, 1545.
The Works of Geber, Englished by Richard Russell, 1678, new edn., E. J. Holmyard, London, 1928.

GEHLER, J. S. T., *Physikalisches Wörterbuch*, 4 vols., Leipzig, 1787–91.

GELLERT, C. E., *Anfangsgründe zur metallurgischen Chymie*, 2nd edn., Leipzig, 1776.
Chimie métallurgique, trans., 2 vols., Paris, 1758.

GERHARDT, C., *Précis de chimie organique*, Paris, 1844, 45.
Traité de chimie organique, 4 vols., Paris, 1853–6.

GESSMANN, G. W., *Die Geheimsymbole der Chemie und Medicin des Mittelalters*, Graz, 1899.

GIRTANNER, C., *Neue Chemische Nomenklatur für die Deutsche Sprache*, Berlin, 1791.

GLASER, C., *The Compleat Chymist*, trans., London, 1677.

GLAUBER, J. R., *Arca Thesauris Opulenta sive Appendix Generalis Omnium Librorum hactenus editorum*, Amsterdam, 1660.
Furni novi philosophici, Amsterdam, 1646–9.
Miraculi Mundi Ander Theil, Amsterdam, 1660.
Tractatus de Natura Salium, Amsterdam, 1658.
Von den Dreyen Anfangen der Metallen, Amsterdam, 1666.
Works, trans. C. Packe, London, 1689.

GMELIN, L., *Handbuch der Chemie*, 4th edn., 10 vols., Heidelberg, 1843–70.

GOETTLING, J. F. A., *Handbuch der theoretischen und praktischen Chemie*, 3 parts, Jena, 1798–1800.

GOLITSUIN, D. A., *Recueil de noms . . . apropriés en minéralogie*, Brunswick, 1801.

GOMME, A. A., *Patents of Invention*, London, 1946.

GRAEBE, C., *Geschichte der organischen Chemie*, vol. i, Berlin, 1920.

GRATACOLLE, W., *The Names of the Philosopher's Stone* in H. P., *Five Treatises of the Philosopher's Stone*, London, 1652.

GREN, F. A. C., *Principles of Modern Chemistry*, 2 vols., London, 1800. *Systematisches Handbuch der gesammten Chemie*, Halle, 1794–6.

GRIER, J., *A History of Pharmacy*, London, 1937.

GRILLOT DE GIVRY, E. A., *Witchcraft, Magic and Alchemy*, trans., London, 1931.

GRIMAUX, E., *Lavoisier*, Paris, 1888.

GRIMAUX, E. and GERHARDT, C. JUNIOR, *Charles Gerhardt, sa vie, son oeuvre, sa correspondance*, Paris, 1900.

GUETTARD, J. E. and MONNET, A. G., *Atlas et description minéralogique de la France*, Paris, 1780.

GUIEBERTUS, N., *De interitu alchemiae*, Tulli, 1614.

GUGLIEMINI, G. D., *De Salibus*, Venice, 1705.

GUYTON DE MORVEAU, L. B., H. MARCET and J. F. DURANDE, *Élémens de Chymie*, 3 vols., Dijon, 1777, 78.

GUYTON DE MORVEAU, L. B., LAVOISIER, BERTHOLLET and FOURCROY *Méthode de nomenclature chimique . . . on y a joint un nouveau système de caractères chimiques adaptés a cette nomenclature par MM. Hassenfratz et Adet*, Paris, 1787.
  —*Method of chymical nomenclature . . . . Translated from the French, and the New Chymical Names adapted to the genius of the English language*, by James St. John, M.D., London, 1788.
  —*Methode der chemischen Nomenklatur für das antiphlogistische System*, trans. Meidinger, Vienna, 1793.

HALL, C. R., *A Scientist in the early republic: S. L. Mitchill*, New York, 1934.

HANIN, M. L., *Vocabulaire médical . . . suivi d'un dictionnaire biographique . . . et d'un tableau des signes chimiques*, Paris, 1811.

HARRIS, J., *Lexicon technicum*, London, 1704.

HASSENFRATZ, J. H. and P. A. ADET, *System der chemischen Zeichen für die antiphlogistische Chemie und ihre Nomenklatur von Herrn Hassenfratz und Adet*, ed. Meidinger, Vienna, 1793
  —see also under GUYTON, *Méthode de nomenclature chimique*.

HELMONT, J. B. VAN, *Opuscula Medica Inaudita, Ortus Medicinae, etc.*, 4 parts, Amsterdam, 1648.
  —*Oriatrike*, trans., London, 1662.

HENRY, W. C., *Memoirs of the life and scientific researches of John Dalton*, London, 1854.

HERMBSTAEDT, S. F., *Systematischer Grundriss der allgemeinen Experimentalchemie*, 3 parts, Berlin, 1791.

HERMETIC MUSEUM, *Musaeum Hermeticum reformatum et amplificatum*, Frankfurt, 1678.

——*The Hermetic Museum restored and enlarged*, ed. A. E. Waite, London, 1893, reprinted 1953.

HIGGINS, W., *Experiments and Observations on the Atomic Theory*, Dublin, 1814.

HITCHCOCK, E. A., *Remarks upon Alchemy and the Alchemists*, Boston, 1857.

HOEFER, J. C. F., *A Chemical Nomenclature and Classification*, trans., London, 1849.

Histoire de la Chimie, 2nd edn., 2 vols., Paris, 1866–9.

HOFFMANN, F., *Dissertationes Physico-Medicae Curiosae selectiores*, Leyden, 1708.

Dissertationes Physico-Medicarum Curiosarum Selectiorum, Pars Altera, Leyden, 1708.

Dissertationum Physico-Chymicarum Trias, Halae Magdeburgicae, 1729.

Exercitatio Medico-Chymica de Cinnabari Antimonii, Frankfurt, 1689.

Observationum Physico-Chymicarum Selectiorum, Libri III, Halle, 1722.

HOFMANN, A. W., *Introductiom to Modern Chemistry*, London, 1865.

HOLLANDUS, I., *Sammlung Chymischer Schriften*, Vienna, 1773.

HOLMYARD, E. J., *Chemistry to the time of Dalton*, London, 1925.

Outlines of Organic Chemistry, 2nd edn., London, 1936.

HOLMYARD, E. J. and W. G. PALMER, *A Higher School Inorganic Chemistry*, 2nd edn., London, 1952.

HOPKINS, A. J., *Alchemy, Child of Greek Philosophy*, New York, 1934.

HOPSON, C. R., *A General System of Chemistry . . . taken chiefly from the German of M. Wiegleb*, London, 1789.

HUET, P. D., *M. Manlii Astronomicon. Accesserunt P. D. Hueti animadversiones*, Paris, 1679.

HUME, G. L., *Chemical Attractions*, Cambridge, 1835.

IANUENSIS, S., *Clavis Sanationis*, Venice, 1514.

INTERNATIONAL UNION OF PURE AND APPLIED CHEMISTRY, *Nomenclature of Organic Chemistry, 1957*, London, 1958.

ISIDORUS *Etymologiarum sive Originum Libri XX*, ed. W. M. Lindsay, 2 vols., Oxford, 1911.

JABIR IBN HAYYAN, *Contribution à l'histoire des idées scientifiques dans l'Islam*, ed. P. Kraus, *Mémoires présentés à l'Institut d'Egypte*, Cairo, *44, 45,* (1943, 42).

JACQUIN, J. F. VON, *Lehrbuch der allgemeinen und medicinischen Chymie*, 2 vols., Vienna, 1793.

JACQUIN, N. F., *Examen Chemicum Doctrinae Meyerianae de Acido Pingui, et Blackianae de Aere Fixo Respectu Calcis*, Vienna, 1769.

JAMES, R., *Medical Dictionary*, 3 vols., London, 1743–5.

JOHNSON, W., *Lexicon Chymicum . . . editio ultima, prioribus longe auctior et correctior*, Frankfurt & Leipzig, 1678.

JOHNSTON, J. F. W., *Chemical tables exhibiting the present state of our knowledge in regard to the chemical and physical properties of simple and compound bodies*, Part 1, Edinburgh, 1836.

JUENGKEN, J. H., *Chymia Experimentalis Curiosa*, Frankfurt, 1681.

JUNG, C. G., *Psychologie und Alchemie*, Zürich, 1944.

—trans. *Psychology and Alchemy*, London, 1953.

KAHLBAUM, G. W. A. and A. HOFFMANN, *Die Einführung der Lavoisierschen Theorie im Besonderen in Deutschland*, Leipzig, 1897.

KEIR, J., *First Part of a Dictionary of Chemistry*, Birmingham, 1789.

A Treatise on the various kinds of permanently elastic fluids or gases, 2nd edn., London, 1779.

KEKULÉ, F. A., *Lehrbuch der organischen Chemie*, 4 vols., Erlangen, 1861–87.

KERZENMACHER, P., *Alchimia*, Frankfurt, 1589.

KIRCHER, A., *Mundus subterraneus*, Amsterdam, 1665.

—another edn., Amsterdam, 1678.

KIRWAN, R., *Elements of Mineralogy*, 1st. edn., London, 1784.

—2nd edn., 2 vols., London, 1794, 96.

Essay on the Analysis of Mineral Waters, London, 1799.

An Essay on Phlogiston, London, 1787.

—new edn., London, 1789.

KLAPROTH, M. H., *Beiträge zur Chemischen Kenntniss der Mineralkörper*, 6 vols., Berlin, 1795—1815.

KOLBE, H., *Ausführliches Lehrbuch der organischen Chemie*, 3 vols., Brunswick, 1854–76.

KOPP, H., *Die Alchemie in älterer und neuerer Zeit*, 2 parts, Heidelberg, 1886.

Beiträge zur Geschichte der Chemie, Brunswick, 1869–75.

Geschichte der Chemie, 4 vols., Brunswick, 1843–7.

KOPP, U. F., *Palaeographia critica*, 4 parts, Mannheim, 1817–29.

KÖRNER, W., *Über die Bestimmung des Chemischen Ortes bei den aromatischen Substanzen*, (1866–74), (Ostwald's Klassiker No. 174), Leipzig, 1910.

KRIEGSMANN, W., *Taaut, oder Ausslegung der Chemischen Zeichen*, Frankfurt, 1665.

KUNCKEL, J., *Chymische Anmerkungen*, Wittenberg, 1677.

Laboratorium Chymicum, Hamburg & Leipzig, 1716.

Nützliche Observationes oder Anmerckungen, Hamburg, 1676.
An experimental confirmation of chymical philosophy, trans., London, 1705.

LADENBURG, A., *Lectures on the history of the development of chemistry since the time of Lavoisier*, trans., 2nd edn., Edinburgh, 1905.
LAGERCRANTZ, C. O., *Papyrus Graecus Holmiensis*, Uppsala, 1913.
LAURENT, A., *Méthode de chimie*, Paris, 1854.
——*Chemical Method, Notation, Classification and Nomenclature*, trans. W. Odling, London, 1855.
LAVOISIER, A. L., *Oeuvres*, 6 vols., Paris, 1862–93, *Correspondance*, ed. R. Fric, vol. i, Paris, 1955.
Opuscules physiques et chymiques, Paris, 1774.
Traité élémentaire de chimie, présenté dans un ordre nouveau et d'après les découvertes modernes, 2 vols., Paris, 1789.
Elements of Chemistry, trans. J. Kerr, Edinburgh, 1790.
——2nd edn., Edinburgh, 1793.
——5th edn., 2 vols., Edinburgh, 1802.
System der antiphlogistischen Chemie, 2 vols., Berlin & Stettin, 1792.
LA WALL, C. H., *Four Thousand Years of Pharmacy*, Philadelphia & London, 1927.
LE BEGUE, J., *Tabula de vocabulis synonymis et equivocis colorum*, etc., (1431)—Merrifield, *Original Treatises on the Arts of Painting*, London, 1849, vol. i.
LE FEBURE, N., *A Compendious Body of Chymistry*, 2 vols., London, 1664.
Traité de Chymie, 2 vols., Paris, 1669.
LEICESTER, H. M., *The Historical Background of Chemistry*, New York, 1956.
LEICESTER, H. M. and KLICKSTEIN, H. S., *A Source Book of Chemistry*, New York, 1952.
LEMERY, N., *Cours de Chymie*, Paris, 1697.
——nouvelle édition, ed. Baron, Paris, 1756.
A Course of Chemistry, trans., London, 1686.
Traité universel des drogues simples, Paris, 1698.
Pharmacopée universelle, Paris, 1697.
LEWIS, W., *Course of practical chemistry*, London, 1746.
LIBAVIUS, A., *Alchymia . . . recognita, emendata et aucta tum dogmatibus et experimentis nonnullis, tum commentario medico-physico-chemico*, 3 parts, Frankfurt, 1606.
Rerum chymicarum Epistolica, Frankfurt, 1595.
Syntagmatis, Arcanorum, Frankfurt, 1660.
LIEBIG, J. VON, *Aus Justus Liebig's und Friedrich Wöhler's Briefwechsel in den Jahren 1829–73*, ed. A. W. Hofmann, 2 vols., Brunswick, 1888.
LIEBIG, J. VON and J. C. POGGENDORFF, *Handwörterbuch der reinen und ungewandeten Chemie*, 8 vols., Braunschweig, 1837–59.

LIMBOURG, J. P. DE, *Dissertation sur les affinités chymiques*, Liège, 1761.

LINDROTH, S. (ed.) *Swedish men of science 1650–1950*, Stockholm, 1952.

LINK, C. F., *Beyträge zur Physik und Chemie*, 3 vols., Rostock & Leipzig, 1795—7.

LINNAEUS, C. VON, *Critica Botanica*, Leyden, 1737.

—trans. Sir A. Hort, Ray Society, London, 1938.

The Elements of Botany . . . being a translation of the Philosophia Botanica and other treatises of the celebrated Linnaeus by H. Rose, London, 1775.

Systema Naturae, 1st edn., Leyden, 1735.

—10th edn., 2 vols., Holmiae, 1758, 59.

LIPPMANN, E. O. VON, *Abhandlung und Vorträge zur Geschichte der Naturwissenschaften*, 2 vols., Leipzig, 1906–13.

Entstehung und Ausbreitung der Alchemie, 3 vols., Berlin, 1919–54.

LISTER, M., *Novae et Curiosae Exercitationes et Descriptiones Thermarum ac Fontium Medicatorum Angliae*, editio ultima, Leyden, 1686.

LOCKE, J., *Essay concerning human understanding*, (Everyman edn.), London, 1947.

LOSCHMIDT, J., *Chemische Studien, I. Constitutions Formeln der organischen Chemie in graphischer Darstellung*, Vienna, 1861.

LOWRY, T. M., *Historical Introduction to Chemistry*, 3rd impression, London, 1936.

LUEDY, F., *Alchemistische und chemische Zeichen*, Berlin, 1929.

LULL, R., *De secretis naturae*, Cologne, 1567.

McKIE, D., *Antoine Lavoisier, the father of modern chemistry*, London, 1935.

Antoine Lavoisier: scientist, economist, social reformer, London, 1952.

MACQUER, P. J., *Dictionnaire de Chymie*, 2 vols., Paris, 1766.

—2nd edn., 2 vols., Paris, 1778.

Dictionary of Chemistry, trans. J. Keir, London, 1771.

Chymisches Wörterbuch, trans. J. G. Leonhardi, 6 vols., Leipzig, 1781–3.

Dizionario di Chimica, trans. G. A. Scopoli, 11 vols., Pavia, 1783–4.

Élémens de Chymie-Pratique, 2 vols., Paris, 1751.

Élémens de Chymie Théorique, Paris, 1749.

MACQUER, P. J. and A. BAUMÉ, *Plan d'un Cours de Chymie Expérimentale et Raisonnée*, Paris, 1757.

MAIER, M., *Atalanta Fugiens*, Oppenheim, 1618.

Tripus Aureus, Frankfurt, 1618.

MAIMONIDES, *Guide to the Perplexed*, London, 1947.

MANGET, J. J. (ed.), *Bibliotheca Chemia Curiosa*, 2 vols., Geneva, 1702.

MANLIIS DE BOSCO *Luminare Maius*, Venice, 1566.

MARGGRAF, A. S., *Opuscules Chimiques*, 2 vols., Paris, 1762.

MARSIGNY, J. C. DE, *Traitté des élémens chimiques*, Rouen, 1671.

368   Bibliography

MARTYN, T., *The language of Botany*, 2nd edn., London, 1796.
MAYOW, J., *Medico-Physical Works* (1674), Alembic Club Reprint, No. 17, Edinburgh, 1907.
MEDICINISCH, *Medicinisch-Chemisch und Alchemistiches Oraculum*, Ulm 1772.
MEISSNER, B., *Babylonien und Assyrien*, 2 vols., Heidelberg, 1920, 25.
MEURDRAC, M., *La Chimie charitable et facile en faveur des dames*, 3rd edn., Paris, 1687.
MEYER, E. VON, *A History of Chemistry*, trans., 2nd edn., London, 1898.
MEYER, L., *Die modernen Theorien der Chemie*, Breslau, 1864.
MIELI, A., *La science arabe*, Leyden, 1938.
MINDERERUS, R., *De calcantho seu vitriolo*, Augustae Vindelicorum, 1617.
MITCHELL, A. D., *British Chemical Nomenclature*, London, 1948.
MITSCHERLICH, E., *Lehrbuch der Chemie*, Berlin, 1831–40.
MONNET, A. G., *Nouveau Système de minéralogie*, Bouillon, 1779.
MOORE, F. J., *A History of Chemistry*, 3rd edn., New York & London, 1939.
MORIENUS ROMANUS, *De metallorum transmutatione*, Paris, 1564.
MOSTRÖM, B., *T. Bergman—A bibliography of his works*, Stockholm, 1957.
MOWAT, J. L. G. (ed.), *Sinonoma Bartholomei*, Oxford, 1882.
  Alphita, A Medico-Botanical Glossary, Oxford, 1887.
MUHAMMAD IBN ABI TALIB, *Manuel de la Cosmographie du Moyen Âge*, ed. Mehren, Copenhagen, 1874.
MUHAMMAD IBN ZAKARIYA, *Das Buch der Alaune und Salze*, trans. J. Ruska, Berlin, 1935.
MUIR, M. M. P., *The story of alchemy and the beginnings of chemistry*, London, 1902.
MÜLLER, P., *Miracula Chymica*, [Wittenberg?], 1611.
MUNRO, D., *A treatise on medical and pharmaceutical chemistry*, 3 vols., London, 1788.
MURATORI, L. A., *Antiquitates Italiae medii aevi*, 6 vols., Mediolani, 1738–42.
MYLIUS, J., *Philosophia Reformata*, Frankfurt, 1622.
MYNSICHT, A. a., *Thesaurus et Armamentarium medico-chymicum*, Rothomagi, 1651.
MYREPSUS, N., *De compositione medicamentorum*—H. Estienne, *Medicae Artis Principes*, Paris, 1567.

NEUMANN, C., *Chemical Works*, trans. Lewis, London, 1759.
  Chymiae Medicae Dogmatico-Experimentalis, ed. C. Kessel, 4 vols., Züllichau, 1749–55.
  Lectiones Publicae von Salibus alkalino-fixis, Berlin, 1727.

Lectiones Publicae von . . . Salpeter, Schwefel, Spiess-Glas und Eisen, Berlin, 1732.

NEWTON, I., *A Catalogue of the Portsmouth Collection of Books and Papers . . . of Sir Isaac Newton,* Cambridge, 1888.

Opticks, 3rd edn., London, 1721.

NICHOLSON, W., *A Dictionary of Chemistry,* 2 vols., London, 1795.

The First Principles of Chemistry, 2nd edn., London, 1792.

NORDENSKIÖLD, E., *The History of Biology,* London, 1929.

NORTON, T., *The Ordinall of Alchimy,* facsimile, London, 1928.

NUISEMENT, J. DE, *Traittez de l'harmonie et constitution générale du vray sel secret des philosophes,* Paris, 1621.

OERSTED, J. C., *Tentamen nomenclaturae chemicae omnibus linguis Scandinavico-Germanicis communis,* Copenhagen, 1814.

ONIANS, C. T. (ed.), *Shorter Oxford English Dictionary,* 3rd edn., 2 vols., Oxford, 1944.

ONIANS, R. B., *The Origins of European Thought,* Cambridge, 1951.

ORIGEN, *Contra Celsum—Migne, Patriologia, Series Graeca,* vol. 11, Paris, 1857.

PACKE, C., *Mineralogia,* London, 1693.

PAGEL, W., *Paracelsus,* Basel & New York, 1958.

PALISSY, B., *Oeuvres,* Paris, 1777.

Oeuvres complètes, ed. P. A. Cap, Paris, 1844.

PARACELSUS, *The Hermetic and Alchemical Writings of Aureolus Philippus Theophrastus Bombast called Paracelsus,* trans. A. E. Waite, 2 vols., London, 1894.

Sämtliche Werke, 1 Abteilung: Medicinische, naturwissenschaftliche und philosophische Schriften, ed. K. Sudhoff, 14 vols., Munich & Berlin, 1922–33.

PARIS (CITY), *Notices et Extraits des Manuscrits de la Bibliotheque Nationale,* vol. 5. 1798–9.

PARIS, J. A., *The Elements of Medical Chemistry,* London, 1825.

Pharmacologia, 7th edn., 2 vols., London, 1829.

PARKINSON, J., *Chemical Pocket Book,* 2nd edn., London, 1801.

—3rd edn., London, 1803.

PARTINGTON, J. R., *Everyday Chemistry,* 3rd edn., London, 1952.

Origin and Development of Applied Chemistry, London, 1935.

A Short History of Chemistry, 2nd edn., London, 1951.

PASTEUR, L., *Leçons de chimie professés en 1860,* Paris, 1861.

PEARSON, G., *A Translation of the Table of Chemical Nomenclature . . . with additions and alterations; to which are prefixed an explanation of the terms and some observations on the new system of chemistry,* London, 1794.

—2nd edn., enlarged and corrected, London, 1799.

PEMBERTON, H., *A Course of Chemistry*, London, 1771.

PERNETY, A.-J., *Dictionnaire Mytho-Hermétique*, Paris, 1787.

Les Fables Égyptiennes et Grecques dévoilées et réduites au même principe, 2 vols., Paris, 1758.

PETTUS, SIR J., *Fleta Minor*, London, 1683.

PHARMACOPOEIAS

AUGSBURG: *A Facsimile of the first edition of the Pharmacopoeia Augustana with introductory essays by T. Husemann*, Madison, Wisconsin, 1927.

Pharmacopoeia Augustana, 1653.

EDINBURGH: *The Edinburgh New Dispensatory . . . being an improvement of the New Dispensatory of Dr. Lewis*, ed. J. Duncan, 1786.

—another edn., 1791.

—4th edn., ed. J. Rotheram, 1794.

—5th edn., ed. J. Rotheram, 1797.

Pharmacopoeia Nosocomii Regii Edinburgensis, 1804.

Pharmacopoeia Collegii Regii Medicorum Edinburgensis, 1805.

DUBLIN: *The Pharmacopoeia of the King and Queen's College of Physicians in Ireland*, trans. T. Morison, 1807.

LONDON: *Pharmacopoeia Londinensis*, 2nd edn., Dec. 1618, with a historical introduction by G. Urdang, 1944.

—another edn., 1650.

—another edn., 1721.

A Draught for the reformation of the London Pharmacopoeia, 1742.

Pharmacopoeia Reformata or an Essay for the Reformation of the London Pharmacopoeia, London, 1744.

Pharmacopoeia Londinensis, 1746.

The Dispensatory of the Royal College of Physicians of London translated with remarks by H. Pemberton, London, 1746.

The British Dispensatory, containing a faithful translation of the New London Pharmacopoeia . . . to which are joined . . . the whole contents of the Edinburgh Pharmacopoeia, 1747.

Pharmacopoeia Londinensis, 1788.

The New Pharmacopoeia of the Royal College of Physicians, translated with notes by T. Healde, M.D., F.R.S., London, 1788.

Cursory Remarks on the New Pharmacopoeia by 'Liquor Volatilis Cornu Cervis', 1788.

Pharmacopoeia Londinensis, trans. R. Powell, 2nd edn., London, 1809.

Foreign editions:

Pharmacopoeia Londinensis, Amsterdam, 1722.

Pharmacopoeia Londinensis, Amsterdam, 1746.

Pharmacopoeia Londinensis, Leyden, 1788.

Pharmacopoeia Londinensis, Paris, 1788.

Pharmacopoeia Londinensis, Ticino, 1788.

Translations:
> *Pharmacopée du Collège Royal des Médecins de Londres*, vol. i, Paris, 1761., vol. ii, Paris, 1771.

NUREMBERG: *Nuremberg Pharmacopoeia*, 1666.

PRUSSIA: *Pharmacopoeia Borussica*, Berlin, 1799.

SPAIN: *Pharmacopoeia Hispanica*, Madrid, 1794.

SWEDEN: *Pharmacopoeia Suecicca*, Holmiae, 1775.
> —editio altera emendata, Holmiae, 1779.
> —3rd edn., Holmiae, 1784.

SWITZERLAND: *Pharmacopoeia Helvetica*, Basle, 1771.

PITTON DE TOURNEFORT, J., *Institutiones Rei Herbariae*, 2nd edn., 3 vols., Paris, 1700.

PLANIS CAMPY, D. DE, *Bouquet composé des plus belles fleurs chimiques*, Paris, 1623.

PLINY, *Historia Naturalis*, Loeb edn., 10 vols., London, 1938 etc.

POGGENDORFF, J. C., *Biographisch-Literarisches Wörterbuch zur Geschichte der Exacten Wissenschaften*, vols., 1 & 2, Leipzig, 1863.

POISSON, A., *Nicolas Flamel*, Paris, 1893.
> *Théories et symboles des alchimistes*, Paris, 1891.

POMET, P., *A Compleat History of Drugs*, London, 1712.

PORTA, G. B. DELLA, *De Occultis Literarum Notis*, Argentorati, 1606.
> *Magiae Naturalis. Libri XX*, Amsterdam, 1664.

POTT, J. H., *Dissertations Chymiques*, trans. Demachy, 4 vols., Paris, 1759.

PRIESTLEY, J., *Considerations of the doctrine of phlogiston*, Philadelphia, 1796.
> *Experiments and observations on different kinds of air*, 3 vols., London, 1774-7.
> *Experiments and observations relating to various branches of natural philosophy; with a continuation of the observations on air*, vol. 1, London, 1779; vols., 2 & 3, Birmingham, 1781, 86.
> *Experiments and observations on different kinds of air and other branches of natural philosophy*, 3 vols., Birmingham, 1790.
> *Scientific Correspondence of Joseph Priestley*, ed. H. C. Bolton, New York, 1892.

PROBIERBÜCHLEIN—see BERGBÜCHLEIN.

PYE, C., *The new chemical nomenclature, selected from the most distinguished modern writers on chemistry, designed for the use of students in pharmacy, druggists, apothecaries and others*, London, 1802.

READ, J., *The alchemist in life, literature and art*, London, 1947.
> *Prelude to chemistry*, London, 1936.

REMLER, J. C. W., *Neues Chemisches Wörterbuch*, Erfurt, 1793.

REUSSNER, H., *Pandora: Das ist, Die edelst Gab Gottes*, Basle, 1588.

REUVENS, C. J. C., *Lèttres à M. Letronne sur les papyrus bilingues et grecs, etc.*, Leyden, 1830.

RICHTER, J. B., *Ueber die neuern Gegenstände der Chymie*, 10 parts, Breslau, 1791–1800.

RIVERIUS, L., *Observationum medicarum et curationum insignium*, Hague, 1657.

ROMÉ DE L'ISLE, J. B. L. DE, *Essai de cristallographie*, Paris, 1772. *Cristallographie*, 2nd edn., 3 vols., Paris, 1783.

ROSARIUM PHILOSOPHORUM, *Secunda Pars Alchimiae . . . cum Figuris rei perfectionem ostendentibus*, Frankfurt, 1550.

ROSCOE, H. E. and A. HARDEN, *A new view of the origin of Dalton's atomic theory*, London, 1896.

ROSENCREUTZER, M. F., *Astronomia inferior*, Nuremberg, 1674.

ROYAL SOCIETY, LONDON, *Catalogue of Scientific Papers*, 19 vols., 1867–1925.

RULAND, M., *Lexicon Alchemiae*, Prague, 1612.

RUSKA, J. (ed.), *Studien zur Geschichte der Chemie*, Festgabe E. O. von Lippmann, Berlin, 1927.

SAGE, B. G., *Exposé des effets de la contagion nomenclative*, Paris, 1810. *Mémoires de Chimie*, Paris, 1773.

SALA, A., *Anatomia Vitrioli*, 3rd edn., Leyden, 1617. *Collectanea Chimica Curiosa*, Frankfurt, 1693.

SALLWIGT, G. A., *Tractatus Mago-Cabbalistico Chymicus*, Salzburg, 1729.

SALMASIUS, L., *Plinianae Exercitationes*, Trajecti ad Rhenum, 1689.

SALMON, W., *Medicina Practica* London, 1707.

SARTON, G. A. L., *A History of Science, Ancient Science through the Golden Age of Greece*, London, 1953.
Introduction to the History of Science, Washington, 1927–48.
Six Wings: men of science in the Renaissance, Bloomington, U.S., 1957.

SCHEELE, C. W., *Chemische Abhandlung von der Luft und dem Feuer*, Uppsala & Leipzig, 1777.
Chemical Observations and Experiments on Air and Fire, trans. Forster, London, 1780.
The collected papers of C. W. Scheele, trans. L. Dobbin, London, 1931.
The early history of chlorine. Papers by C. W. Scheele, C. L. Berthollet, Guyton de Morveau, J. L. Gay-Lussac and L. J. Thenard, A. C. R. No. 13, Edinburgh, 1905.
Mémoires de Chimie de Scheele, Dijon, 1785.
Nachgelassene Briefe und Aufzeichnungen, ed. A. E. Nordenskiöld, Stockholm, 1892.
Sämtliche Physische und Chemische Werke, ed. and trans. S. F. Hermbstädt (1793), facsimile, Berlin, 1891.

SCHELHAMMER, G. C., *De nitro*, Amsterdam, 1709.

SCHENNIS, H. VON, *Spagyrische Hauss und Rayss Apotheca*, trans. Zürich, 1628.

SCHERER, A. N. *Nachträge zu den Grundzügen der neuern chemischen Theorie*, Jena, 1796.

SCHERER, J. A., *Versuch einer neuen Nomenklatur für Deutsche Chymisten*, Vienna, 1792.

SCHORLEMMER, C., *The Rise and Development of Organic Chemistry*, 2nd edn., London, 1894.

SCHRADER, O., *Sprachvergleichung und Urgeschichte*, 2nd edn., Jena, 1890.

SCHROEDER, J., *Pharmacopoeia medico-chymica*, Ulmae Suevorum, 1685.

SELENUS, G., *Cryptomenytices et cryptographiae*, Lunaeburgi, 1624.

SEVRIN, L.-J., *Dictionnaire des nomenclatures chimiques et minéralogiques anciennes comparées aux nomenclatures chimiques et minéralogiques modernes*, Paris, 1807.

SIGAUD DE LA FOND, J. A., *Essai sur différentes espèces d'air fixe ou de Gaz*, nouvelle édition, Paris, 1785.

SIGGEL, A., *Decknamen in der arabischen alchemistischen Literatur— Deutsche Akademie der Wissenschaften zu Berlin; Institut für Orientforschung*, Veröffentlichung Nr. 5, 1951.

SINGER, C., *The earliest chemical industry*, London, 1948.

SINGER, D. W., *Catalogue of Latin and Vernacular Alchemical Manuscripts in Great Britain and Ireland dating from before the 16th century*, 3 vols., Brussels, 1928–31.

SMITH, SIR J. E., *Correspondence of Linnaeus and other naturalists*, 2 vols., London, 1821.

SMITH, R. A., *The life and works of Thomas Graham*, Glasgow, 1884.

SÖDERBAUM, H. G., *Berzelius' Werden und Wachsen, 1779–1821*, Leipzig, 1899.
(see also under BERZELIUS)

SOMMERHOFF, J. C., *Lexicon Pharmaceutico-Chymicum*, Nuremberg, 1701.

SPALDING, L., *A new nomenclature of chemistry proposed by Messrs. de Morveau, Lavoisier, Berthollet and Fourcroy with additions and improvements by Lyman Spalding, M.B.*, Hanover, (N.H.), 1799.

SPIELMANN, J. R., *Instituts de Chymie*, trans., 2 vols., Paris, 1770.

STAHL, G. E., *Fundamenta Chymiae Dogmaticae et Experimentalis*, Nuremberg, 1723.
Fundamenta Chymiae Dogmatico-Rationalis, Nuremberg, 1732.
Nützliche Bedencken . . . von dem sogennanten Sulphure, trans., *Traité du Soufre*, Paris, 1766.

STEELE, R., *Mediaeval Lore from Bartholomew Anglicus*, London, 1905.

STILLMAN, J. Y., *Paracelsus*, Chicago & London, 1920.
The Story of Early Chemistry, New York & London, 1924.

STOLCIUS, D., *Viridarium Chymicum Figuris adornatum*, Frankfurt, 1624.

SUIDAS, *ΣΟΥΙΔΑΣ. Suidae Lexicon Graece et Latine*, 2 vols., Halle & Brunswick, 1853.

SYLVATICUS, J. B., *Galeni Historiae Medicinalis*, Hanoviae, 1605.

SYLVESTER, C., *An elementary treatise on chemistry*, Liverpool, 1809.

TABULA SMARAGDINA, ed. J. Ruska, Heidelberg, 1926.

TACHENIUS, O., *Hippocrates Chimicus*, Brunswick 1668.
—trans., London, 1690.
Hippocraticae Medicinae Clavis, Frankfurt, 1669.

TATON, R. (ed.), *Histoire générale des sciences*, 2 vols., Paris, 1957, 58.

TAYLOR, F. S., *The Alchemists, founders of modern chemistry*, London, 1951.
A History of Industrial Chemistry, London, 1957.

TESTI, G., *Dizionario di Alchimia e di Chimica Antiquaria*, Rome, 1950.

TEXTE, *Le texte d'Alchimie et Songe-Verd*, Paris, 1695.

THENARD, L. J., *Traité de chimie élémentaire théorique et pratique*, 4th edn., 5 vols., Paris, 1824.
—6th edn., 5 vols., Paris, 1834.

THEOPHILUS, *Essai sur divers arts*, Paris, 1843.

THEOPHRASTUS, *History of Stones*, trans. J. Hill, London, 1746.

THOMSON, R. C., *Dictionary of Assyrian Chemistry and Geology*, Oxford, 1936.

THOMSON, T., *An attempt to establish the first principles of chemistry by experiment*, 2 vols., London, 1825.
History of Chemistry, 2 vols., London, 1830, 31.
System of Chemistry, 4 vols., Edinburgh, 1802.
—3rd edn., 5 vols., Edinburgh, 1807.
—4th edn., 5 vols., Edinburgh, 1810.
—5th edn., 4 vols., London, 1817.

THORNDIKE, L., *A History of Magic and Experimental Science*, 8 vols., New York, 1923–58.

THORPE, SIR E., *Dictionary of Applied Chemistry*, 4th edn., 12 vols., London, 1937–56.

THURNEYSSER ZUM THURN, L., *Quinta Essentia*, Munster, 1570.

TOLLIUS, J., *Fortuita. In quibus praeter critica nonnulla, tota fabularis historia Graeca, Phoenicea, Aegyptiaca, ad Chemiam pertinere asseritur*, Amsterdam, 1687.

TOXITES, M., *Onomasticon I*, Argentorati, 1574.
Onomastica II, Argentorati, 1583.

TRITHEIM, J., *Polygraphie*, Paris, 1561.

TROMMSDORFF, J. B., *Chemische Receptirkunst*, 2nd edn., Erfurt, 1799.

TURBA PHILOSOPHORUM, ed. J. Ruska, Berlin, 1931.
—trans. A. E. Waite, London, 1896.

TURNER, E., *An introduction to the study of the laws of chemical combination and the atomic theory*, Edinburgh, 1825.

Elements of Chemistry, 1st edn., Edinburgh, 1827.
—4th edn., London, 1833.
—5th edn., London, 1834.
TURQUET DE MAYERNE, T., *Opera Medica*, ed. J. Browne, London, 1700.

VALENTINI, M. B., *Relatio de Magnesia Alba, novo, genuino, polychresto et innoxio pharmaco purgante, Roma nuper advecto, Gissae Hassorum*, 1707.
VALMONT DE BOMARE, J. C., *Minéralogie*, 2 vols., Paris, 1762.
VAN'T HOFF, J. H., *La Chimie dans l'Espace*, Rotterdam, 1875.
VERBESIUS, D., *Disquisitione iatrochymica de calcantho*, Augustae Vindelicorum, 1626.
VIGENÈRE, B. DE, *Traicté du feu et du sel*, Paris, 1618.
VINCENT OF BEAUVAIS, *Speculum Naturale*, Venice, 1494.
VITRUVIUS, *De Architechtura*, Loeb edn., 2 vols., 1931-4.
VOGEL, R., *Lehrsätze der Chemie*, trans. Weigleb, Wiemar, 1775.

WALLERIUS, J. G., *Minéralogie*, 2 vols., Paris, 1753.
WATTS, H. (ed.), *Dictionary of Chemistry*, 5 vols., and Supplement, London, 1866-75.
WEEKS, M. E., *Discovery of the Elements*, 5th edn., Easton, Pa.
WELTZIEN, C., *Systematische Zusammenstellung der organischen Verbindungen*, Brunswick, 1860.
WESTRUMB, J. F., *Versuch eines Beytrages zu den Sprachbereicherungen für die Deutsche Chemie—Kleine Physikalische-Chemische Abhandlungen* by J. F. Westrumb, Band III, Heft 2, Hannover, 1793.
WHEELER, T. S. AND PARTINGTON, J. R., *The Life and Work of William Higgins, Chemist*, Oxford, London & New York, 1960.
WHITE, R., *An Analysis of the New London Pharmacopoeia. A Summary of the Pneumato-Chemical Theory with a table of its nomenclatüre intended as a supplement to the Analysis of the new London Pharmacopoeia*, Newmarket 1792.
WOOTON, A. C., *Chronicles of Pharmacy*, 2 vols., London, 1910.
WURTZ, A., *Dictionnaire de chimie pure et appliquée*, 3 vols., Paris, 1869-78. Supplément, 2 vols., Paris, 1880-6.
Leçons de philosophie chimique, Paris, 1864.

YOUNG, T., *An introduction to medical literature*, London, 1813.
YUHANNA IBN SARAPION, *Insignium Medicarum*, etc., Argentorati, 1531.

ZACAIRE, D., *Opuscule très excellent de la vraye philosophie naturelle des Métaux . . . plus le traité de M. Bernard Trevisan*, Lyon, 1612.

ZETZNER, L. (ed.), *Theatrum chemicum,* 2nd edn., 5 vols., Argentorati, 1613–22.
—another edn., 6 vols., Argentorati, 1659–61.
ZURETTI, C. O., *Alchemistica Signa—Catalogue des Manuscrits Alchimiques Grecs,* vol., 8, *Union Académique Internationale,* Brussels, 1932.
ZWELFER, J., *Appendix ad animadversiones in Pharmacopoeiam Augustanam,* Gouda, 1658.

II. UNPUBLISHED DISSERTATIONS

University of London (H. & P. of S.)
MILLARD, W. F., *The life and chemical works of Thomas Thomson (1773–1852) with special reference to his 'System of Chemistry',* M.Sc., 1955.
PEARSON, F. J., *The influence of chemical theory upon chemical nomenclature and symbolism from the period of Lavoisier to that of Laurent,* M.Sc., 1929.
ROSS, C., *Studies in the chemical work of Claude Louis Berthollet (1748–1822),* M.Sc., 1934.
TASLIMI, M., *A conspectus of recent researches on Arabic chemistry,* M.Sc., 1951.
TRENGOVE, L., *A critical study of the experimental content of John Dalton's 'New System of Chemical Philosophy'* M.Sc., 1954.

III. MANUSCRIPTS

B. M. Sloane, 1754.
B. M. Sloane, 2135.
B. M. Harleian, 3528.

IV. PERIODICALS

Nova Acta Regiae Societatis Scientiarum Upsaliensis, Uppsala.
Acta Societatis Scientiarum Fennica, Helsinki.
Allgemeine chemische Bibliothek des neunzehnten Jahrhunderts, ed. J. B. Trommsdorff, Erfurt.
Allgemeines Journal der Chemie, ed. A. N. Scherer, Leipzig.
Ambix, London.
American Journal of Science and Arts, ed. Silliman, New York.

Annalen der Chemie und Pharmacie, ed. J. von Liebig, Heidelberg & Leipzig.

Annalen der Pharmacie, ed. J. von Liebig, Lemgo & Heidelberg.

Annalen der Physik und Chemie, ed. Poggendorff, Halle.

Annalen der Physik, ed. L. W. Gilbert, Halle.

Annales de Chimie, ed. Morveau, Lavoisier, Monge, Berthollet, de Fourcroy, le Baron de Dietrich, Hassenfratz & Adet, Paris.

Annales de Chimie et de Physique, Paris.

Annals of Philosophy, ed. T. Thomson, London.

Annals of Science, London.

Annual Report of the Board of Regents of the Smithsonian Institution, Washington, D. C.

Archiv der Pharmacie, Hannover.

Archives Internationales d'Histoire des Sciences, Paris.
   —formerly: *Archeion,* Rome & Paris.
   —originally: *Archivio di Storia della Scienze,* Rome.

Archives des Sciences Physiques et Naturelles, Geneva,

Berichte der deutschen chemischen Gesellschaft,

Berichte der königlichen Preuss. Akademie der Wissenschaften zu Berlin.

Bulletin de la Société Chimique de Paris.

Bulletins de l'Académie Royale des Sciences, des Lettres et des Beaux-Arts de Belgique, Brussels.

Chemical News, London.

Chemische Annalen, ed. L. Crell, Helmstadt.

The Chemist and Druggist, London.

Chymia, Philadelphia.

Commentarii Academiae Scientiarum Imperialis Petropolitanae, St. Petersburg.
   also: *Novi Commentarii Academiae Scientiarum Imperialis Petropolitanae.*

Comptes Rendus des Séances de l'Académie des Sciences, Paris.

Comptes Rendus des Travaux de Chimie par MM. Aug. Laurent et Ch. Gerhardt, Paris.

Giornale di Fisica, Chimica e Storia Naturale, Pavia.

Histoire de l'Académie Royale des Sciences, Paris.

Histoire de l'Académie Royale des Sciences de Berlin, Berlin.

Isis, Cambridge, Mass.

Jahresbericht über die Fortschritte der physischen Wissenschaften, ed. Berzelius, trans. C. G. Gmelin and F. Wöhler, Reports presented to the Royal Academy of Sciences at Stockholm, 1822–47, Tübingen, 1822–50.

Journal de l'École Polytechnique, Paris.
Journal de Pharmacie, Paris.
Journal der Pharmacie, ed. J. B. Trommsdorff, Leipzig.
Journal der Physik, ed. F. A. C. Gren, Halle.
  continued as: *Neues Journal der Physik*.
Journal des Sçavans, Paris.
Journal für Chemie und Physik, ed. Schweigger, Nuremberg.
Journal für practische Chemie, Leipzig.
Journal of Chemical Education, Easton, Pa.
Journal of the Chemical Society, London.
Journal of Hellenic Studies, London.
Journal of Natural Philosophy, ed. W. Nicholson, London.
Journal of the Royal Institution, London.

Kungliga Svenska Vetenskaps Akademien, Handlingar, Stockholm.
    also: Nya Handlingar.
    trans. Kästner: Königliche Schwedische Akademie der Wissenschaften, Abhandlungen. Neue Abhandlungen.

Medical Repository, New York.
Mémoires de l'Académie Royale des Sciences, Paris.
Mémoires de l'Académie Royale des Sciences de Berlin, Berlin.
Mémoires de l'Académie Royale des Sciences de Turin, Turin.
Mémoires de mathématiques et de physique présentés a l'Academie des Sciences, Paris.
Memoirs of the Asiatic Society of Bengal, Calcutta.
Memoirs of the Literary and Philosophical Society of Manchester, Manchester.
Miscellanea Berolinensis Societati Regiae Scientiarum, Berlin.

Nature, London.
Neues Journal—see *Journal*.
Nova Acta—see *Acta*.
Novi Comentarii—see *Comentarii*.
Nya Handlingar—see *Kungliga Svenska Vetenskaps Akademien, Handlingar*.

Observations sur la Physique, Paris.
Opuscolti Scelti sulla Scienze e sulle arti, Milan.
Osiris, Bruges.

Philosophical Magazine, London.
Philosophical Transactions of the Royal Society, London.
Proceedings of the Chemical Society, London.
Proceedings of the Royal Society, London.
Proceedings of the Royal Society of Edinburgh.

Quarterly Journal of Science, Literature and the Arts, London.

Repertorium für die Pharmacie, Nuremberg.
Reports of the Meetings of the British Association for the Advancement of Science.
Revue Scientifique et Industrielle, ed. Quesneville, Paris.

Schriften der Gesellschaft naturforschender Freunde zu Berlin, Berlin.
Sitzungsberichte der physikalisch-medicinische Societät, Erlangen.

Taschen-Buch für Scheidekunstler und Apotheker, ed. Göttling, Weimar.
Tidningar om lärda saker, Stockholm.
Transactions of the Linnaean Society, London.
Transactions of the New York Academy of Sciences, New York.
Transactions of the Royal Irish Academy, Dublin.

Zeitschrift für Chemie und Pharmacie, Erlangen.

Index

Index of Names

Index of Subjects and Chemical Names

A CATALOGUE OF SELECTED DOVER BOOKS
IN ALL FIELDS OF INTEREST

A CATALOGUE OF SELECTED DOVER BOOKS
IN ALL FIELDS OF INTEREST

THE NOTEBOOKS OF LEONARDO DA VINCI, edited by J.P. Richter. Extracts from manuscripts reveal great genius; on painting, sculpture, anatomy, sciences, geography, etc. Both Italian and English. 186 ms. pages reproduced, plus 500 additional drawings, including studies for Last Supper, Sforza monument, etc. 860pp. 7⅞ x 10¾.   USO 22572-0, 22573-9 Pa., Two vol. set $15.90

ART NOUVEAU DESIGNS IN COLOR, Alphonse Mucha, Maurice Verneuil, Georges Auriol. Full-color reproduction of Combinaisons ornamentales (c. 1900) by Art Nouveau masters. Floral, animal, geometric, interlacings, swashes — borders, frames, spots — all incredibly beautiful. 60 plates, hundreds of designs. 9⅜ x 8¹/₁₆ .   22885-1 Pa. $4.00

GRAPHIC WORKS OF ODILON REDON. All great fantastic lithographs, etchings, engravings, drawings, 209 in all. Monsters, Huysmans, still life work, etc. Introduction by Alfred Werner. 209pp. 9⅛ x 12¼.   21996-8 Pa. $6.00

EXOTIC FLORAL PATTERNS IN COLOR, E.-A. Seguy. Incredibly beautiful full-color pochoir work by great French designer of 20's. Complete Bouquets et frondaisons, Suggestions pour étoffes. Richness must be seen to be believed. 40 plates containing 120 patterns. 80pp. 9⅜ x 12¼.   23041-4 Pa. $6.00

SELECTED ETCHINGS OF JAMES A. McN. WHISTLER, James A. McN. Whistler. 149 outstanding etchings by the great American artist, including selections from the Thames set and two Venice sets, the complete French set, and many individual prints. Introduction and explanatory note on each print by Maria Naylor. 157pp. 9⅜ x 12¼.   23194-1 Pa. $5.00

VISUAL ILLUSIONS: THEIR CAUSES, CHARACTERISTICS, AND APPLICATIONS, Matthew Luckiesh. Thorough description, discussion; shape and size, color, motion; natural illusion. Uses in art and industry. 100 illustrations. 252pp.
                                        21530-X Pa. $2.50

TEN BOOKS ON ARCHITECTURE, Vitruvius. The most important book ever written on architecture. Early Roman aesthetics, technology, classical orders, site selection, all other aspects. Stands behind everything since. Morgan translation. 331pp.
                                        20645-9 Pa. $3.50

THE CODEX NUTTALL. A PICTURE MANUSCRIPT FROM ANCIENT MEXICO, as first edited by Zelia Nuttall. Only inexpensive edition, in full color, of a pre-Columbian Mexican (Mixtec) book. 88 color plates show kings, gods, heroes, temples, sacrifices. New explanatory, historical introduction by Arthur G. Miller. 96pp. 11⅜ x 8½.   23168-2 Pa. $7.50

How to Solve Chess Problems, Kenneth S. Howard. Practical suggestions on problem solving for very beginners. 58 two-move problems, 46 3-movers, 8 4-movers for practice, plus hints. 171pp. 20748-X Pa. $2.00

A Guide to Fairy Chess, Anthony Dickins. 3-D chess, 4-D chess, chess on a cylindrical board, reflecting pieces that bounce off edges, cooperative chess, retrograde chess, maximummers, much more. Most based on work of great Dawson. Full handbook, 100 problems. 66pp. 7⅞ x 10¾. 22687-5 Pa. $2.00

Win at Backgammon, Millard Hopper. Best opening moves, running game, blocking game, back game, tables of odds, etc. Hopper makes the game clear enough for anyone to play, and win. 43 diagrams. 111pp. 22894-0 Pa. $1.50

Bidding a Bridge Hand, Terence Reese. Master player "thinks out loud" the binding of 75 hands that defy point count systems. Organized by bidding problem—no-fit situations, overbidding, underbidding, cueing your defense, etc. 254pp. EBE 22830-4 Pa. $3.00

The Precision Bidding System in Bridge, C.C. Wei, edited by Alan Truscott. Inventor of precision bidding presents average hands and hands from actual play, including games from 1969 Bermuda Bowl where system emerged. 114 exercises. 116pp. 21171-1 Pa. $1.75

Learn Magic, Henry Hay. 20 simple, easy-to-follow lessons on magic for the new magician: illusions, card tricks, silks, sleights of hand, coin manipulations, escapes, and more —all with a minimum amount of equipment. Final chapter explains the great stage illusions. 92 illustrations. 285pp. 21238-6 Pa. $2.95

The New Magician's Manual, Walter B. Gibson. Step-by-step instructions and clear illustrations guide the novice in mastering 36 tricks; much equipment supplied on 16 pages of cut-out materials. 36 additional tricks. 64 illustrations. 159pp. 6⅝ x 10. 23113-5 Pa. $3.00

Professional Magic for Amateurs, Walter B. Gibson. 50 easy, effective tricks used by professionals —cards, string, tumblers, handkerchiefs, mental magic, etc. 63 illustrations. 223pp. 23012-0 Pa. $2.50

Card Manipulations, Jean Hugard. Very rich collection of manipulations; has taught thousands of fine magicians tricks that are really workable, eye-catching. Easily followed, serious work. Over 200 illustrations. 163pp. 20539-8 Pa. $2.00

Abbott's Encyclopedia of Rope Tricks for Magicians, Stewart James. Complete reference book for amateur and professional magicians containing more than 150 tricks involving knots, penetrations, cut and restored rope, etc. 510 illustrations. Reprint of 3rd edition. 400pp. 23206-9 Pa. $3.50

The Secrets of Houdini, J.C. Cannell. Classic study of Houdini's incredible magic, exposing closely-kept professional secrets and revealing, in general terms, the whole art of stage magic. 67 illustrations. 279pp. 22913-0 Pa. $2.50

MANUAL OF THE TREES OF NORTH AMERICA, Charles S. Sargent. The basic survey of every native tree and tree-like shrub, 717 species in all. Extremely full descriptions, information on habitat, growth, locales, economics, etc. Necessary to every serious tree lover. Over 100 finding keys. 783 illustrations. Total of 986pp.
20277-1, 20278-X Pa., Two vol. set $9.00

BIRDS OF THE NEW YORK AREA, John Bull. Indispensable guide to more than 400 species within a hundred-mile radius of Manhattan. Information on range, status, breeding, migration, distribution trends, etc. Foreword by Roger Tory Peterson. 17 drawings; maps. 540pp. 23222-0 Pa. $6.00

THE SEA-BEACH AT EBB-TIDE, Augusta Foote Arnold. Identify hundreds of marine plants and animals: algae, seaweeds, squids, crabs, corals, etc. Descriptions cover food, life cycle, size, shape, habitat. Over 600 drawings. 490pp.
21949-6 Pa. $5.00

THE MOTH BOOK, William J. Holland. Identify more than 2,000 moths of North America. General information, precise species descriptions. 623 illustrations plus 48 color plates show almost all species, full size. 1968 edition. Still the basic book. Total of 551pp. 6½ x 9¼. 21948-8 Pa. $6.00

AN INTRODUCTION TO THE REPTILES AND AMPHIBIANS OF THE UNITED STATES, Percy A. Morris. All lizards, crocodiles, turtles, snakes, toads, frogs; life history, identification, habits, suitability as pets, etc. Non-technical, but sound and broad. 130 photos. 253pp. 22982-3 Pa. $3.00

OLD NEW YORK IN EARLY PHOTOGRAPHS, edited by Mary Black. Your only chance to see New York City as it was 1853-1906, through 196 wonderful photographs from N.Y. Historical Society. Great Blizzard, Lincoln's funeral procession, great buildings. 228pp. 9 x 12. 22907-6 Pa. $6.00

THE AMERICAN REVOLUTION, A PICTURE SOURCEBOOK, John Grafton. Wonderful Bicentennial picture source, with 411 illustrations (contemporary and 19th century) showing battles, personalities, maps, events, flags, posters, soldier's life, ships, etc. all captioned and explained. A wonderful browsing book, supplement to other historical reading. 160pp. 9 x 12. 23226-3 Pa. $4.00

PERSONAL NARRATIVE OF A PILGRIMAGE TO AL-MADINAH AND MECCAH, Richard Burton. Great travel classic by remarkably colorful personality. Burton, disguised as a Moroccan, visited sacred shrines of Islam, narrowly escaping death. Wonderful observations of Islamic life, customs, personalities. 47 illustrations. Total of 959pp. 21217-3, 21218-1 Pa., Two vol. set $10.00

INCIDENTS OF TRAVEL IN CENTRAL AMERICA, CHIAPAS, AND YUCATAN, John L. Stephens. Almost single-handed discovery of Maya culture; exploration of ruined cities, monuments, temples; customs of Indians. 115 drawings. 892pp.
22404-X, 22405-8 Pa., Two vol. set $8.00